Nonequilibrium Thermodynamics in Biophysics

Harvard Books in Biophysics, Number 1

Nonequilibrium Thermodynamics in Biophysics

A. KATCHALSKY
Polymer Department, Weizmann Institute of Science
Rehoveth, Israel

PETER F. CURRAN
Biophysical Laboratory, Harvard Medical School
Boston, Massachusetts

HARVARD UNIVERSITY PRESS
CAMBRIDGE, MASSACHUSETTS 1967

Second printing

Distributed in Great Britain by Oxford University Press, London

Library of Congress Catalog Card Number 65-22045

Printed in the United States of America

PREFACE

This book is based on lectures delivered by the authors in a biophysics course at Harvard University. The purpose of the course was to introduce graduate students to the thermodynamics of irreversible processes. The interest shown by students and research workers who attended the lectures made us feel more strongly that the approach developed here might be a useful addition to the methods of theoretical biology. Although the book has been written primarily with biophysicists in mind, we hope that it may prove useful to those from other disciplines who desire an introduction to this new branch of thermodynamics. In preparing the material, we have assumed that the reader is more familiar with biological, biochemical, and physiological concepts than with the formalism of thermodynamics and the operations of differential vector analysis. Chapters dealing with essential aspects of these subjects have therefore been included in an effort to present a self-consistent development that does not require extensive training in physics and physical chemistry. It has been our conviction that the purpose of the book would best be served if efforts were made to simplify the material wherever possible, particularly since several admirable presentations on a more advanced level are already available.

Throughout the preparation of the book, we have had continued recourse to the work of the many people who have contributed to both the theory and the experimental application of the nonequilibrium thermodynamics. Since we have not attempted to compile an extensive list of references, we would like to acknowledge our indebtedness to all those whose work has aided us in developing this presentation. In particular, we owe much to the many contributions of Prigogine, de Groot, Kirkwood, and their coworkers.

A. Katchalsky
Peter F. Curran

CONTENTS

5

ISOTHERMAL EQUILIBRIA AND CHEMICAL THERMODYNAMICS

6

FLOWS AND FORCES IN THE THERMODYNAMICS OF IRREVERSIBLE PROCESSES

7

ENTROPY PRODUCTION IN CONTINUOUS SYSTEMS

8

THE PHENOMENOLOGICAL EQUATIONS RELATING FLOWS AND FORCES; ONSAGER'S LAW

9

ISOTHERMAL DIFFUSION AND SEDIMENTATION

10

MEMBRANE PERMEABILITY TO NONELECTROLYTES: DISCONTINUOUS SYSTEMS

11

TRANSPORT PROCESSES IN CONTINUOUS SYSTEMS CONTAINING ELECTROLYTES: IONIC CONDUCTANCE AND DIFFUSION

12

ELECTROCHEMICAL PROCESSES IN DISCONTINUOUS SYSTEMS

13

SYSTEMS WITH TEMPERATURE GRADIENTS

14

RELATIONS BETWEEN CHEMICAL REACTIONS AND DIFFUSION PROCESSES

15

STATISTICAL DERIVATION OF ONSAGER'S LAW

16

STATIONARY STATES: THE PRINCIPLE OF MINIMUM ENTROPY PRODUCTION

Nonequilibrium Thermodynamics in Biophysics

INTRODUCTION

CLASSICAL thermodynamics is one of the outstanding achievements of the scientific mind and may be compared favorably with the harmonious and self-consistent structures of Euclidean geometry and analytical mechanics. It is founded on a small number of basic principles and operational postulates from which a vast number of correlations, adequately describing observable phenomena, may be deduced. The impact of classical thermodynamics on physical chemistry and biochemistry cannot be overestimated. For example, the very ascription of thermodynamic characteristics to numerous important metabolites has provided a quantitative basis for the development of dynamic biochemistry and aided the growth of quantitative biology.

Classical thermodynamics is, however, limited in its scope. It is essentially a theory describing systems in equilibrium or undergoing reversible processes and is particularly applicable to closed systems. Since living organisms are nonequilibrium, open systems in which irreversible processes are occurring, thermodynamics has so far played only a minor role in describing the over-all processes taking place in living systems. In the case of such irreversible processes, the laws of classical thermodynamics provide a set of inequalities describing only the direction of change. Consequently, biological phenomena such as transport of matter, nerve conduction, muscle contraction, and others must be described quantitatively by *kinetic* equations that are based on specific models. Such kinetic or statistical models not only are intellectually satisfying but contribute substantially to the understanding and visualization of biological processes. However, the development of an adequate kinetic description of the phenomena often requires more detailed information than is available or readily obtainable. It may, therefore, be advantageous to have a method by which phenomena could be correlated in an alternative, more formal manner independent of specific kinetic or statistical models, and which may offer additional insight into the factors influencing the phenomena in question. An important step in this direction is the application of the formalism of the thermodynamics of irreversible processes to the investigation of the living organism.

These modern developments of thermodynamics have made it possible to replace the inequalities of classical thermodynamics with equalities, and hence have led to a quantitative description of irreversible processes. Some of the early steps in the development of the thermodynamics of irreversible processes took place a hundred years ago, concurrently with the formulation of the fundamental laws of classical thermodynamics, and many pioneering contributions may be found in papers dating from the late 19th and early 20th centuries.[1] However, the cornerstone of the modern theory was laid in 1931 by Onsager, who formulated the law of the symmetry of the coefficients in phenomenological equations of flow.[2] Onsager's law was derived from statistical considerations. It has, however, been verified experimentally for a large number of phenomena and may be regarded as a general statement on macroscopic systems, although of a more limited validity than the first and second laws of thermodynamics. A coordinated theory of the thermodynamics of irreversible processes based on the fundamental work of Onsager has been developed over the past 20 years by Casimir,[3] Prigogine,[4] de Groot,[5] Meixner,[6] and many others.[7]

This book represents an attempt to introduce students of biophysics, physical biochemistry, and physiology to this new branch of thermodynamics, and to suggest some possible applications of the theory to biological problems. A number of texts dealing with the thermodynamics of irreversible processes have appeared during the last 15 years, including works by Denbigh,[8] de Groot,[9] Prigogine,[10] Fitts,[11] and de Groot and Mazur.[12] These are, however, directed more toward the student of theoretical physics and chemistry and give little attention to those branches of quantitative biology which can be interpreted by the thermodynamic formalism. Since this book is intended more for those interested in biological problems, greater stress will be placed on understanding of the physical concepts related to living systems than on precise and detailed mathematical development or on actual experimental detail. In order to make the text complete in itself, the first part is devoted to a summary of those aspects of classical thermodynamics that are required for further study of the subject. The second part deals with the fundamentals of the thermodynamics of irreversible processes, and the final section with specific examples of the application of the thermodynamic formalism.

CHAPTER 1

THE FIRST LAW OF THERMODYNAMICS

1.1. Systems and Characteristic Parameters

THERMODYNAMICS is concerned with a description of the world by means of concepts and laws derived from a study of macroscopic phenomena. Since the "world" as a whole is not readily amenable to experimental study, certain parts of it must be isolated from their surroundings and subjected to controlled experimental conditions. Those parts of the observable world isolated for thermodynamic study are called *thermodynamic systems* or simply *systems*. There are numerous methods of isolation; the simplest is to enclose the system within some type of wall, but the isolation may also be effected by energy barriers or by other more sophisticated devices. However, for the sake of simplicity, we shall consider only walls or barriers which bring about three fundamental forms of isolation and which lead to a definition of three basic types of systems:

1. *Adiabatic systems* are enclosed by walls that prevent exchange of both matter and thermal energy between the system and its surroundings. Perfect adiabatic walls are an ideal limiting case which can, however, be approached rather closely by certain experimental devices. An adiabatic system is only partly prevented from interacting with the external world; it can perform mechanical work or can be acted upon by mechanical means, but this action may not be accompanied by any exchange of heat or matter.

2. *Closed systems* are surrounded by *diathermal* walls, which allow an exchange of heat or thermal energy with the surroundings but prevent the transfer of matter into or out of the system. There are many types of diathermal walls. Some, such as metallic heat conductors, allow rapid exchange of thermal energy, while others, such as imperfect thermal insulators, permit only a slow exchange of heat to occur. The limiting case of poor heat conductors is clearly the adiabatic wall discussed above.

3. *Open systems* are enclosed by walls that allow exchange of both matter and energy with the surroundings. The study of such systems has particular importance for the understanding of biological phenomena, since living organisms constantly exchange both matter and thermal energy with their external environment. For the sake of simplicity, we shall start

our considerations with the analysis of adiabatic and diathermal systems, which are the primary objects of classical thermodynamics. As we proceed with the subject of the thermodynamics of irreversible processes, we shall find that our primary concern will be with open systems.

Any description of a thermodynamic system is based on the specification of a set of parameters, which may be either *external* or *internal.* The very process of isolation is based on the fixation of some external parameters, such as the ones defining geometric dimensions. The volume of the system, the external pressure exerted by the surroundings on its walls, and the electrical state of the external bodies in contact with the system are examples of external parameters. These parameters are functions of the generalized coordinates characterizing the external bodies with which the system can interact. For a complete description, we also require a set of internal parameters, which describe the local and temporary properties of the system. The momentary distribution of concentrations in a diffusional process and the distribution of pressures during a rapid compression are examples of internal parameters. The internal parameters are determined both by the external parameters and by the positions and velocities of the molecules composing the system. For example, if we subject a body to the action of an electric field, the field strength, which is determined by the position and charge density of the external bodies, is an external parameter. The electrical state of the molecules or their degree of polarization is an internal parameter of the system.

The thermodynamic parameters may be divided into two classes: *extensive parameters,* such as volume and mass, which depend on the size of the system as a whole and on the amounts of the various substances present, and *intensive parameters,* such as pressure and concentrations, which have definite values at each point in the system and do not depend on its size. The *state* or condition of a thermodynamic system may be defined by specifying the values of a number of these parameters. Any function determined *completely* by such parameters is a *function of state.* More explicitly, a state function is a total derivative of the thermodynamic parameters as variables. Thus, the quantity Z, as a function of pressure P, volume V, and number of moles n_i, will be a function of state if the total differential dZ is given by

$$dZ = \left(\frac{\partial Z}{\partial P}\right)_{V,n_i} dP + \left(\frac{\partial Z}{\partial V}\right)_{P,n_i} dV + \sum_{i=1}^{k} \left(\frac{\partial Z}{\partial n_i}\right)_{P,V,n_j} dn_i. \tag{1-1}$$

An important property of the state function Z, defined by Eq. (1-1), is that the change in Z accompanying the transition of the system from one state to another depends only on the initial and final states and not on the path between them.

Among the possible states that a system can assume, a particularly important one is that of *thermodynamic equilibrium*. This is the state reached by a system that is left for a long time with no external restraints. An important property of systems at equilibrium is that the internal parameters are fully determined by the external ones. In other words, at equilibrium, the external parameters may be used as parameters of state. This important property leads to considerable simplification in the description of such systems and is one of the reasons why classical thermodynamics has dealt primarily with states of equilibrium. The description of systems in flow, such as those generally encountered in nature, requires a larger number of parameters and must include explicit consideration of the internal parameters and their variation in space and time.

1.2. The Work Principle for Adiabatic Systems

If an adiabatic system is subjected to the operation of external forces X_i which cause the external parameters of the system a_i to change by an amount da_i, a quantity of work dW is performed according to Eq. (1-2):

$$dW = \sum_{i=1}^{n} X_i da_i. \tag{1-2}$$

Thus, if the external force is an isobaric pressure P, changing the volume by an amount dV, the work performed is $dW = PdV$. Work done by the system is considered positive, since it is gained by the external world. Work done by the operator on the system is lost by the external world and is considered negative. Since an adiabatic system is not influenced by changes in external temperature and cannot exchange matter with the surroundings, the changes in the external parameters fully determine the change in the state of the system.

Many experiments, particularly those of Joule, have established that the work accompanying the transition of an adiabatic system from one state to another is independent of the physical path. Thus, the work of compression W_{12}, given by

$$W_{12} = \int_1^2 PdV, \tag{1-3}$$

required to take an adiabatic system from state 1 to state 2 is independent of the intermediate values assumed by P and is fully determined by the initial and final states of the system. As discussed above, this implies that under these conditions dW is a total differential whose integral is independent of the path and is determined uniquely by the boundaries of integration. In other words, there exists a potential function of state U whose differential decrease represents the element of work:

$$-dU = dW. \tag{1-4}$$

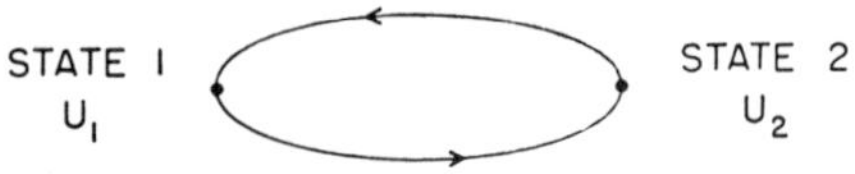

Fig. 1. Internal energy changes in a cyclic process.

The function U is called the *internal energy* of the system. For an integral process, the relation between internal energy and work is given by

$$W_{12} = \int_1^2 dW = -\int_1^2 dU = U_1 - U_2. \tag{1-5}$$

An important property of total differentials is that they vanish when integrated around a closed cycle. Thus, for the cycle illustrated in Fig. 1,

$$-\oint dW = \oint dU = \int_1^2 dU + \int_2^1 dU = U_2 - U_1 + U_1 - U_2 = 0, \tag{1-6}$$

and any complete cyclic change of an adiabatic system leaves the internal energy unchanged.

1.3. The Zeroth Law of Thermodynamics

The parameters discussed in Sec. 1.1 are the usual physical and geometric properties of any system. However, thermodynamics requires an additional parameter of a thermal nature, *the temperature*. Experimental study of closed systems shows that two systems in thermal contact undergo change until a state of equilibrium is attained. This state is defined uniquely by the new parameter, the temperature. If system 1 maintains thermal equilibrium with system 2 and system 2 maintains equilibrium with system 3, then upon bringing 1 into contact with 3 we shall find that 1 is also in thermal equilibrium with 3. In contradistinction to chemical equilibrium, which may be defined by an equilibrium for one chemical species in systems 1 and 2 and for another species in systems 2 and 3, thermal equilibrium is characterized by the equality of a *single* parameter for all systems. This parameter, the temperature, is a universal function and may be written as $T = \Phi(a_i, U_i)$ in which the a_i are the state parameters and U_i the energy of the ith system. This unique property of thermal equilibria was first stated clearly by Joseph Black in the 18th century. Recently, Guggenheim suggested that the principle be called the *zeroth law of thermodynamics* since the first and second places in the sequence of thermodynamic principles were already occupied. This law implies the possibility of constructing a universal temperature scale. We shall not discuss the development of such a scale but shall point out the fundamental assumptions involved. For a system in thermal equilibrium, the energy is assumed to be distributed uniquely over all the parts of the system. An increase in the energy of the system as a whole is assumed to raise the energy level of all parts of the system, and, finally, the temperature of the system is considered to increase monotonically with its energy content. The last condition, $(\partial U/\partial T) > 0$, defines the direction of the temperature scale.

1.4. The First Law of Thermodynamics

The considerations of Sec. 1.2 for an adiabatic system can be readily generalized to include a closed system separated by a diathermal wall from a large heat reservoir. In order to analyze such a system, we shall enclose both the closed system under investigation A and the heat reservoir B by a common adiabatic wall, as illustrated in Fig. 2, and shall assign to the system as a whole an internal energy content U. Since the internal energy has the dimensions of work, it is an extensive property and the total internal energy of the system is the sum of the internal energy of the working system, U_A, and that of the reservoir, U_B:

$$U = U_A + U_B. \tag{1-7}$$

Any work performed by the closed system A is now carried out by an adiabatic system consisting of subsystems A and B. According to Eq. (1-4), the work is equal to the decrease of the internal energy of the system as a whole:

$$-dU = -dU_A - dU_B = dW, \tag{1-8}$$

or

$$dU_A = -dU_B - dW. \tag{1-9}$$

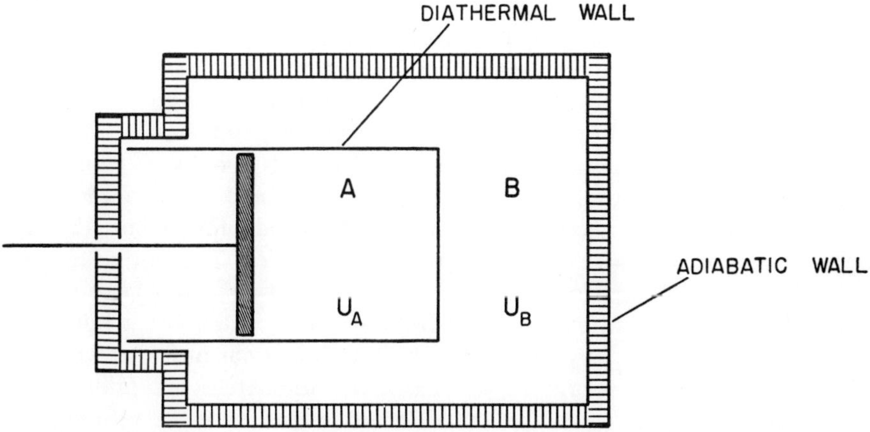

Fig. 2. Model for analysis of changes in internal energy of a closed system; A is the closed system under consideration and B is a heat reservoir. The total system, $A + B$, is surrounded by an adiabatic wall.

Since the complete system is adiabatic, the decrease in the energy of the reservoir, $-dU_B$, must be due to transport of energy from B to A. We shall define *energy transported from one system to another as heat* and denote it by the symbol Q. Thus, for the system under discussion, $dQ = -dU_B$ and Eq. (1-9) becomes

$$dU_A = dQ - dW. \tag{1-10}$$

Equation (1-10) is the mathematical statement of the *first law of thermodynamics*. In adiabatic systems, $dQ = 0$ and Eq. (1-10) reduces to Eq. (1-4). In closed systems, which may exchange energy with their surroundings, dW is not a state function or total differential, and the integral of dW becomes dependent on the path followed between the initial and final states. Similarly, dQ is not a total differential but represents a small quantity of energy transported from the reservoir to the closed system. On the other hand, U is a state function whose magnitude is fully determined by the parameters of the system. For a cyclic process, we may write

$$\oint dU = 0 = \oint dQ - \oint dW. \tag{1-11}$$

However, neither $\oint dQ$ nor $\oint dW$ will vanish unless the process is adiabatic.

Equation (1-10) expresses the law of conservation of energy as formulated by Helmholtz in 1847. Similar laws, such as the laws of conservation of mass and of mechanical energy, had been known since the 17th century. The first law of thermodynamics expresses, however, a conservation principle of a wider nature, for it includes various forms of energy, the work function, the thermal energy, and the internal energy. It implies a more profound insight into the nature of energy and predicts the possibility of converting one form of energy into another.

The difficulty of grasping the unifying concept of energy prevented scientists of the 19th century from immediately accepting R. Meyer's bold declaration of the first law in 1842. However, the law of conservation of energy as formulated by Helmholtz withstood all revolutions in physics and is now accepted not only in thermodynamics but also in the theory of relativity and in quantum mechanics. The law is also a statement on impossible processes, as are all laws of conservation. It states that energy can be converted from one form into another but cannot be obtained from any type of machinery that is not provided with an adequate source of energy. Historically, it summarizes all failures to build engines of perpetual motion of the first kind and is a recognition of human inability to create something out of nothing. This "impotence," which is imposed by all laws of nature, is equivalent to the realization that natural phenomena obey certain sets of regulations and restrictions.

It is only the recognition of these limitations and the apprehension of the orderly structure of the world that make possible prediction and scientific planning. More extensive discussion of the basic principles considered in this and the following four chapters may be found in texts of classical thermodynamics, some of which are listed in the reference section of this chapter.

CHAPTER 2

THE SECOND LAW OF THERMODYNAMICS

2.1. Quasi-equilibrium Processes

THE second law of thermodynamics is the product of a long attempt to find an adequate quantitative expression defining the directional properties of *natural* or *spontaneous processes.* Idealized processes may be reversible and proceed indefinitely in the forward or backward directions, but all natural processes proceed in only one direction, toward an equilibrium state, and upon reaching this state they come to a halt. A mathematical pendulum may swing periodically an infinite number of times, but an actual pendulum will stop moving after a time owing to friction in the bearings or to the frictional resistance of the air. Thus, spontaneous processes dissipate their moving power. This dissipative aspect attracted the attention of the thermodynamicists of the 19th century, who felt that a criterion of unidirectional progress of spontaneous processes might be found in the degradation of motile energy. However, idealized reversible processes had to serve as the starting point for the theoretical development of the pertinent concepts. These ideal processes have the advantage of mathematical simplicity and the expressions derived for them may be extended to apply to real irreversible processes.

The thermodynamic equivalent of a reversible mechanical process is a quasi-equilibrium or quasi-static process. At equilibrium the internal parameters of a system are single-valued functions of the external parameters so that specification of the external parameters describes the state of the system fully. If the rate of change in external parameters is so slow that the internal parameters are able to adjust their values at every instant to those of the external ones, the process is quasi-static. This type of process may be considered as a sequence of equilibrium states and can be treated by the equations obtained for systems in equilibrium. For such a quasi-equilibrium process, reversal of the direction of change in the external parameters will cause the inner parameters to retrace exactly the path of their change so that these processes are truly reversible.

2.2. Kelvin's Formulation of the Second Law and the Principle of Carathéodory

The second law of thermodynamics may be stated in several equivalent forms, but for our purpose the expression of Kelvin is the most convenient. This formulation states that it is impossible to devise an engine operating in a cycle that produces positive work as a result of the cooling of a single reservoir. In other words, no device can produce positive work in a cyclic operation from the cooling of a single body without concomitant changes in surrounding bodies. (Thomson's (Lord Kelvin's) formulation is found in the famous article of 1853.[1] The original wording of the statement is as follows: "It is impossible by means of inanimate material agency to derive mechanical effect from any portion of matter by cooling it below the temperature of the coldest of the surrounding objects.") This statement is similar in nature to the first law since it summarizes the failure to construct machines based on a *perpetual motion of the second kind*. It states, for example, that the cooling of a single body, the ocean, cannot provide the useful energy required to drive a ship, even though the absorption of thermal energy from the water and its cyclic transformation into mechanical work would not violate the first law. Another, more restricted version of Kelvin's statement is that any closed system which undergoes an isothermal cyclic process cannot produce positive work.

In mathematical terms, the principle states that

$$\oint (dW)_T \leq 0, \tag{2-1}$$

in which the subscript T indicates that the temperature is constant throughout the cycle. In a reversible process, the work gained in the first part of any cycle,

$$\int_1^2 dW_T = W_{12},$$

is exactly compensated by the work required to bring the system isothermally back to its starting point,

$$\int_2^1 dW_T = -W_{12},$$

and hence the cyclic integral is zero. For all natural, irreversible processes, the inequality in Eq. (2-1) holds and the cyclic integral is negative. This means that, as a result of irreversible losses, the work required to restore the initial state is greater than any possible gain.

The requirement that the work integral is zero for a reversible cyclic process carried out under isothermal conditions is equivalent to a statement that positive work can be derived from a decrease in a potential function. Thus, in accordance with the discussion in Sec. 1.2,

$$dW_T = -dF_T. \tag{2-2}$$

The isothermal thermodynamic potential, F, is the *free-energy* function introduced by Helmholtz in 1882. In correspondence with Eq. (1-2), we may now write for isothermal work

$$dW_T = \sum X_i da_i = -dF_T.$$

The forces, X_i, are then given by

$$X_i = -\left(\frac{\partial F}{\partial a_i}\right)_{a_j, T}. \tag{2-3}$$

For example, if an isothermal system undergoes an expansion dV at a pressure P with investment of work given by PdV and an increase in length dl at a force f with performance of work $-fdl$,

$$dW = PdV - fdl,$$

and the forces are related to the free energy by the expressions

$$P = -\left(\frac{\partial F}{\partial V}\right)_{l, T}, \qquad f = \left(\frac{\partial F}{\partial l}\right)_{V, T}. \tag{2-4}$$

At the beginning of this century, Carathéodory[2] arrived at an important conclusion concerning adiabatic processes which may be derived from Kelvin's statement of the second law. Although Carathéodory's statement lacks the physical concreteness of Kelvin's formulation, it is a convenient starting point for an alternative mathematical development of the second law.[3] The statement may be expressed as follows: *there exist states that cannot be reached by a homogeneous system undergoing any adiabatic process*, whether reversible or irreversible. To derive this conclusion from Kelvin's principle, we shall consider a hypothetical cycle, consisting of two steps. In the first step, the system passes isothermally from state 1 to state 2, and in the second step, we assume that it can be made to return adiabatically from state 2 to state 1. According to the first law, the change in internal energy accompanying the first step is

$$U_2 - U_1 = Q_{12} - W_{12}, \tag{2-5}$$

in which Q_{12} is the heat absorbed from a reservoir with which the system maintained thermal contact during the first step, and W_{12} is the work obtained during the process. The energy change during the second step would be

$$U_1 - U_2 = -W_{21}. \tag{2-6}$$

There is no heat term in Eq. (2-6), since heat cannot be exchanged with the surroundings during an adiabatic process. Adding Eqs. (2-5) and (2-6), we obtain, for the work W resulting from the complete cycle,

$$W = \oint dW = W_{12} + W_{21} = Q_{12}. \tag{2-7}$$

This expression is, however, untenable because of the restriction imposed by Kelvin's law. If Eq. (2-7) were correct, we could obtain positive work from the cooling of a single body—the heat reservoir applied in the first step. Since this is not allowed, we must conclude that upon reaching state 2 it is impossible to return adiabatically to state 1, or, as concluded by Carathéodory, there are states that cannot be reached by an adiabatic process. This alternative formulation of the second law leads to a proof for the existence of an integrating factor for the heat term, dQ, and to the definition of a new and important state function, the *entropy.*

2.3. The Entropy

In order to illustrate the mathematical treatment leading to the concept of entropy, we must consider, very briefly, a group of differential expressions of the Pfaffian form,

$$dw = \mathcal{P}dx + \mathcal{R}dy + \mathcal{S}dz, \tag{2-8}$$

and the associated Pfaffian equations

$$dw = 0, \tag{2-9}$$

in which $\mathcal{P}$, $\mathcal{R}$, and $\mathcal{S}$ are functions of x, y, and z. The integrability of these equations depends on whether dw is an exact or an inexact differential in the sense discussed in Sec. 1.1. If dw is exact,

$$dw = d\eta(x, y, z),$$

the integral of dw is independent of the path and the Pfaffian equation has a solution

$$\eta(x, y, z) = c,$$

in which c is a constant. If dw is an inexact differential, an attempt can be made to find a multiplier, an integrating factor, which when multiplied by dw gives a product that is an exact differential of x, y, and z.

It can be shown that a Pfaffian expression in two variables,

$$dw = \mathcal{P}dx + \mathcal{R}dy,$$

always has an integrating factor. However, if the equation has more than two variables, the existence of an integrating factor cannot be generally assumed. According to Carathéodory, the condition of integrability for such an expression can be stated topologically. A Pfaffian in three or more variables will have an integrating factor only if there exist points in the neighborhood of a given point that cannot be reached along curves representing solutions of the Pfaffian equation. The connection between this mathematical theorem of Carathéodory and his statement concerning adiabatic processes is apparent. His physical statement may be regarded as the mathematical requirement for the existence of an integrating factor for the Pfaffian equations of thermodynamics.

We may illustrate this point briefly for a two-dimensional Pfaffian. In this case, an integrating factor, λ, must exist, so that we may write

$$\lambda dw = d\eta = \lambda \mathcal{P} dx + \lambda \mathcal{R} dy, \tag{2-10}$$

in which $d\eta$ is an exact differential. The integrated form of the associated Pfaffian equation $d\eta = 0$ is

$$\eta(x, y) = c,$$

in which the constant c can have any value. Figure 3 shows hypothetical solutions for two values of c. Starting from a point on the plane $\eta = c_1$, any other point on the plane can be reached along curves representing a solution of the Pfaffian equation. However, it is impossible to pass from any point on the plane $\eta = c_1$ to the plane $\eta = c_2$. Thus, there exist in the neighborhood of $\eta = c_1$ an infinite number of points that cannot be reached by any variation in x and y.

We can illustrate the application of these mathematical considerations to thermodynamics by writing the first law in the following form:

$$dQ = dU + dW = dU + \sum X_i da_i, \tag{2-11}$$

where dQ is substituted for the differential dw. If the process under consideration is reversible, all the forces X_i are fully determined by the external parameters a_i and we may write $X_i = X_i(a_i)$, or

$$dQ = dU + \sum X_i(a_i) da_i. \tag{2-12}$$

In this form Eq. (2-12) is a Pfaffian equation of the type (2-8) in terms of the independent variables a_i, equivalent to x, y, and z.

According to Carathéodory's statement, starting from a given state,

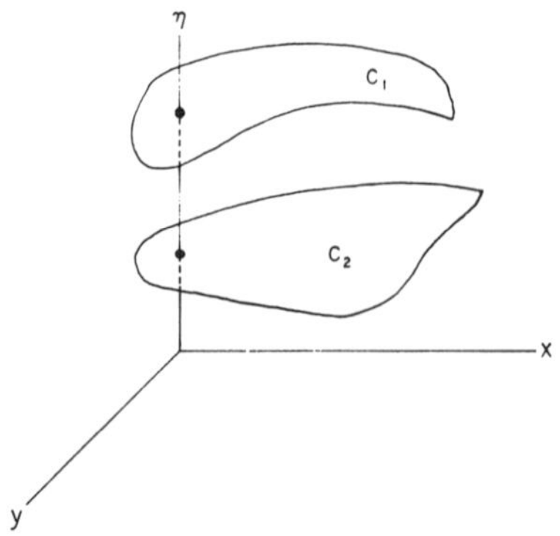

Fig. 3. Hypothetical solutions for a two-dimensional Pfaffian equation.

there are many states that cannot be reached by an adiabatic process along the path $dQ = 0$. This condition ensures the existence of an integrating factor for dQ, so that we may write

$$\lambda dQ = d\eta,$$

in which, for a reversible process, $d\eta$ is a total differential of the thermodynamic variables a_i equivalent to x and y in Eq. (2-10). Therefore, η must be a function of the state parameters a_i. This new state function is called the *entropy* and is denoted by S. It can be shown that the integrating factor is equal to $1/T$ in which T is the absolute temperature. We thus arrive at the conclusion that

$$dS = \frac{dQ}{T}. \tag{2-13}$$

Equation (2-13) may be considered as the mathematical statement of the second law of thermodynamics for reversible processes. It is important to stress that this proof is valid for reversible processes only. The treatment of entropy in natural irreversible processes is considered in Chapter 4.

This development of the concept of entropy is perhaps somewhat abstract, but it is more straightforward than the classical approach using ideal heat engines and may serve to remove some of the mystery from the entropy concept, particularly for those preferring a more mathematical approach. We have obviously made no attempt at a rigorous mathematical analysis but have merely sketched its outline. More complete discussion of this approach can be found in the article of M. Born[3] or in the texts of Margenau and Murphy[4] and Kirkwood and Oppenheim.[5]

Introducing Eq. (2-13) into Eq. (1-10), we obtain the expression for the combined first and second laws,

$$dU = TdS - dW, \tag{2-14}$$

which summarizes all that has been discussed in the previous sections. In an adiabatic process, $dQ = 0$ and hence $dS = 0$, and

$$dU = -dW,$$

as stated in the work principle for adiabatic systems. In a reversible isothermal cycle,

$$\oint dU = T \oint dS - \oint dW, \tag{2-15}$$

and, since both dU and dS are total differentials,

$$\oint dW = 0, \tag{2-16}$$

which corresponds to Kelvin's principle for an isothermal reversible cycle.

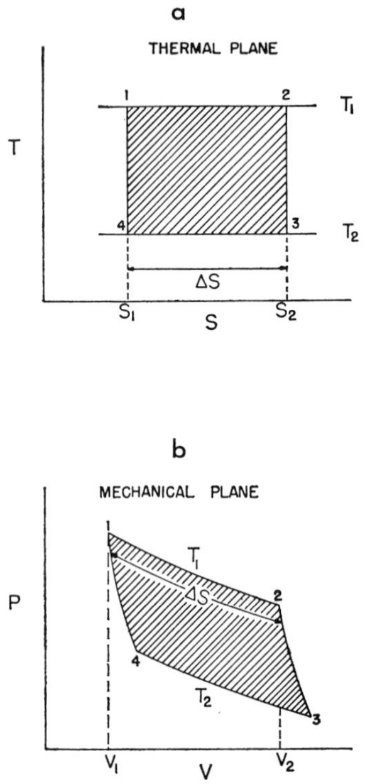

Fig. 4. Diagrammatic representation of a cyclic reversible process in (*a*) thermal and (*b*) mechanical planes.

If the temperature is not kept constant during such a cycle, the integral $\oint TdS$ does not vanish and positive work may be obtained. This may be illustrated by considering the simple case of a reversible engine operating between a higher temperature T_1 and a lower one T_2. The work cycle for such an engine is shown schematically in Fig. 4, representing projection of the cycle on a thermal plane and on a mechanical plane. The mechanical plane, Fig. 4*b*, represents the changes in volume and pressure accompanying the work of a gas engine of the type considered by Carnot.[6] The gas in state 1 (P_1, V_1, T_1) is allowed to expand isothermally to state 2 maintaining contact with a heat reservoir of temperature T_1. The work obtained by the surroundings in this process is

$$W_{12} = \int_1^2 PdV$$

and is represented by the area V_1–1–2–V_2. During the process, heat is absorbed from the reservoir in an amount represented in the thermal plane by

$$Q_{12} = \int_1^2 T_1 dS = T_1(S_2 - S_1) = T_1 \Delta S,$$

or by the rectangular area S_1–1–2–S_2 in Fig. 4*a*. In the next step, the gas is allowed to expand adiabatically from state 2 to state 3 and further work, given by

$$W_{23} = \int_2^3 PdV,$$

is obtained. However, no heat is exchanged, so that $Q_{23} = 0$ and the entropy remains at the constant value S_2. From state 3, the engine is brought back to its initial state by work introduced from the surroundings. The total work supplied in the two steps $3 \to 4$ and $4 \to 1$ is

$$W_{34} + W_{41} = \int_3^4 PdV + \int_4^1 PdV.$$

During the step $3 \to 4$, the engine is in contact with a heat reservoir at a temperature T_2 ($T_2 < T_1$) and heat is given off by the engine in an amount

$$Q_{34} = \int_3^4 T_2 dS = T_2(S_4 - S_2).$$

According to Fig. 4*a*,

$$Q_{34} = T_2(S_1 - S_2) = -T_2 \Delta S.$$

The last step from state 4 to state 1 is adiabatic, so that $S_4 = S_1$.

The work obtained in the complete cycle is given by

$$\oint dW = W = W_{12} + W_{23} + W_{34} + W_{41}. \tag{2-17}$$

The total work is represented by the shaded area in Fig. 4*b*. The sum of the heat terms for the complete cycle gives

$$\oint dQ = Q_{12} + Q_{34} = (T_1 - T_2)\Delta S. \tag{2-18}$$

Using the combined first and second laws, represented by Eq. (2-14), we obtain

$$\oint dU = \oint dQ - \oint dW = \oint TdS - \oint dW.$$

Since $\oint dU$ is always zero,

$$\oint TdS = (T_1 - T_2)\Delta S = \oint dW = W. \tag{2-19}$$

This conclusion states that the mechanical area in the P–V plane in Fig. 4*b* is equal to the thermal area in the T–S plane of Fig. 4*a*. The equality does not hold for every step and it is only the balance in a cyclic process that leads to the equality of the mechanical and thermal terms.

Equation (2-19) illustrates another aspect of the second law; it shows that work can be obtained by the transport of entropy across a temperature difference. When the temperature difference goes to zero, no work can be obtained. (This statement is equivalent to the famous formulation of the second law of thermodynamics by Clausius,[7] which states that it is impossible to transfer heat from a reservoir and transform it all into work in a cyclic process without transferring, at the same time, a certain amount of heat from a hotter to a colder body.) As discussed below, the principle of Kelvin can be generalized to show that positive work can be obtained when there exists a difference of potential across which a conjugated extensive quantity is transported. Equation (2-19) shows that in the conversion of thermal energy into work the quantity transported is an extensive or capacitative quantity, the entropy, while the temperature plays the role of an intensive or potential quantity. From this point of view, the introduction of the integrating factor for dQ leads to a decomposition of the thermal energy into an extensive factor, S, and an intensive factor, T. In the following chapter we shall consider all energy terms, except the internal energy, as the products of capacitative and intensive terms.

The physical meaning of entropy has intrigued physicists and philosophers since its introduction by Clausius in 1865. Clausius himself recognized that entropy is not a conservative quantity and, as will be shown below, that it increases in irreversible processes. In spite of its mathematical clarity, the notion of entropy is not one of the elementary concepts of physics that conveys a direct intuitive idea. However, the advent of statistical mechanics has succeeded in removing some of the mystery attached to this capacity of thermal energy. Boltzmann has shown that entropy is proportional to the number of configurations Ω in which a system can be realized, according to the relation

$$S = k \ln \Omega, \tag{2-18}$$

in which k is the Boltzmann constant. An increase in the number of arrangements or configurations that a system can assume increases its entropy, while any restriction in the modes of realization decreases entropy. Thus, mixing, disorganization, and randomization increase entropy, while organization and ordering decrease it. The concept of entropy as a measure of order is slowly gaining ground in modern science and has recently penetrated such fields as the theories of communication and information. For our purpose, however, the classical concept of Clausius is sufficient and we may consider dS as the total differential assigned to heat changes in reversible processes and S as the capacitative conjugate of temperature in thermal energy.

CHAPTER 3

THE GIBBS EQUATION

3.1. The Differential Form of the Gibbs Equation

BEFORE discussing changes in entropy during irreversible processes, we shall consider some further implications of the second law as stated in the previous chapter and shall extend our analysis to open systems. All the systems considered in the first two chapters were surrounded by walls preventing exchange of matter with the surroundings. The formalism that has been developed is, however, sufficient to remove this restriction and to consider also open systems. This step was taken by Gibbs[1] in his famous treatise on thermodynamics and we shall follow his procedure by analyzing the work term, dW, in greater detail.

In introducing dW in the previous chapters, we have implied that the work under consideration was essentially mechanical work. A system can, however, perform numerous other types of work. If the system is a contractile fiber that shortens by an amount $-dl$ under a force f, it performs work equal to $-fdl$, or if a quantity of electricity $-de$ is given off by a system at an electric potential ψ, electrical work, equal to $-\psi de$, is obtained. If $-dn_i$ moles of the ith component are transported from the system to the surroundings, chemical work, given by $-\mu_i dn_i$, is performed. The intensive factor, μ_i, which relates chemical work to the number of moles transported, was called by Gibbs the chemical potential of the ith component. On the basis of these considerations, we may write the work term in a more general form,

$$dW = PdV - fdl - \psi de - \sum_{i=1}^{k} \mu_i dn_i + \cdots , \tag{3-1}$$

in which the summation is carried out over all chemical components that are transported between the system and its surroundings. Introducing Eq. (3-1) into Eq. (2-14) we obtain the equation of Gibbs,

$$dU = TdS - PdV + fdl + \psi de + \sum_{i=1}^{k} \mu_i dn_i + \cdots . \tag{3-2}$$

Equation (3-2) is valid for open as well as for closed and adiabatic systems. It takes into account all possible changes in extensive properties (dS, dV,

dl, dn_i, de) and relates the total change in internal energy to the sum of products of intensive quantities (T, P, f, μ_i, and ψ) and changes in capacities. In this chapter, we shall use Eq. (3-2) for the more limited case in which ψde and the additional nonspecified terms are taken equal to zero. Thus, Eq. (3-2) becomes

$$dU = TdS - PdV + fdl + \sum_{i=1}^{k} \mu_i dn_i. \tag{3-3}$$

Equation (3-3) defines the chemical potential as the change in internal energy due to addition of dn_i moles of the ith component to the system at constant S, V, l and, n_j, where j denotes all species other than the ith. Thus,

$$\mu_i = \left(\frac{\partial U}{\partial n_i}\right)_{S,V,l,n_j}. \tag{3-4}$$

In a later section, we shall define μ_i in another way more accessible to experimental determination.

In a cyclic reversible process, all extensive properties of a system must be conserved, so that $\oint dS = \oint dV = \oint dl = \oint dn_i = 0$. This permits us to obtain from Eq. (3-3) the generalization of Kelvin's formulation mentioned above. The method may be illustrated by a simple example.[2] We shall consider a reversible cyclic process in which temperature, pressure, and the number of moles of all species but one remain constant. The mathematical description of such a process is

$$\oint dU = T \oint dS - P \oint dV + \oint fdl + \oint \mu dn, \tag{3-5}$$

or, since $\oint dU = \oint dS = \oint dV = 0$,

$$W = -\oint fdl = \oint \mu dn. \tag{3-6}$$

The integral $-\oint fdl$ could represent, for example, the contractile work W of a fiber that can operate in a manner similar to muscle upon interaction with a specific chemical agent. Equation (3-6) is then the expression for the transformation of chemical into mechanical energy in an isothermal, isobaric cycle. If μ is constant throughout the cycle, $\oint \mu dn = 0$ and no contractile work can be obtained; hence, in order to transform chemical energy into useful work, a difference in chemical potential is required. As an example, we shall consider the simplest case using two chemical potentials, $\mu_1 > \mu_2$. The cyclic process involved is illustrated schematically in Fig. 5, representing a projection on both mechanical and chemical planes. For this cycle,

$$\oint \mu dn = \int_1^2 \mu_1 dn + \int_3^4 \mu_2 dn = \mu_1(n_2 - n_1) + \mu_2(n_4 - n_3). \tag{3-7}$$

The transitions 2 → 3 and 4 → 1 are made at constant n and do not contribute to the integral. Since $n_3 = n_2$ and $n_4 = n_1$, Eq. (3-7) becomes

$$\oint \mu dn = (\mu_1 - \mu_2)\Delta n, \tag{3-8}$$

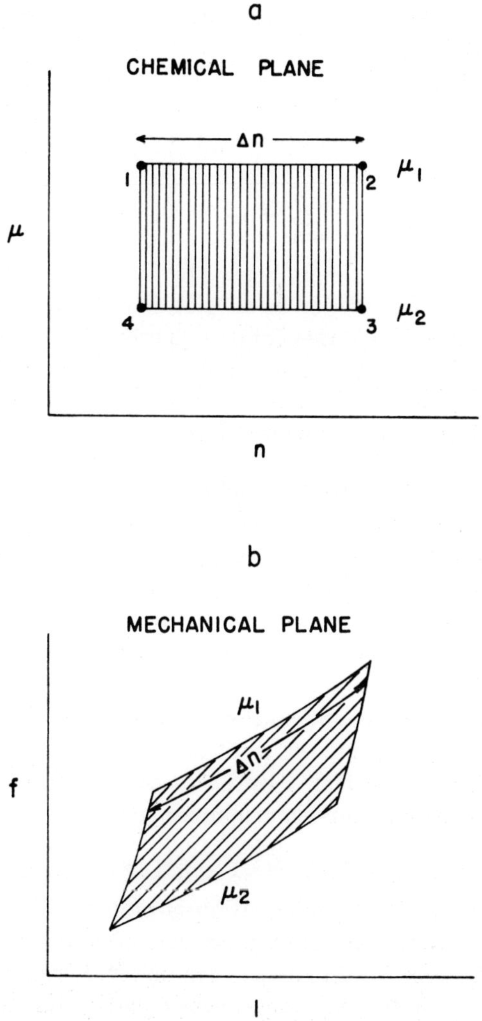

Fig. 5. Diagrammatic representation of a mechanicochemical system in (a) chemical and (b) mechanical terms. The cyclic operation of the system is assumed to take place under isothermal and isobaric conditions.

in which $\Delta n = n_2 - n_1$ is the amount of substance absorbed at the higher chemical potential, μ_1. From Eq. (3-6),

$$W = (\mu_1 - \mu_2)\Delta n. \tag{3-9}$$

Equation (3-9) indicates that the transport of Δn moles through a chemical potential difference will produce positive work in a mechanicochemical engine, in the same way that the transfer of entropy ΔS across a temperature difference yields work in a thermomechanical engine. Similar conclusions can be reached by considering thermoelectric, electromechanical, or electrochemical engines. Brønsted[3] has summarized these results in his work principle which states that the over-all work ΔW performed by a system is the sum of contributions due to transport of extensive quantities ΔK_i across a difference of conjugated potentials $\mathcal{P}_{i(1)} - \mathcal{P}_{i(2)}$:

$$\Delta W = \sum_{i=1}^{k} (\mathcal{P}_{i(1)} - \mathcal{P}_{i(2)})\Delta K_i, \tag{3-10}$$

in which for example $\mathcal{P}_{i(1)} - \mathcal{P}_{i(2)}$ may be $T_1 - T_2$, $\mu_1 - \mu_2$, or $\psi_1 - \psi^2$ and the ΔK_i will be ΔS, Δn, or Δe respectively. Brønsted's principle may evidently be derived from the Gibbs equation. The equation of Gibbs has, however, a wider range of applicability, is not restricted to two values of the potential terms, and leads to numerous other conclusions which will be discussed in the following sections.

3.2. The Integration of the Gibbs Equation—The Gibbs–Duhem Equation

Much additional information can be obtained from Eqs. (3-2) and (3-3) if an integration is carried out on the Pfaffian form. This is not a trivial step since the intensive properties are functions of all the independent parameters of the system. Thus the integration of the term PdV cannot be carried out in a straightforward manner since P is a function not only of V but also of the temperature, of the number of moles, of the electric state of the system, and possibly of other parameters. In order to carry out the integration, we shall use an important relation for homogeneous equations discovered by Euler. An equation, $\Phi(x, y, z) = 0$, is a homogeneous equation of the nth order if

$$\Phi(\lambda x, \lambda y, \lambda z) = \lambda^n \Phi(x, y, z). \tag{3-11}$$

Thus, if every variable of the equation is multiplied by a factor λ, the resulting expression will be the same as that obtained by multiplying the equation as a whole by λ raised to the nth power. For example, the expression $ax + by + cz = 0$ is a homogeneous equation of the first order, and $ax^2 + bxy + cz^2 = 0$ is a homogeneous equation of the second order. Let us now differentiate $\Phi(\lambda x, \lambda y, \lambda z)$ with respect to λ keeping x, y, z constant:

$$\frac{\partial\Phi(\lambda x, \lambda y, \lambda z)}{\partial\lambda} = x\left(\frac{\partial\Phi}{\partial\lambda x}\right)_{\lambda y,\lambda z} + y\left(\frac{\partial\Phi}{\partial\lambda y}\right)_{\lambda x,\lambda z} + z\left(\frac{\partial\Phi}{\partial\lambda z}\right)_{\lambda x,\lambda y}. \tag{3-12}$$

However, in view of Eq. (3-11), Eq. (3-12) should be equal to

$$\frac{\partial\lambda^n\Phi(x, y, z)}{\partial\lambda} = n\lambda^{n-1}\Phi(x, y, z). \tag{3-13}$$

Assuming that $\lambda = 1$ and equating Eqs. (3-12) and (3-13), we obtain Euler's relation:

$$n\Phi = x\left(\frac{\partial\Phi}{\partial x}\right)_{y,z} + y\left(\frac{\partial\Phi}{\partial y}\right)_{x,z} + z\left(\frac{\partial\Phi}{\partial z}\right)_{x,y}. \tag{3-14}$$

All extensive properties of the thermodynamic system are homogeneous functions of the first order in the mass of the system. For example, the internal energy, $U(S, V, l, n_i)$ is doubled by doubling the mass of the system without changing its composition, so that

$$U(2S, 2V, 2l, 2n_i) = 2U(S, V, l, n_i). \tag{3-15}$$

Therefore, according to Euler's relation, $U(S, V, l, n_i)$ may be written as follows:

$$U = S\left(\frac{\partial U}{\partial S}\right)_{V,l,n_i} + V\left(\frac{\partial U}{\partial V}\right)_{S,l,n_i} + l\left(\frac{\partial U}{\partial l}\right)_{S,V,n_i} + \sum_{i=1}^{k} n_i\left(\frac{\partial U}{\partial n_i}\right)_{S,V,l,n_j}. \tag{3-16}$$

From the Gibbs equation, Eq. (3-3), we may obtain the following set of relations for the partial derivatives in Eq. (3-16):

$$\begin{aligned} \left(\frac{\partial U}{\partial S}\right)_{V,l,n_i} &= T, \\ \left(\frac{\partial U}{\partial l}\right)_{S,V,n_i} &= f, \\ \left(\frac{\partial U}{\partial V}\right)_{S,l,n_i} &= -P, \\ \left(\frac{\partial U}{\partial n_i}\right)_{S,V,l,n_j} &= \mu_i. \end{aligned} \tag{3-17}$$

Introducing these into Eq. (3-16), we obtain the integrated form of the Gibbs equation:

$$U = TS - PV + fl + \sum_{i=1}^{k} \mu_i n_i. \tag{3-18}$$

This remarkably simple result leads to conclusions that will be used extensively in the following chapters.

The value of dU obtained by differentiating Eq. (3-18) is different from that given by Eq. (3-3), which served as the starting point for our integration. The differentiation yields

$$dU = TdS + SdT - PdV - VdP + fdl + ldf + \sum_{i=1}^{k} \mu_i dn_i + \sum_{i=1}^{k} n_i d\mu_i. \tag{3-19}$$

If Eqs. (3-3) and (3-19) are to be identical, the following relation must hold:

$$ldf + SdT - VdP + \sum_{i=1}^{k} n_i d\mu_i = 0. \tag{3-20}$$

Equation (3-20) is the important *Gibbs-Duhem equation.* It is particularly useful in the study of isothermal, isobaric systems in which df is also zero. Under these conditions,

$$\sum_{i=1}^{k} n_i d\mu_i = 0. \tag{3-21}$$

The meaning of this equation may be clarified by pointing out that it may be regarded as an abbreviated notation for a set of equations,

$$\sum_{i=1}^{k} n_i \left(\frac{\partial \mu_i}{\partial n_j}\right)_{n_l} = 0. \qquad \begin{matrix}(j = 1, 2, \cdots, k) \\ (l \neq j)\end{matrix} \tag{3-22}$$

This set of k equations correlates changes in the chemical potentials of all components with the addition of any component to the system.

3.3. Thermodynamic Potentials and Cross Relations

3.3.1. At equilibrium, the extensive parameters U, S, V, l, n_i are functions of state, and linear combinations of these parameters are also state functions. Helmholtz, Gibbs, and others have considered such combinations and have found that these are often more useful than the internal energy for describing systems under ordinary experimental conditions. Such combinations are called *thermodynamic potentials.* They are extensive quantities and must not be confused with the ordinary potentials, which are derivatives of the thermodynamic potentials and are intensive quantities. The first such potential introduced was the *Helmholtz free energy* F given by

$$F = U - TS. \tag{3-23}$$

This function is useful in treating systems of constant volume under isothermal conditions. At constant temperature,

$$(dF)_T = dU - TdS. \tag{3-24}$$

From Eq. (2-14), this becomes

$$-(dF)_T = dW. \tag{3-25}$$

Thus, the total reversible work performed by an isothermal system is equal to the decrease in the Helmholtz free energy. As pointed out in Chapter 2, the existence of a potential function for the reversible work of an isothermal system may be deduced directly from Kelvin's law. This function is now identified with the thermodynamic potential of Helmholtz given by Eq. (3-23).

The change in F under any conditions is given by

$$dF = dU - TdS - SdT. \tag{3-26}$$

With Eq. (3-3) for dU, Eq. (3-26) becomes

$$dF = -SdT - PdV + fdl + \sum_{i=1}^{k} \mu_i dn_i. \tag{3-27}$$

Equation (3-27) leads to a new definition of the chemical potential:

$$\mu_i = \left(\frac{\partial F}{\partial n_i}\right)_{T,V,l,n_j}. \tag{3-28}$$

Another important thermodynamic potential is the *Gibbs free energy* G, given by the expression

$$G = U - TS + PV. \tag{3-29}$$

This function is particularly useful at constant temperature and pressure, the conditions that are the easiest to maintain in the laboratory. Under these conditions,

$$(dG)_{T,P} = dU - TdS + PdV. \tag{3-30}$$

Using Eq. (2-14), we obtain

$$-(dG)_{T,P} = dW - PdV. \tag{3-31}$$

Equation (3-31) shows that the decrease in G is equal to the total work minus the work of compression, which Gibbs called the *useful work*, $dW - PdV = dW'$; it is that part of the work contributed by chemical reactions or by the transport of electricity. In the study of condensed systems such as solutions, living tissues, or solid material, PdV is usually small and generally does not contribute significantly to the total work, so that the choice of G as the characteristic potential is common practice. The value of dG under any conditions is given by

$$dG = dU - TdS - SdT + PdV + VdP. \tag{3-32}$$

With Eq. (3-3) for dU, Eq. (3-32) becomes

$$dG = -SdT + VdP + fdl + \sum_{i=1}^{k} \mu_i dn_i. \tag{3-33}$$

This expression defines the chemical potential in its most familiar form,

$$\mu_i = \left(\frac{\partial G}{\partial n_i}\right)_{P,T,l,n_j}. \tag{3-34}$$

Another common thermodynamic potential is the *enthalpy* H, defined by the equation

$$H = U + PV. \tag{3-36}$$

The physical significance of enthalpy becomes apparent if a closed system ($dn_i = 0$, $dl = 0$) under isobaric conditions is considered. Since

$$dH = dU + PdV + VdP, \tag{3-37}$$

we find that at constant pressure

$$(dH)_P = dU + PdV. \quad (3\text{-}38$$

However, if $dn_i = 0$ and $dl = 0$,

$$dU + PdV = (dQ)_P,$$

and hence

$$(dH)_P = (dQ)_P. \tag{3-39}$$

Thus, the enthalpy is a measure of the heat exchanged with the surroundings by a closed system during an isobaric process. If dU is expressed in terms of Eq. (3-3), the general expression for dH, Eq. (3-37), becomes

$$dH = VdP + TdS + fdl + \sum_{i=1}^{k} \mu_i dn_i. \tag{3-40}$$

Inserting Eq. (3-36) into Eq. (3-29), we find that the free energy is related to the enthalpy by the expression

$$G = H - TS. \tag{3-41}$$

3.3.2. There are many other possible linear combinations of state functions, but these are of limited importance in the thermodynamic description of phenomena. They may, however, be of value for derivation of useful cross relations of the type first noted by Maxwell. These so-called *Maxwell relations* are of considerable importance and will be discussed in some detail. The method of obtaining all possible cross relations depends on an important condition for total differentials derived by Cauchy.

As is well known, the second derivative of a function $\Phi(x, y)$ with respect to x and y is independent of the order of differentiation so that

$$\left[\frac{\partial}{\partial y}\left(\frac{\partial \Phi}{\partial x}\right)_y\right]_x = \left[\frac{\partial}{\partial x}\left(\frac{\partial \Phi}{\partial y}\right)_x\right]_y. \tag{3-42}$$

Now let

$$d\Phi = Mdx + Ndy + Pdz,$$

in which $d\Phi$ is a total differential. Then

$$M = \left(\frac{\partial \Phi}{\partial x}\right)_{y,z}, \qquad N = \left(\frac{\partial \Phi}{\partial y}\right)_{x,z}, \qquad P = \left(\frac{\partial \Phi}{\partial z}\right)_{x,y},$$

and, using Eq. (3-42), we obtain

$$\frac{\partial M}{\partial y} = \frac{\partial N}{\partial x}, \qquad \frac{\partial N}{\partial z} = \frac{\partial P}{\partial y}, \qquad \frac{\partial P}{\partial x} = \frac{\partial M}{\partial z}. \tag{3-43}$$

The conditions given by Eqs. (3-43) can be applied immediately to the differentials of the thermodynamic potentials. Since these potentials are functions of state, their differentials are total differentials and the coefficients of their variables must fulfill the Cauchy condition. For example, comparison of the first two terms on the right-hand side of Eq. (3-27) yields the relation

$$\left(\frac{\partial S}{\partial V}\right)_{T,l,n_i} = \left(\frac{\partial P}{\partial T}\right)_{V,l,n_i}, \tag{3-44}$$

which may be used for the construction of important thermodynamic *equations of state*. Thus, if we consider the behavior of a closed system undergoing only compressional change at constant temperature, we may use Eq. (2-14) to obtain

$$\left(\frac{\partial U}{\partial V}\right)_T = T\left(\frac{\partial S}{\partial V}\right)_T - P. \tag{3-45}$$

Introducing Eq. (3-44), we obtain

$$\left(\frac{\partial U}{\partial V}\right)_T = T\left(\frac{\partial P}{\partial T}\right)_V - P. \tag{3-46}$$

If the system is a mole of ideal gas obeying the equation $P = RT/V$,

$$\left(\frac{\partial P}{\partial T}\right)_V = \frac{R}{V},$$

or

$$T\left(\frac{\partial P}{\partial T}\right)_V = \frac{RT}{V} = P.$$

Equation (3-46) then becomes

$$\left(\frac{\partial U}{\partial V}\right)_T = P - P = 0. \tag{3-47}$$

Thus, the internal energy of an ideal gas is independent of the volume and is a function of temperature only; this is the usual criterion of ideality for gaseous systems.

In another context, we may obtain an equation of state for contractile materials such as rubber or steel. A consideration of the free energy change, dG, for a closed system, Eq. (3-33), leads to the cross relation

$$\left(\frac{\partial f}{\partial T}\right)_l = -\left(\frac{\partial S}{\partial l}\right)_T. \tag{3-48}$$

Equation (3-48) has been tested on rubberlike materials and on steel springs. For steel, f is practically independent of temperature and $(\partial f/\partial T)_l = 0$; the entropy of a steel spring does not change upon stretching. In terms of the Boltzmann interpretation of entropy, the crystalline order of the structure is hardly affected by the stretching force. On the other hand, for rubberlike materials, $(\partial f/\partial T)_l$ is large and positive, which means that $(\partial S/\partial l)_T < 0$; the entropy of rubber decreases with stretching. This result fits the accepted picture of rubber molecules as more or less randomly kinked coils which are elongated and oriented upon stretching, thereby decreasing their entropy content.

The cross relation (3-48) may be used to give an equation of state for contractile materials in closed systems. Equation (3-3) then becomes

$$dU = TdS - PdV + fdl,$$

and

$$\left(\frac{\partial U}{\partial l}\right)_T = T\left(\frac{\partial S}{\partial l}\right)_T - P\left(\frac{\partial V}{\partial l}\right)_T + f. \tag{3-49}$$

In rubber and steel $(\partial V/\partial l)_T$ may be neglected, so that Eq. (3-49) reduces to

$$\left(\frac{\partial U}{\partial l}\right)_T = f - T\left(\frac{\partial f}{\partial T}\right)_l. \tag{3-50}$$

As we saw earlier, for steel $(\partial f/\partial T)_l = 0$. Thus, $f = (\partial U/\partial l)_T$, and the major contribution to the elastic force of steel is the increase in the internal energy with increasing distance between the iron atoms. For rubberlike materials, it has been found that $T(\partial f/\partial T)_l = f$ at low degrees of stretch, so that $(\partial U/\partial l)_T = 0$. These findings show that the elasticity of rubber resembles that of a gas; the major component of the elastic force is the entropic contribution. The equation of state (3-50) holds only for closed systems. For open systems, a more general expression must be used.

3.3.3. The Cauchy condition applied to reversible changes may also lead to the establishment of interesting cross relations. As an example, we may consider a rectangular rubber sheet that is subject to stretch by two perpendicular forces, f_x and f_y, under isothermal conditions. On a priori grounds, each force may depend on the extent of stretching in both the x and y directions, so that, in general,

$$f_x = M_{11}\Delta x + M_{12}\Delta y \tag{3-51.1}$$

and

$$f_y = M_{21}\Delta x + M_{22}\Delta y. \tag{3-51.2}$$

Here M_{11} and M_{22} are the ordinary elastic moduli in the x and y directions, defined by the expressions

$$M_{11} = \left(\frac{\partial f_x}{\partial x}\right)_y, \qquad M_{22} = \left(\frac{\partial f_y}{\partial y}\right)_x,$$

and M_{12} and M_{21}, defined by the relations

$$M_{12} = \left(\frac{\partial f_x}{\partial y}\right)_x, \qquad M_{21} = \left(\frac{\partial f_y}{\partial x}\right)_y,$$

are the coupling moduli relating the force in one direction to the stretch in the other direction.

According to Eq. (2-4),

$$f_x = \left(\frac{\partial F}{\partial x}\right)_y, \qquad f_y = \left(\frac{\partial F}{\partial y}\right)_x, \tag{3-52}$$

in which F is the Helmholtz free energy. Using Eq. (3-42), we find that

$$\left(\frac{\partial f_x}{\partial y}\right)_x = \frac{\partial^2 F}{\partial x \partial y} = \left(\frac{\partial f_y}{\partial x}\right)_y, \tag{3-53}$$

which requires that

$$M_{12} = M_{21}. \tag{3-54}$$

Thus, thermodynamics requires that the matrix of the moduli,

$$\begin{vmatrix} M_{11} & M_{12} \\ M_{21} & M_{22} \end{vmatrix},$$

be symmetric. In subsequent chapters, we shall be interested in the symmetry of similar matrices that arise in the thermodynamic description of irreversible processes.

These examples illustrate some of the conclusions that may be obtained from the Gibbs equation. This equation is one of the most important expressions in the thermodynamics of irreversible processes and we shall use it extensively in the following chapters. However, before discussing further uses of the Gibbs equation, we must consider the entropy itself in more detail and investigate more closely its change during irreversible processes.

CHAPTER 4

ENTROPY CHANGE IN IRREVERSIBLE PROCESSES

4.1. Increase of Entropy in an Adiabatic Process

4.1.1. In Chapter 2 the concept of entropy and its quantitative formulation for quasi-static processes were discussed. During such processes, the external parameters define the state of the system completely and the thermodynamic potentials are functions of state. These considerations will now be extended to nonequilibrium processes and a suitable treatment for systems in a state of flow will be developed. As shown below, the function that can be used to distinguish between reversible and irreversible processes is the entropy, which is a total differential only for quasi-static processes ($dS = dQ/T$). The simplest case to consider is an adiabatic system, for which we know that in any change, reversible or irreversible, the change in internal energy is a total differential, independent of the manner in which the change was brought about. In a reversible adiabatic process the entropy remains constant since $dQ = 0$ and hence $dS = 0$.

We shall now consider the change in entropy in an irreversible adiabatic process, following a method used by Kirkwood and Oppenheim.[1] The analysis is carried out in terms of a T–S diagram (Fig. 6) similar to that used in the thermal description of the Carnot cycle. The initial state of the system (state 1) will be characterized by a temperature T_1 and an entropy S_1. Any reversible adiabatic change will leave the entropy constant so that all states which can be attained by such quasi-equilibrium processes must lie on the line AB which is perpendicular to the S-axis and passes through the point 1. Since $(\partial U/\partial T)_S > 0$, work done on the system will raise the temperature, while work done by the system will lower the temperature. We allow the system to change irreversibly, with performance of work, to a state 2 lying on the isotherm T_2. Work will then be performed on the system to bring it reversibly, at constant entropy, back to its original temperature, T_1. Finally, a cycle will be completed by removing the adiabatic restriction and taking up heat from a reservoir at constant temperature, so as to bring the system reversibly

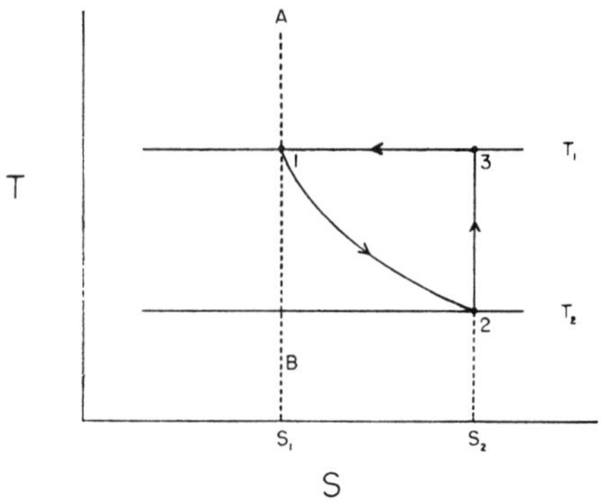

Fig. 6. Representation of an irreversible process ($1 \rightarrow 2$) in the thermal plane. The steps $2 \rightarrow 3$ and $3 \rightarrow 1$ complete a cycle that makes possible determination of the location of state 2 relative to the line of constant entropy AB.

back to its initial state 1. Applying the first law to the process as a whole, we obtain

$$\oint dU = 0 = \oint dQ - \oint dW, \tag{4-1}$$

in which the integral $\oint dW$ is the work obtained in the cycle. Since we had access during the process to only one heat reservoir, the isothermal reservoir applied in step $3 \rightarrow 1$, by Kelvin's principle the work cannot be positive, or

$$\oint dW \leq 0. \tag{4-2}$$

Hence, according to Eq. (4-1),

$$\oint dQ \leq 0. \tag{4-3}$$

This heat integral represents the thermal energy absorbed reversibly from the reservoir, so that $dQ = TdS$ and

$$\oint dQ = \int_3^1 TdS = T_1(S_1 - S_3) \leq 0. \tag{4-4}$$

Now T is positive, so that $S_3 \geq S_1$, and therefore $S_2 \geq S_1$ since $S_2 = S_3$. If the equality sign applies, the process of $1 \rightarrow 2$ must have been reversible, which is contrary to our original assumption. We may conclude, therefore, that for the actual irreversible process $S_2 > S_1$ and the entropy of the system has increased. Thus, if the system can go from state 1 to state 2 by an irreversible adiabatic process, there must be an increase in entropy of the system. In terms of the T–S diagram, states on the isotherm T_2 that can be reached by an irreversible adiabatic process must lie to the right of the line AB. If any such state were to the left of this line, the process would lead to a violation of Kelvin's statement of the second law. All points to the left of AB thus represent "unnatural" states, which cannot be reached by any spontaneous change taking place in an adiabatic system, in agreement with the principle of Carathéodory.

4.1.2. There was no fundamental difficulty in assigning entropy values to the initial and final states of an adiabatic system undergoing an irreversible transition. We must now consider the question whether measurable entropy values can be assigned to intermediate states during the irreversible process itself. The answer to this question is the basis of the thermodynamics of irreversible processes, and the procedure outlined below is, therefore, of primary importance.

Measurement of entropy at any stage of an irreversible process is based on the assumption that the entropy is a unique function of the external and internal parameters, a_k and ξ_k respectively, whatever the energy and work content of the system. We can reach the same distribution of internal parameters, for a given set of external parameters, in several ways, both reversible and irreversible. Generally speaking, different paths leading to the same distribution will be accompained by different expenditures of work and by different energy changes in the system. It is, however, assumed that the *entropy is determined only by the configuration*, by the set of local parameters that fully characterize the state of the system at a given moment. With this assumption, we may devise an *ideal* process that would bring the system *reversibly* to any of the momentary configurations through which a system passes during an irreversible process. The entropy of the system in the reversible process is well defined and the values of the entropy thus obtained may be regarded as the corresponding entropies of the *real* system at any time.

To clarify the meaning of these statements, let us consider, for example, a diffusion process. Diffusion is a nonequilibrium process and its characterization requires detailed specification of the internal parameters, the local distribution of concentrations within the system. Now let us assume that we apply reversibly a suitable centrifugal field to the system in order to maintain the same distribution of concentrations in a state of equilibrium. Clearly, the energy of the system and the work required to develop reversibly the centrifugal field will differ appreciably from those of the system in an irreversible diffusion process. Thus, the thermodynamic states of the system undergoing an irreversible process and of the corresponding equilibrium system are different. However, the entropy will be the same in both systems and, moreover, the entropy is measurable and given by the parameters of the equilibrium state.

Let us denote by X_k the additional external parameters that have to be introduced in order to maintain the nonequilibrium distribution of internal parameters ξ_k in a state of equilibrium. These additional parameters establish a field of forces whose potential energy is $-\sum_{k=1}^{n} \xi_k X_k$. The internal energy of the equilibrium system, U^*, is then related to the internal energy of the nonequilibrium system, U, by the equation

$$U^* = U - \sum_{k=1}^{n} \xi_k X_k. \tag{4-5}$$

The additional work of the external parameters, maintaining the given distribution of internal parameters, is $\sum \xi_k dX_k$. Hence the differential of the work, dW^*, required to reach reversibly the given configuration is related to the work dW expended in reaching the same configuration irreversibly by

$$dW^* = dW + \sum_{k=1}^{n} \xi_k dX_k. \tag{4-6}$$

Now the entropy change in the corresponding reversible process is given by Eq. (2-14),

$$TdS = dU^* + dW^*. \tag{4-7}$$

Introducing dU^* from Eq. (4-5) and dW^* from Eq. (4-6), we obtain

$$\begin{aligned} TdS &= dU - \sum_{k=1}^{n} X_k d\xi_k - \sum_{k=1}^{n} \xi_k dX_k + dW + \sum_{k=1}^{n} \xi_k dX_k \\ &= dU + dW - \sum_{k=1}^{n} X_k d\xi_k. \end{aligned} \tag{4-8}$$

The entropy term, TdS, in Eq. (4-8) is the same for the irreversible process and the corresponding reversible process; Eq. (4-8) represents, therefore, the Gibbs equation for irreversible processes. According to the first law, $dU + dW = dQ$, and hence

$$TdS = dQ - \sum_{k=1}^{n} X_k d\xi_k. \tag{4-9}$$

For an adiabatic process, $dQ = 0$ and

$$TdS = -\sum_{k=1}^{n} X_k d\xi_k. \tag{4-10}$$

In Eq. (4-10), the change in entropy during an irreversible process in an adiabatic system is expressed as a function of the internal parameters and the external parameters that make entropy measurable.

4.1.3. We are now in a position to extend the conclusion of Sec. 4.1.1 and to prove that there is an increase in entropy throughout any spontaneous process. The procedure is essentially the same as that used previously, except that the external force has to be applied at pertinent

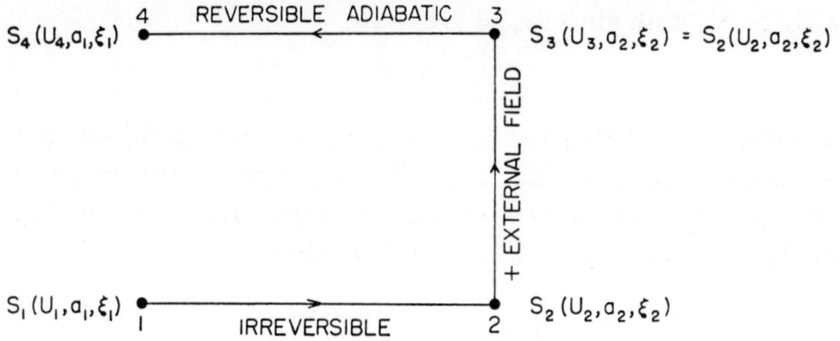

Fig. 7. Scheme for demonstrating an increase in entropy in a spontaneous adiabatic process. The symbols a and ξ denote, respectively, the external and internal parameters of the system.

points of a cycle such as that shown in Fig. 7. The system is allowed to pass from state 1 to state 2 by an irreversible process. In the transition 1 to 2, the internal energy changes from U_1 to U_2 and the external and internal parameters change from a_1 and ξ_1 to a_2 and ξ_2. Our problem is to evaluate the relation between the entropy in state 1, $S_1(U_1, a_1, \xi_1)$, and the entropy in state 2, $S_2(U_2, a_2, \xi_2)$. Upon reaching state 2 let us apply the external field at constant a_2, ξ_2 so that the system reaches a state of equilibrium. The introduction of the additional parameters changes the internal energy, so that we now have $S_3(U_3, a_2, \xi_2)$. Since the configuration, a_2, ξ_2, is unchanged, S_2 and S_3 are equal. The external parameters are now made to change so as to bring the system back reversibly and adiabatically to its original configuration (a_1, ξ_1). The work performed changes the internal energy to a new value, U_4, but the entropy does not change, since this step is both adiabatic and reversible. Thus,

$$S_4(U_4, a_1, \xi_1) = S_3(U_3, a_2, \xi_2) = S_2(U_2, a_2, \xi_2). \tag{4-11}$$

A comparison of S_4 with S_1 is equivalent to a comparison of S_2 with S_1 and permits us to determine the direction of entropy change during the irreversible step.

Comparison of states 4 and 1 can be made according to the procedure of Sec. 4.1.1. We pass from state 4 to state 1 by an isothermal step during which an amount of heat ΔQ is absorbed from a reservoir at constant temperature. For the complete cycle, $\oint dU = 0$ and

$$\oint dQ = \oint dW < 0.$$

Since all steps except the last are adiabatic,

$$\oint dQ = \Delta Q = T \int_4^1 dS = T(S_1 - S_4) < 0. \tag{4-12}$$

Hence $S_4 > S_1$, and, since $S_4 = S_3 = S_2$,

$$S_2 > S_1. \tag{4-13}$$

We have thus proved that the entropy increases during the whole progress of an irreversible process since states 1 and 2 may be any two subsequent states of the system during the change. Applying Eq. (4-13) to Eq. (4-10), we find that throughout the irreversible process

$$dS = -\sum_{k=1}^{n} \frac{X_k d\xi_k}{T}. \tag{4-14}$$

Equation (4-14) can be regarded as an expression for the change in entropy during a spontaneous adiabatic process. Dividing both sides of Eq. (4-14) by dt, where t denotes time, we obtain the rate of increase in entropy, dS/dt, in an adiabatic process as a function of the rate of change in the internal parameters, $d\xi_k/dt$:

$$\frac{dS}{dt} = -\sum_{k=1}^{n} \frac{X_k}{T} \frac{d\xi_k}{dt}. \tag{4-15}$$

In Eq. (4-15) we encounter the fundamental form of the rate of increase in entropy in an irreversible process, given as the sum of the products of the "affinities" X_k/T and the flows of the internal parameters $d\xi_k/dt$. We shall show later that this form is generally valid and describes the rate of entropy production in irreversible processes.

4.2. Conditions of Equilibrium for an Adiabatic System

4.2.1. In every natural adiabatic process, the entropy continues to increase until a state of equilibrium is reached. At equilibrium, $dS = 0$ and the entropy has an extreme value which must be a maximum. At equilibrium, dS vanishes for any variation in the parameters ξ_i of the system, or

$$\left(\frac{\partial S}{\partial \xi_i}\right)^0_{\xi_j} = 0, \tag{4-16}$$

in which the superscript 0 indicates the value of the partial derivative at equilibrium. On the other hand, the very fact that entropy reaches a maximum at equilibrium may be expressed mathematically by the condition

$$(d^2S)^0 < 0.$$

Let us denote the equilibrium value of the ith internal parameter by ξ_i^0 and the fluctuating deviation from the equilibrium value by $\alpha_i = \xi_i - \xi_i^0$. Then the fact that the equilibrium entropy is maximal with respect to any deviation may be also written in the form

$$\sum_{i,j=1}^{n} \left(\frac{\partial^2 S}{\partial \alpha_i \partial \alpha_j}\right)^0 \alpha_i \alpha_j \leq 0. \tag{4-17}$$

Without going into detailed considerations, it can easily be shown that any fluctuation in the ξ_i from their equilibrium values brings the system into a less probable state of lower entropy. Natural processes which tend to increase entropy will then develop instantaneously, bringing the entropy of the system back toward its maximal value. The state of equilibrium is, therefore, a stable state provided with a thermodynamic restoring mechanism for any possible deviation. The stability of thermodynamic equilibria and their passive resistance to change is the essence of the famous theorem of Le Chatelier and Braun.

4.2.2. The discovery of the directional properties of the entropy and the realization that entropy increases in natural adiabatic processes deeply impressed scientific thought. Clausius, who coined the term entropy, and studied the properties of this state function, believed that the world is a closed adiabatic system and that the laws of thermodynamics have a universal validity, transcending the realm of human experience. His paper of 1865 was headed by the famous statement, "Die Energie der Welt ist konstant, die Entropie der Welt strebt einem Maximum zu,"[2] which summarizes the first and second laws of thermodynamics. Numerous speculations resulted from this sweeping and stimulating generalization. The first conclusion was that when the entropy of the world reached a maximum all natural processes would cease. When universal equilibrium was attained, no directional change would be possible and the chaotic thermal movements of a disorganized structure would fill the cosmic space. Evidently life could not continue and the ultimate state of the universe was defined as the "thermal death of the world." A consideration in the reverse direction led to the conclusion that cosmic entropy must have had a zero point when all processes started. This state might play the role of creation when the material world, in the physical sense, started to develop. Indeed, some modern cosmologies have paid considerable attention to these possibilities and attempted to construct an evolutionary theory of the cosmos corresponding to the universal increase in entropy from zero at creation to a maximum at thermal death.

Whatever be our attitude toward the doubtful assumption that the world is an adiabatic system enclosed in "cosmic walls," there is no doubt that the recognition of the nonconservative nature of entropy and its increase during natural processes has implications beyond the limits of thermodynamics in a strict sense. It gives a quantitative measure of irreversibility and spontaneity, but it also explains in a suggestive manner the direction of time. The concept of time is implied in the very notion of a process; it is indeed the "event" that is perceived directly as a four-dimensional space-time entity. Only through a long and involved process of abstraction was time isolated as an independent analytic coordinate. The time of classical physics, introduced by the founders of mechanics into all equations of motion, is a directionless quantity, which may go from future to past as well as from past to future without discrimination. This is obvious if we consider any of the equations of classical physics, such as the one describing wave propagation,

$$\frac{1}{C^2}\frac{\partial^2 u}{\partial t^2} = \frac{\partial^2 u}{\partial x^2},$$

in which C is the velocity of propagation and u is the amplitude of the wave. The substitution of $-t$ for t leaves the expression unchanged. The reason for this behavior of the time coordinate is evidently the fact that the processes considered by the physicists were reversible or quasi-reversible. However, in the description of even the simplest cases of irreversible processes, time appears as a first-order differential. For example, conduction of heat may be described by the equation of Fourier,

$$\frac{1}{\lambda}\frac{\partial T}{\partial t} = \frac{\partial^2 T}{\partial x^2},$$

in which T is temperature and λ is the coefficient of heat conduction. The substitution of $-t$ for t in this equation leads to an entirely different result, suggesting that in a process of this nature time has a specified direction of change. Time can, of course, be measured by reversible periodic phenomena, such as the oscillations of a pendulum or the rotations of a star, and the amount of time can be given as the number of periods of the chosen standard process, but the direction of time cannot be determined by such measurements. The problem of the direction of time seems to be related to the unidirectional increase of entropy in all natural processes. Both entropy increase and time are intimately associated with the pattern of natural events, and the fundamental law for adiabatically closed systems that

$$\frac{dS}{dt} > 0$$

may be regarded, according to Eddington,[3] as the pointer of the "arrow of time."

4.3. Examples of the Increase in Entropy During Adiabatic Irreversible Processes

4.3.1. We shall first consider a two-compartment system enclosed by rigid adiabatic walls so that no external work can be performed. The two compartments will be separated by a rigid diathermal wall so that energy can pass from one compartment to the other but no mechanical work can be done within the system. The internal energy U of this system as a whole is composed of the sum of the energies of the compartments, U_1 and U_2. Since no work can be done by the system, and no heat can be exchanged with the surroundings,

$$U = U_1 + U_2 = \text{constant}, \tag{4-18}$$

and any change in the internal energy of either compartment is constrained by the condition

$$dU_1 = -dU_2. \tag{4-19}$$

The total entropy of the system, S, is the sum of the entropies of the individual compartments, so that

$$dS = dS_1 + dS_2. \tag{4-20}$$

The entropies of the compartments can change only as a result of changes in energy, since all other parameters of the system are fixed. Therefore,

$$dS = \frac{\partial S_1}{\partial U_1}\,dU_1 + \frac{\partial S_2}{\partial U_2}\,dU_2 = dU_1\left(\frac{\partial S_1}{\partial U_1} - \frac{\partial S_2}{\partial U_2}\right), \tag{4-21}$$

in which Eq. (4-19) has been used. From Eq. (3-3), $(\partial S/\partial U)_V = 1/T$ and Eq. (4-21) becomes

$$dS = dU_1\left(\frac{1}{T_1} - \frac{1}{T_2}\right). \tag{4-22}$$

Equation (4-22) is a special case of Eq. (4-10) in which the role of the affinity or force is played by $\Delta(1/T) = (1/T_1) - (1/T_2)$ and the internal energy is the internal parameter. For an irreversible process $dS > 0$ or

$$dU_1\left(\frac{1}{T_1} - \frac{1}{T_2}\right) > 0. \tag{4-23}$$

Equation (4-23) shows that thermal energy flows from a higher to a lower temperature. If $T_1 > T_2$, $(1/T_1) - (1/T_2) < 0$ and thus, $dU_1 < 0$; energy will flow from compartment 1 to 2. The irreversible process continues until thermal equilibrium is attained. At equilibrium, $dS = 0$, and from Eq. (4-23) the condition of thermal equilibrium is $T_1 = T_2$. This condition is in agreement with the considerations of Sec. 1.3 regarding the zeroth law of thermodynamics.

4.3.2. The example in the previous section can be easily extended to the more general case, illustrated in Fig. 8, in which the partition between the compartments is movable and permeable to one component of the system. The system will still be considered enclosed by a rigid adiabatic

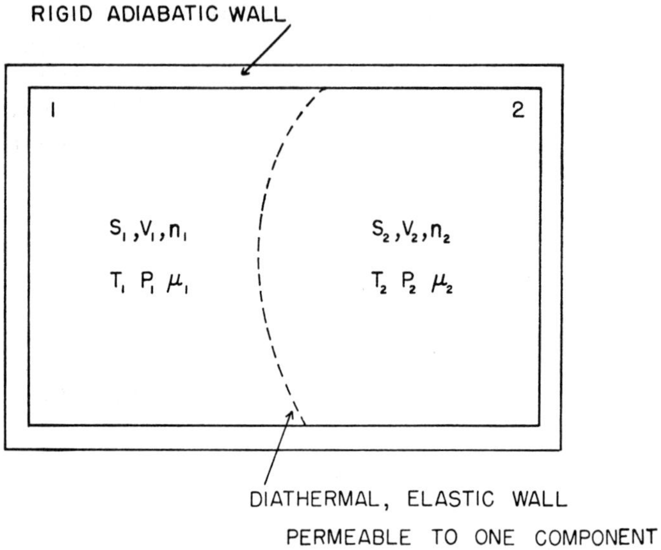

Fig. 8. System for considering entropy changes in an adiabatic system. The two compartments are separated by a diathermal, elastic barrier that is permeable to one of the components in the system.

wall so that Eq. (4-18) remains valid. However, the change in the entropy of the compartments is now given by the sum of the partial changes due to the transport of energy, volume, and matter:

$$dS = \frac{\partial S_1}{\partial U_1}\,dU_1 + \frac{\partial S_1}{\partial V_1}\,dV_1 + \frac{\partial S_1}{\partial n_1}\,dn_1 + \frac{\partial S_2}{\partial U_2}\,dU_2 + \frac{\partial S_2}{\partial V_2}\,dV_2 + \frac{\partial S_2}{\partial n_2}\,dn_2. \tag{4-24}$$

Since the total energy, volume, and amount of substance are constants,

$$dU_1 = -dU_2, \qquad dV_1 = -dV_2, \qquad dn_1 = -dn_2.$$

Introducing these conditions into Eq. (4-24) we obtain

$$dS = dU_1\left(\frac{\partial S_1}{\partial U_1} - \frac{\partial S_2}{\partial U_2}\right) + dV_1\left(\frac{\partial S_1}{\partial V_1} - \frac{\partial S_2}{\partial V_2}\right) + dn_1\left(\frac{\partial S_1}{\partial n_1} - \frac{\partial S_2}{\partial n_2}\right). \tag{4-25}$$

As can be seen from Eq. (3-3),

$$\left(\frac{\partial S}{\partial U}\right)_{V,n} = \frac{1}{T}, \qquad \left(\frac{\partial S}{\partial V}\right)_{U,n} = \frac{P}{T}, \qquad \left(\frac{\partial S}{\partial n}\right)_{U,V} = \frac{-\mu}{T}.$$

With these relations, Eq. (4-25) becomes

$$dS = dU_1\left(\frac{1}{T_1} - \frac{1}{T_2}\right) + dV_1\left(\frac{P_1}{T_1} - \frac{P_2}{T_2}\right) - dn_1\left(\frac{\mu_1}{T_1} - \frac{\mu_2}{T_2}\right). \quad (4\text{-}26)$$

Equation (4-26) shows that the entropy increase in this system is given by the sum of products of changes in the three internal parameters, U, V, and n, multiplied by suitable affinities, $(1/T_1) - (1/T_2)$, $(P_1/T_1) - (P_2/T_2)$, and $(\mu_1/T_1) - (\mu_2/T_2)$. Equation (4-26) thus has the form required by Eq. (4-10). When thermal equilibrium is reached, $T_1 = T_2$ and the energy flow no longer contributes to the entropy production. When $T_1 = T_2$, mechanical equilibrium will be established when $P_1 = P_2$ and the volume flow will cease to cause an increase in entropy. It is of interest to examine the last term in Eq. (4-26) when $T_1 = T_2$ and $P_1 = P_2$. In this case,

$$dS = -dn_1 \frac{\mu_1 - \mu_2}{T} > 0. \quad (4\text{-}27)$$

Equation (4-27) indicates that, if $\mu_1 > \mu_2$, dn_1 must be negative and that matter will be transported from the higher to the lower chemical potential. This justifies the term "chemical potential," since the gradient of this quantity acts as the driving force for the transport of matter. Again dS will become zero when $\mu_1 = \mu_2$; this is the condition for chemical equilibrium, which is analogous to the conditions $T_1 = T_2$ and $P_1 = P_2$ for thermal and mechanical equilibria. Equation (4-26) may be cast in another form, which will be useful in the following chapters. Let us denote the bracketed differences in this equation by Δ so that

$$\Delta\left(\frac{1}{T}\right) = \frac{1}{T_1} - \frac{1}{T_2},$$

$$\Delta\left(\frac{P}{T}\right) = \frac{P_1}{T_1} - \frac{P_2}{T_2},$$

$$\Delta\left(\frac{-\mu}{T}\right) = -\left(\frac{\mu_1}{T_1} - \frac{\mu_2}{T_2}\right).$$

Further, let us divide both sides of Eq. (4-26) by the time change dt, and denote the flow of energy dU_1/dt by J_U, the flow of volume dV_1/dt by J_v, and the flow of matter dn_1/dt by J_n. Equation (4-26) may then be written in a form equivalent to that of Eq. (4-15):

$$\frac{dS}{dt} = J_u\Delta\left(\frac{1}{T}\right) + J_v\Delta\left(\frac{P}{T}\right) + J_n\Delta\left(\frac{-\mu}{T}\right). \quad (4\text{-}28)$$

Equation (4-28) demonstrates more clearly the idea implied in Eq. (4-15) that the rate of entropy production in adiabatic irreversible processes is the sum of the products of individual flows each multiplied by a corresponding affinity, the flow of energy by $\Delta(1/T)$, the flow of volume by $\Delta(P/T)$, and the flow of matter by $\Delta(-\mu/T)$.

4.4. Entropy Changes in Isothermal Processes

4.4.1. In order to evaluate the change in entropy accompanying an isothermal irreversible process, we shall consider the simple cycle shown in Fig. 9. The system, enclosed by diathermal walls, is allowed to pass isothermally and irreversibly from state 1 to state 2, maintaining contact with a reservoir at constant temperature. Upon reaching state 2, the process is reversed and the system brought back to state 1 in a reversible manner, maintaining contact with the same reservoir applied in the step 1 to 2. For the complete cycle

$$\oint dU = 0 = \oint dQ - \oint dW.$$

According to Kelvin's principle, $\oint dW = W \leq 0$, since the work is the result of the cooling of a single body—the heat reservoir used in both steps. Thus,

$$\oint dQ = \int_1^2 dQ + \int_2^1 dQ \leq 0. \tag{4-29}$$

The integral $\int_1^2 dQ$ is the heat absorbed from the reservoir in the irreversible step and may be written as $\int_1^2 dQ = \Delta Q^{\text{irr}}$. During this heat absorption, the reservoir is assumed to operate reversibly so that Clausius' equation, $dS = dQ/T$, will apply to the external surroundings:

$$\int_1^2 dQ = \Delta Q^{\text{irr}} = T\Delta_e S, \tag{4-30}$$

in which $\Delta_e S$ denotes the entropy exchanged between the system and its surroundings. For the reversible process, $2 \rightarrow 1$, $dQ = TdS$ and

$$\int_2^1 dQ = T\int_2^1 dS = T(S_1 - S_2) = -T\Delta S. \tag{4-31}$$

Introducing Eqs. (4-30) and (4-31) into Eq. (4-29), we obtain

$$\Delta Q^{\text{irr}} - T\Delta S = T\Delta_e S - T\Delta S \leq 0, \tag{4-32}$$

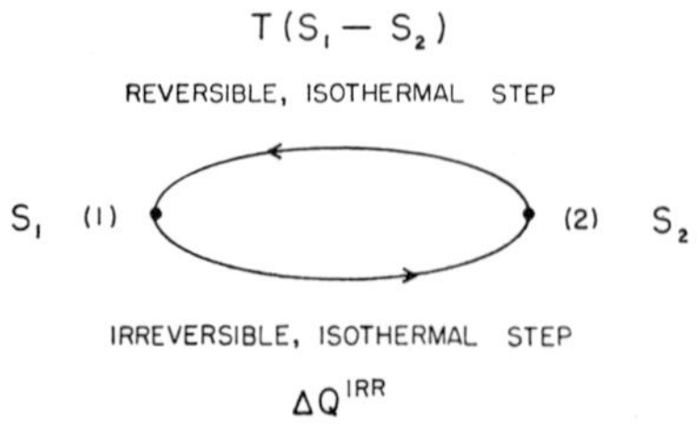

Fig. 9. Cyclic process for considering the entropy change in an isothermal irreversible process.

or

$$\Delta S \geq \Delta_e S. \tag{4-33}$$

As previously discussed, the equality sign would apply if the process $1 \rightarrow 2$ were reversible. Since we have assumed that it is irreversible, the inequality must apply. Equation (4-33) was written by Clausius in different forms, the best known being that given in 1854:

$$dS \geq \frac{dQ}{T} \quad \text{or} \quad \Delta S \geq \frac{\Delta Q}{T}. \tag{4-34}$$

The physical meaning of Eq. (4-33) or (4-34) is that in an isothermal natural process the entropy of the system increases more than can be accounted for by absorption of entropy from the surroundings. Therefore, a process has taken place within the system that creates entropy in the same manner as in a spontaneous adiabatic process. This *entropy creation* will be called internal production of entropy, d_iS, and is equivalent to the "uncompensated heat" of Clausius. We shall now postulate that the total change in entropy is the sum of the entropy exchanged with the surroundings and the entropy created in the system[4] and shall replace the inequality of Eq. (4-33) by the equality

$$dS = d_iS + d_eS. \tag{4-35}$$

The inequality may then be written as

$$d_iS \geq 0. \tag{4-36}$$

Thus, the internal entropy production is positive-definite; it is greater than zero for all irreversible processes and equal to zero for reversible changes. Equations (4-35) and (4-36) summarize all the information of this chapter for both adiabatic and isothermal systems. In an adiabatic process there is no exchange of entropy with the surroundings, so that

$$d_eS = 0$$

and

$$dS = d_iS \geq 0.$$

We assume that Eqs. (4-35) and (4-36) hold for any possible change in a material system. To complete the argument, we postulate that these equations hold not only for the system as a whole but for all parts of the system. Any element of the system may exchange entropy with its surroundings and d_eS may be either positive or negative, but any entropy change resulting from irreversible processes taking place within the element must be positive-definite. At equilibrium all macroscopic processes stop

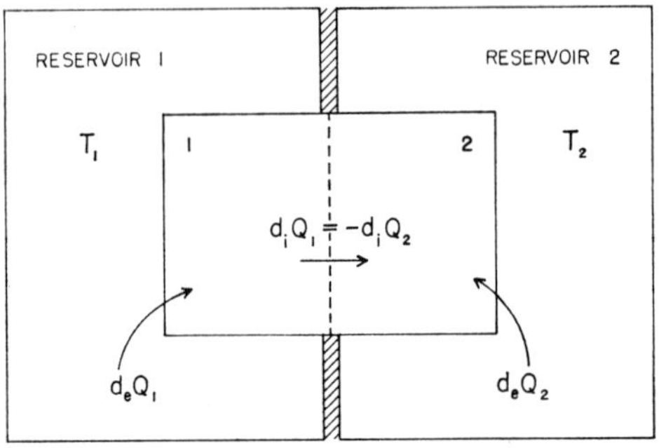

Fig. 10. Two-compartment system having diathermal walls. The barrier between the compartments is rigid and diathermal. Each compartment is in contact with a separate heat reservoir.

and no entropy is created; hence the condition $d_iS = 0$ is an additional criterion for a state of equilibrium.

4.4.2. A simple example will clarify the concepts of "internal" and "external" entropy changes and will demonstrate the meaning of the statement $d_iS \geq 0$. We shall consider again the two-compartment system discussed in Sec. 4.3.1 but shall assume that the wall surrounding the container is diathermal. Further, as shown in Fig. 10, compartments 1 and 2 will be kept in equilibrium with heat reservoirs at different temperatures, T_1 and T_2. The total change in thermal energy of compartment 1 at a given moment, dQ_1, is given by the expression

$$dQ_1 = d_eQ_1 + d_iQ_1, \tag{4-37}$$

in which d_eQ_1 is the heat exchanged with the reservoir at temperature T_1 and d_iQ_1 is the heat exchanged with compartment 2. Similarly for compartment 2,

$$dQ_2 = d_eQ_2 + d_iQ_2. \tag{4-38}$$

Evidently,

$$d_iQ_1 + d_iQ_2 = 0. \tag{4-39}$$

We may now write for the entropy change of the system as a whole,

$$dS = \frac{dQ_1}{T_1} + \frac{dQ_2}{T_2} = \frac{d_eQ_1}{T_1} + \frac{d_eQ_2}{T_2} + \frac{d_iQ_1}{T_1} + \frac{d_iQ_2}{T_2}. \tag{4-40}$$

With Eq. (4-39), Eq. (4-40) becomes

$$dS = \frac{d_eQ_1}{T_1} + \frac{d_eQ_2}{T_2} + d_iQ_1\left(\frac{1}{T_1} - \frac{1}{T_2}\right). \tag{4-41}$$

The total change in entropy consists of two parts, a term due to exchange of heat with the surroundings,

$$d_eS = \frac{d_eQ_1}{T_1} + \frac{d_eQ_2}{T_2}, \tag{4-42}$$

and a term due to inner, irreversible flow of heat from one compartment to the other

$$d_iS = d_iQ_1\left(\frac{1}{T_1} - \frac{1}{T_2}\right). \tag{4-43}$$

The condition given by Eq. (4-36) requires that

$$d_iQ_1\left(\frac{1}{T_1} - \frac{1}{T_2}\right) > 0,$$

which again expresses the fact that heat flows from the compartment of higher temperature to that of lower temperature. The decomposition of dS into internal and external parts is carried out in a direct manner by writing specifically all the energy terms of the process. As will be shown later, such a decomposition can be carried out in all cases and the internal entropy production can always be isolated. This quantity is the fundamental property of all irreversible processes.

CHAPTER 5

ISOTHERMAL EQUILIBRIA AND CHEMICAL THERMODYNAMICS

5.1. Conditions of Equilibrium for Free Energy

5.1.1. As was pointed out in Sec. 3.3, the entropy and internal energy may not always be the most suitable thermodynamic functions to describe a given system. Under ordinary laboratory conditions, where pressure and temperature are easily controlled, the Gibbs free energy G is usually more convenient. It is, therefore, important to consider the change in G during an irreversible process and the value attained at equilibrium. For isothermal, isobaric conditions,

$$(dG)_{T,P} = dU + PdV - TdS. \tag{5-1}$$

However, according to the considerations of Sec. 4.4,

$$dQ - TdS \leq 0. \tag{5-2}$$

Further, according to the first law applied to closed systems,

$$dU + PdV = dQ, \tag{5-3}$$

if the only work performed is that of compression. Introducing Eq. (5-3) into Eq. (5-1), we find that

$$(dG)_{T,P} = dQ - TdS. \tag{5-4}$$

Hence, by Eq. (5-2),

$$(dG)_{T,P} \leq 0, \tag{5-5}$$

in which the inequality applies to irreversible processes and the equality to reversible processes and equilibrium. Thus, the free energy or work potential decreases in any isothermal, isobaric process and reaches a constant, minimal value at equilibrium. Since the free energy is minimal at equilibrium,

$$(d^2G)^0_{T,P} > 0, \tag{5-6}$$

in which the superscript 0 refers to equilibrium. In terms of fluctuations α_i of the parameters ξ_i of a system from their equilibrium values, we may write

$$\sum_{i,j=1}^{n} \left(\frac{\partial^2 G}{\partial \alpha_i \partial \alpha_j}\right)^0 \alpha_i \alpha_j > 0. \tag{5-7}$$

Thus, any fluctuations that shift a system from its equilibrium state will increase its free energy and give rise to processes tending to restore equilibrium. The stability of the equilibrium state is thereby insured. The conclusions of Eqs. (5-6) and (5-7) may be summarized in different ways, one of which is the statement that a system whose sole external sources are heat and work, and whose surroundings are maintained at constant temperature and pressure, will assume, among all possible configurations, that stable configuration for which the free energy takes a minimum value.

5.2. Chemical Transformations and Equilibria

5.2.1. For the purpose of the present discussion, we shall assume that fdl is equal to zero and write Eq. (3-33) in the form

$$dG = -SdT + VdP + \sum_{i=1}^{k} \mu_i dn_i. \tag{5-8}$$

The change in the Gibbs free energy under isothermal, isobaric conditions is then related to the change in the number of moles of the chemical components as follows:

$$(dG)_{T,P} = \sum_{i=1}^{k} \mu_i dn_i. \tag{5-9}$$

In view of Eq. (5-5),

$$\sum_{i=1}^{k} \mu_i dn_i \leq 0 \tag{5-10}$$

for any change in chemical composition at constant temperature and pressure. Equation (5-10) will be the basis of our considerations of chemical transformations in closed systems. We may begin by considering a closed system of two phases, 1 and 2, in which the chemical potentials of the ith substance are $\mu_{i(1)}$ and $\mu_{i(2)}$ respectively. We shall assume that there is a change in the number of moles of the ith component in phase 1, given by $dn_{i(1)}$, and a corresponding change in phase 2 given by $dn_{i(2)}$. The total change in free energy of the system will then be

$$dG = \mu_{i(1)} dn_{i(1)} + \mu_{i(2)} dn_{i(2)}.$$

If the ith component is not subject to chemical change,

$$dn_{i(1)} + dn_{i(2)} = 0,$$

since the total system is closed. The change in free energy then becomes

$$dG = (\mu_{i(1)} - \mu_{i(2)}) dn_{i(1)}, \tag{5-11}$$

or

$$dG = \Delta\mu_i dn_{i(1)} \leq 0, \tag{5-12}$$

in which $\Delta\mu_i = \mu_{i(1)} - \mu_{i(2)}$. If $\mu_{i(1)} > \mu_{i(2)}$, $\Delta\mu_i > 0$, so that $dn_{i(1)}$ must be negative in an irreversible process. Thus, the number of moles in the phase of higher chemical potential must diminish and, as previously discussed, the *i*th component moves from higher toward lower potential. At equilibrium, the equality sign in Eq. (5-12) holds and, since $dn_{i(1)}$ is arbitrary, the condition of equilibrium is

$$\mu_{i(1)} = \mu_{i(2)}. \tag{5-13}$$

Equations (5-12) and (5-13) again indicate as in Eq. (4-27) that a difference in chemical potential provides the driving force for the flow of matter and that at equilibrium the driving force disappears.

5.2.2. Equation (5-9) can be generalized to describe chemical reactions in a closed system. In order to do this, we must introduce a new concept, the degree of advancement of a chemical reaction, $d\xi$. The meaning of $d\xi$ can best be clarified by considering an elementary example such as the formation of water from hydrogen and oxygen by the reaction

$$2H_2 + O_2 \rightarrow 2H_2O.$$

If dn_{O_2} moles of oxygen are converted to water by reaction with dn_{H_2} moles of hydrogen, $dn_{H_2} = 2dn_{O_2}$ and $dn_{H_2O} = 2dn_{O_2}$. Moreover, while oxygen and hydrogen disappear, water is formed. This may be taken into account by introducing a negative sign for the change in the number of moles of *reactants* and a positive sign for the change in the number of moles of *products* of the reaction. For a consistent treatment we choose the change in the number of moles of the substance whose stoichiometric coefficient is unity as a measure of the advancement of the reaction, $d\xi$. Thus

$$dn_{O_2} = -d\xi, \qquad dn_{H_2} = -2d\xi, \qquad dn_{H_2O} = 2d\xi.$$

In an exactly equivalent manner, we may write for the formation of ammonia,

$$3H_2 + N_2 \rightarrow 2NH_3;$$

$$dn_{N_2} = -d\xi, \qquad dn_{H_2} = -3d\xi, \qquad dn_{NH_3} = 2d\xi.$$

For a general chemical reaction, such as

$$\nu_A A + \nu_B B + \cdots \rightleftharpoons \nu_C C + \nu_D D + \cdots,$$

we may write

$$dn_A = -\nu_A d\xi, \qquad dn_B = -\nu_B d\xi, \quad \ldots, \tag{5-14}$$

for the reactants and

$$dn_C = \nu_C d\xi, \qquad dn_D = \nu_D d\xi, \ \ldots, \tag{5-15}$$

for the products of the reaction.

According to Eq. (5-9), the free-energy change accompanying this general chemical process will be

$$(dG)_{T,P} = (\mu_A dn_A + \mu_B dn_B + \cdots) + (\mu_C dn_C + \mu_D dn_D + \cdots).$$

From Eqs. (5-14) and (5-15), this becomes

$$(dG)_{T,P} = \sum_{i=1}^{k} \mu_i dn_i = \sum_{i=1}^{k} \nu_i \mu_i d\xi \leq 0, \tag{5-16}$$

in which the stoichiometric coefficients ν_i are taken as negative for the reactants and positive for the products. Since $d\xi$ represents a positive advancement of the reaction,

$$\sum_{i=1}^{k} \nu_i \mu_i \leq 0. \tag{5-17}$$

The sum $-\sum \nu_i \mu_i$ is called the affinity, A, of the reaction.[1] This quantity is the driving force for the reaction in the same way as $\Delta\mu_i$ is the driving force for the transport of matter.

We may obtain additional insight into the meaning of the affinity by considering the entropy changes occurring in a closed system that performs work and exchanges energy with the surroundings and in which an irreversible change takes place owing to chemical reaction. The Gibbs equation for this system will be

$$TdS = dU + dW - \sum_{i=1}^{k} \mu_i dn_i. \tag{5-18}$$

Equation (5-18) is identical in form with Eq. (4-8) and here the role of the additional term, $\sum X_k d\xi_k$, is played by the contribution of the chemical reaction, $\sum \mu_i dn_i$. Using the first law for a closed system, we obtain from Eq. (5-18)

$$dS = \frac{dQ}{T} - \frac{1}{T} \sum_{i=1}^{k} \mu_i dn_i, \tag{5-19}$$

in which dQ is the heat exchanged with the surroundings. From Eq. (5-16),

$$\sum_{i=1}^{n} \mu_i dn_i = d\xi \sum_{i=1}^{k} \nu_i \mu_i = -A d\xi. \tag{5-20}$$

Inserting Eq. (5-20) into Eq. (5-19), we obtain

$$dS = \frac{dQ}{T} + \frac{A}{T} d\xi. \tag{5-21}$$

Equation (5-21) again illustrates the way of separating the total entropy change into a term due to entropy exchanged with the surroundings,

$$d_e S = \frac{dQ}{T},$$

and a term representing the internal production of entropy,

$$d_i S = \frac{A}{T}\, d\xi > 0. \tag{5-22}$$

Equation (5-22) can also be written as a time differential of the entropy production:

$$\frac{d_i S}{dt} = \frac{A}{T}\frac{d\xi}{dt} = \frac{A}{T}\, v, \tag{5-23}$$

in which $v = d\xi/dt$ is the velocity of the chemical reaction. Equation (5-23) is the general form for entropy production due to a chemical reaction; entropy is created by the flow of the reaction driven by its conjugate force, the affinity.

If several reactions take place simultaneously in the system, Eq. (5-23) is easily generalized to give

$$\frac{d_i S}{dt} = \frac{1}{T}\sum_{r=1}^{k} A_r v_r \geq 0, \tag{5-24}$$

in which the summation is over the k different reactions. In this case the requirement that internal entropy must increase applies to the sum of the products and does not impose the restriction that each term separately should be greater than zero. Thus, in the case of two simultaneous reactions,

$$A_1 v_1 + A_2 v_2 \geq 0. \tag{5-25}$$

For example, $A_1 v_1$ may be negative if $A_2 v_2$ is positive and greater in absolute value than $A_1 v_1$. Thus, on the basis of thermodynamic considerations, one of the reactions may progress in a direction opposite to that predicted by its own affinity ($A_i v_i < 0$) if another reaction provides the necessary positive entropy production to make a spontaneous process possible. Such thermodynamically coupled reactions are well known in biochemistry.

When a chemical reaction reaches a state of equilibrium, dG becomes zero and

$$A\, d\xi = 0. \tag{5-26}$$

Since $d\xi$ is arbitrary, A must vanish, and the fundamental condition of chemical equilibrium is

$$A = -\sum_{i=1}^{k} \nu_i \mu_i = 0. \tag{5-27}$$

5.3. Consideration of a Mechanicochemical System

Some of the conclusions that can be drawn from the equations of this and the previous chapters may be demonstrated in the thermodynamic treatment of a mechanicochemical system. In such a system, chemical energy is transformed directly into mechanical work and, conversely, mechanical work can be converted into chemical energy under isobaric and isothermal conditions. Muscles and other motile organs of living systems are, of course, examples of such mechanicochemical systems.

We shall consider a fiber stretched to an extent dl by a force f, and shall assume that a chemical reaction occurs simultaneously in the fiber. The affinity of the reaction is A and its degree of advancement, at the moment of our consideration, is $d\xi$. Under isothermal, isobaric conditions, the free-energy change accompanying the simultaneous stretch and advancement of the reaction is

$$(dG)_{T,P} = f_i dl - A d\xi, \tag{5-28}$$

as indicated by Eqs. (3-33) and (5-20). Equation (5-28) may be interpreted as defining the internal mechnical force, f_i, within the fiber and the affinity of the internal reaction in terms of the free energy. Thus,

$$f_i = \left(\frac{\partial G}{\partial l}\right)_{\xi,P,T}, \tag{5-29}$$

$$A = -\left(\frac{\partial G}{\partial \xi}\right)_{l,P,T}. \tag{5-30}$$

The free energy of the mechanicochemical system near equilibrium may be treated according to a procedure discussed by Meixner.[2] We consider a deviation from equilibrium due to a small stretch, Δl, and a small advancement of reaction, $\Delta\xi$, and denote the free energy in the fluctuation state by $G(\Delta l, \Delta\xi)$. Expansion of the free energy in a Maclaurin series, retaining only quadratic terms, yields

$$G(\Delta l, \Delta\xi) = G(0, 0) + \left(\frac{\partial G}{\partial l}\right)_{\xi}^{0} \Delta l + \left(\frac{\partial G}{\partial \xi}\right)_{l}^{0} \Delta\xi + \frac{1}{2}\left(\frac{\partial^2 G}{\partial l^2}\right)^{0} (\Delta l)^2 + \left(\frac{\partial^2 G}{\partial l \partial \xi}\right)^{0} \Delta l \Delta\xi + \frac{1}{2}\left(\frac{\partial^2 G}{\partial \xi^2}\right)(\Delta\xi)^2, \tag{5-31}$$

in which $G(0, 0)$ is the equilibrium value of the free energy, and the superscript 0 on the differentials indicates that these are equilibrium values. According to Eq. (5-5), at equilibrium, the change in free energy with any fluctuating quantity will be zero, so that

$$\left(\frac{\partial G}{\partial l}\right)_{\xi}^{0} = 0,$$

$$\left(\frac{\partial G}{\partial \xi}\right)_{l}^{0} = 0.$$

Further, $G(0, 0)$ is a constant so that Eq. (5-31) becomes

$$G(\Delta l, \Delta\xi) = \text{const.} + \frac{1}{2}\left(\frac{\partial^2 G}{\partial l^2}\right)^0 (\Delta l)^2 + \left(\frac{\partial^2 G}{\partial l \partial \xi}\right) \Delta l \Delta \xi + \frac{1}{2}\left(\frac{\partial^2 G}{\partial \xi^2}\right)(\Delta\xi)^2. \quad (5\text{-}32)$$

Taking the partial derivatives of Eq. (5-32) with respect to l and ξ and using Eqs. (5-29) and (5-30), we obtain

$$\left(\frac{\partial G}{\partial l}\right)_\xi = f_i = \left(\frac{\partial^2 G}{\partial l^2}\right)^0 \Delta l + \left(\frac{\partial^2 G}{\partial l \partial \xi}\right)^0 \Delta\xi = \left(\frac{\partial f_i}{\partial l}\right)_\xi \Delta l + \left(\frac{\partial f_i}{\partial \xi}\right)_l \Delta\xi, \quad (5\text{-}33)$$

$$\left(\frac{\partial G}{\partial \xi}\right)_l = -A = \left(\frac{\partial^2 G}{\partial l \partial \xi}\right)^0 \Delta l + \left(\frac{\partial^2 G}{\partial \xi^2}\right)^0 \Delta\xi = -\left(\frac{\partial A}{\partial l}\right)_\xi \Delta l - \left(\frac{\partial A}{\partial \xi}\right)_l \Delta\xi. \quad (5\text{-}34)$$

Equations (5-33) and (5-34) also provide a set of thermodynamic cross relations for a system undergoing an irreversible process similar to those discussed in Sec. 3.3 for reversible changes. The equations show that if there exists a mechanicochemical coupling, if the advancement of reaction changes the force exerted by the system, then the affinity of the reaction will change with stretch. In mathematical terms,

$$\left(\frac{\partial f_i}{\partial \xi}\right)_l = \left(\frac{\partial^2 G}{\partial l \partial \xi}\right)^0 = -\left(\frac{\partial A}{\partial l}\right)_\xi.$$

Thus, if

$$\left(\frac{\partial f_i}{\partial \xi}\right)_l \neq 0,$$

then

$$-\left(\frac{\partial A}{\partial l}\right)_\xi \neq 0.$$

This discussion illustrates that cross relations appear naturally in the thermodynamic analysis of irreversible processes.

5.4. The Chemical Potential

5.4.1. Further progress in using the concepts of chemical thermodynamics may be made if the chemical potential is considered in more detail and expressed as a sum of explicit terms. In order to do this, we have to evaluate some of the partial differential coefficients of the chemical potential with respect to the variables that determine its behavior.

We shall begin by considering the dependence of the chemical potential on pressure under conditions of constant temperature and composition, $(\partial\mu_i/\partial P)_{T,n_i}$. According to the definition of the chemical potential,

$$\mu_i = \left(\frac{\partial G}{\partial n_i}\right)_{P,T,n_j}, \quad (5\text{-}35)$$

so that

$$\left(\frac{\partial \mu_i}{\partial P}\right)_{T,n_i} = \left[\frac{\partial}{\partial P}\left(\frac{\partial G}{\partial n_i}\right)_{P,T,n_j}\right]_{T,n_i}. \tag{5-36}$$

In view of Cauchy's condition for partial differentiation, Eq. (3-42), the order of differentiation in Eq. (5-36) may be reversed so that

$$\left(\frac{\partial \mu_i}{\partial P}\right)_{T,n_i} = \left[\frac{\partial}{\partial n_i}\left(\frac{\partial G}{\partial P}\right)_{T,n_i}\right]_{T,P,n_j}. \tag{5-37}$$

In Eqs. (5-36) and (5-37), the subscript n_i means that the number of moles of each component is kept constant, while the subscript n_j means that the number of moles of each component except the ith is kept constant. According to Eq. (5-8),

$$\left(\frac{\partial G}{\partial P}\right)_{T,n_i} = V. \tag{5-38}$$

Inserting Eq. (5-38) into Eq. (5-37), we find that the dependence of μ_i on pressure is given by the dependence of the volume on the number of moles of the ith component:

$$\left(\frac{\partial \mu_i}{\partial P}\right)_{T,n_i} = \left(\frac{\partial V}{\partial n_i}\right)_{T,P,n_j}. \tag{5-39}$$

The partial derivative of volume with respect to n_i is called the *partial molar volume* of the ith component and is denoted by $\bar{V}_i$:

$$\left(\frac{\partial V}{\partial n_i}\right)_{T,P,n_j} = \bar{V}_i. \tag{5-40}$$

The quantity $\bar{V}_i$ is a representative example of various possible partial molar quantities, all of which are partial derivatives of extensive quantities with respect to the number of moles. Thus, the chemical potential itself is the *partial molar free energy*, Eq. (5-35), and we may define, in a similar manner, partial molar internal energy $\bar{U}_i$, partial molar enthalpy $\bar{H}_i$, or partial molar entropy $\bar{S}_i$. Since, at constant temperature and pressure, extensive quantities are homogeneous functions of the first order in the number of moles of the components, Euler's equation, Eq. (3-14), may be applied, for example to the volume, to give

$$V = n_1\left(\frac{\partial V}{\partial n_1}\right)_{T,P,n_j} + n_2\left(\frac{\partial V}{\partial n_2}\right)_{T,P,n_j} + \cdots = \sum_{i=1}^{k} n_i\left(\frac{\partial V}{\partial n_i}\right)_{T,P,n_j},$$

or, in view of Eq. (5-40),

$$V = \sum_{i=1}^{k} n_i \bar{V}_i. \tag{5-41}$$

By similar reasoning, we may show, for example, that

$$H = \sum_{i=1}^{k} n_i \bar{H}_i, \tag{5-42}$$

$$S = \sum_{i=1}^{k} n_i \bar{S}_i. \tag{5-43}$$

Experimental evidence has indicated in many cases that the partial molar volumes of the components in liquid mixtures are approximately constant, so that the expression

$$\left(\frac{\partial \mu_i}{\partial P}\right)_{T,n_i} = \bar{V}_i, \tag{5-44}$$

obtained by inserting Eq. (5-40) into Eq. (5-39), can be integrated with respect to pressure to give

$$\mu_i = \bar{V}_i P + \mu_i^c. \tag{5-45}$$

The constant of integration, μ_i^c, in Eq. (5-45) may depend on temperature and composition (the variables that were kept constant during the integration), but it is independent of pressure.

5.4.2. In order to obtain insight into the nature of μ_i^c, we shall turn our attention to the form assumed by the Gibbs–Duhem equation at constant temperature. Under this condition ($dT = 0$), Eq. (3-20) becomes

$$VdP - \sum_{i=1}^{k} n_i d\mu_i = 0, \tag{5-46}$$

if df is zero. Introducing μ_i from Eq. (5-45) into Eq. (5-46), we obtain

$$VdP - \sum_{i=1}^{k} n_i \bar{V}_i dP - \sum_{i=1}^{k} n_i d\mu_i^c = 0.$$

In view of Eq. (5-41), the pressure terms cancel and we obtain the important relation

$$\sum_{i=1}^{k} n_i d\mu_i^c = 0, \tag{5-47}$$

which holds for all pressures.

Let us now consider an osmotic experiment, such as that illustrated in Fig. 11, in which a solution containing several solutes maintains equilibrium, across an ideal semipermeable membrane, with an infinite reservoir of pure solvent. The assumption of a semipermeable membrane implies that only the solvent can pass through the membrane. We shall assume that the solvent is water and denote its chemical potential by μ_w. As is well known, the maintenance of equilibrium in such a system requires

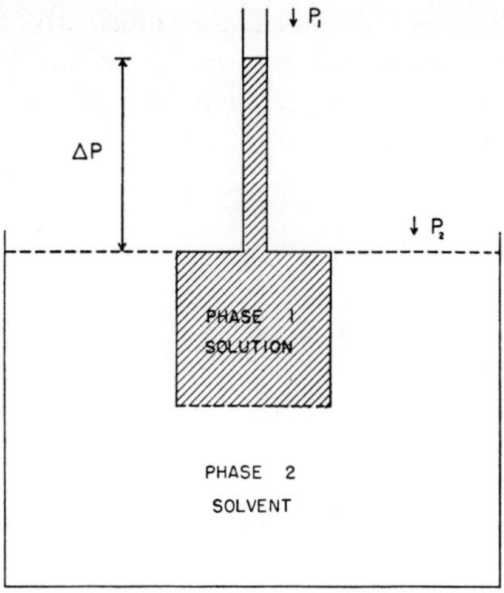

Fig. 11. Illustration of an osmotic-pressure experiment. The membrane separating the solution from the pure solvent is permeable to the solvent only. ΔP represents the equilibrium pressure difference required to prevent flow of solvent from phase 2 to phase 1.

a positive pressure on the solution, as indicated in Fig. 11. Any change in the solution contained in the membrane cell, whether in composition or in pressure, will leave μ_w in the solution unchanged since its value remains equal to the constant potential of the pure external solvent. Thus, the condition of osmotic equilibrium through a membrane permeable to solvent only may be expressed as

$$d\mu_w = 0, \tag{5-48}$$

in which μ_w refers to the chemical potential of water in the solution. In view of Eq. (5-45), Eq. (5-48) can be written

$$d\mu_w = \bar{V}_w dP + d\mu_w^c = 0,$$

or

$$d\mu_w^c = -\bar{V}_w dP. \tag{5-49}$$

Now Eq. (5-47) can be rewritten, for the solution,

$$\sum_{j=1}^{k-1} n_j d\mu_j^c = -n_w d\mu_w^c, \tag{5-50}$$

in which the summation goes over all the components except the solvent. Introducing Eq. (5-49) into Eq. (5-50), we obtain

$$\sum_{j=1}^{k-1} n_j d\mu_j^c = n_w \bar{V}_w dP. \tag{5-51}$$

Generally, the solutions considered are sufficiently dilute to make the volume contribution of the solvent, $n_w \bar{V}_w$, to the total volume of the solution V overwhelmingly larger than that of the other components. Thus, to a good approximation,

$$n_w \bar{V}_w \cong V,$$

and Eq. (5-51) can be written

$$dP = \sum_{j=1}^{k-1} \frac{n_j}{V} d\mu_j^c. \tag{5-52}$$

The number of moles of component j per unit volume is the molar concentration $c_j = n_j/V$. The equilibrium pressure of a solution maintaining osmotic equilibrium with the solvent is called the osmotic pressure, π, so that, under the present conditions, the variation in P is identical with the change in osmotic pressure:

$$dP = d\pi.$$

Hence, Eq. (5-52) can also be written

$$d\pi = \sum_{j=1}^{k-1} c_j d\mu_j^c. \tag{5-53}$$

If there is only one solute in the osmotic cell, Eq. (5-53) reduces to the simple form

$$d\pi = c_s d\mu_s^c, \tag{5-54}$$

in which the subscript s denotes the single solute.

Numerous experiments have shown that the osmotic pressure of dilute, ideal solutions follows the laws of ideal gases, or

$$\pi = RTc_s. \tag{5-55}$$

Equation (5-55) is the well-known van't Hoff law for the osmotic pressure of dilute solutions. In this case,

$$d\pi = RTdc_s,$$

and Eq. (5-54) may be written

$$RTdc_s = c_s d\mu_s^c,$$

or

$$d\mu_s^c = RTd \ln c_s. \tag{5-56}$$

At constant temperature, Eq. (5-56) can be integrated to give the desired expression for μ_s^c of an ideal solution:

$$\mu_s^c = RT \ln c_s + \mu_s^0 (T), \tag{5-57}$$

in which μ_s^0 is the integration constant, which may be a function of the temperature only. Combining Eqs. (5-45) and (5-57), we obtain, for the chemical potential of an ideal solution,

$$\mu_i = \mu_i^0(T) + \bar{V}_i P + RT \ln c_i. \tag{5-58}$$

5.4.3. Real solutions approach the behavior predicted by Eq. (5-58) only at infinite dilution. To account for the deviation from ideality, the common practice is to introduce an activity coefficient, γ_i, by which c_i is multiplied to give the "active concentration" or activity, a_i:

$$a_i = \gamma_i c_i.$$

This procedure leads to the correct chemical potential for a real solution,

$$\mu_i = \mu_i^0 + \bar{V}_i P + RT \ln \gamma_i c_i. \tag{5-59}$$

The activity coefficient has the property that $\gamma_i \to 1$ as $c_i \to 0$, so that Eq. (5-59) reduces to Eq. (5-58) at infinite dilution.

It is worth noting that in the case of ideal nonelectrolyte solutions, the chemical potential of the ith component is independent of the concentration of all other components, so that

$$\left(\frac{\partial \mu_i}{\partial n_j}\right)_{T,P,nk} = 0, \qquad i \neq j.$$

On the other hand, the activity coefficient, which expresses the deviation from ideality and represents possible interactions with other components, may depend on the concentrations of all other components. Thus, from Eq. (5-59),

$$\left(\frac{\partial \mu_i}{\partial n_j}\right)_{T,P,nk} = RT\left(\frac{\partial \ln \gamma_i}{\partial n_j}\right)_{T,P,nk}. \tag{5-60}$$

Since

$$\frac{\partial \mu_i}{\partial n_j} = \frac{\partial}{\partial n_j}\frac{\partial G}{\partial n_i}$$

and

$$\frac{\partial \mu_j}{\partial n_i} = \frac{\partial}{\partial n_i}\frac{\partial G}{\partial n_j},$$

Cauchy's condition for partial derivatives, Eq. (3-42), requires that

$$\left(\frac{\partial \mu_i}{\partial n_j}\right)_{P,T,nk} = \left(\frac{\partial \mu_j}{\partial n_i}\right)_{P,T,nk}. \tag{5-61}$$

Introducing Eq. (5-60) into Eq. (5-61), we find that the dependence of γ_i, the activity coefficient of the ith component, on n_j is equal to the dependence of γ_j on n_i, or

$$\left(\frac{\partial \ln \gamma_i}{\partial n_j}\right)_{P,T,nk} = \left(\frac{\partial \ln \gamma_j}{\partial n_i}\right)_{P,T,nk}. \tag{5-62}$$

5.4.4. We shall finally consider in a more explicit manner the dependence of the chemical potential on temperature. Following the same procedure as that used in Sec. 5.4.1, we may write

$$\left(\frac{\partial \mu_i}{\partial T}\right)_{P,n_i} = \left[\frac{\partial}{\partial T}\left(\frac{\partial G}{\partial n_i}\right)_{P,T,n_j}\right]_{P,n_i} = \left[\frac{\partial}{\partial n_i}\left(\frac{\partial G}{\partial T}\right)_{P,n_i}\right]_{P,T,n_j}. \tag{5-63}$$

According to Eq. (5-8),

$$\left(\frac{\partial G}{\partial T}\right)_{P,n_i} = -S,$$

and since

$$\frac{\partial S}{\partial n_i} = \bar{S}_i,$$

we find that

$$\left(\frac{\partial \mu_i}{\partial T}\right)_{P,n_i} = -\bar{S}_i. \tag{5-64}$$

Equation (5-64) may be used advantageously for the evaluation of the partial molar enthalpy of the ith component. From the relation between free energy and enthalpy,

$$G = H - TS,$$

and the definition of the chemical potential we may obtain the relation

$$\mu_i = \left(\frac{\partial G}{\partial n_i}\right)_{T,P,n_j} = \left(\frac{\partial H}{\partial n_i}\right)_{T,P,n_j} - T\left(\frac{\partial S}{\partial n_i}\right)_{P,T,n_j},$$

or

$$\bar{H}_i = \mu_i + T\bar{S}_i. \tag{5-65}$$

Introducing Eq. (5-64) into Eq. (5-65), we obtain the important Gibbs–Helmholtz equation for the partial molar enthalpy in terms of the partial molar free energy or chemical potential:

$$\bar{H}_i = \mu_i - T\left(\frac{\partial \mu_i}{\partial T}\right)_{P,n_i}. \tag{5-66}$$

In concluding this section, we would like to summarize all the information concerning the chemical potential in a single equation. We have seen that the chemical potential is a function of temperature, pressure, and the number of moles of all components, so that we may write the general expression for the differential of μ_i as

$$d\mu_i = \left(\frac{\partial \mu_i}{\partial T}\right)_{P,n_i} dT + \left(\frac{\partial \mu_i}{\partial P}\right)_{T,n_i} dP + \sum_{j=1}^{n}\left(\frac{\partial \mu_i}{\partial n_j}\right)_{P,T,n_k} dn_j. \tag{5-67}$$

Introducing Eqs. (5-44), (5-45), and (5-64) into Eq. (5-67), we obtain

$$d\mu_i = -\bar{S}_i dT + \bar{V}_i dP + \sum_{j=1}^{n} \left(\frac{\partial \mu_i^c}{\partial n_j}\right)_{P,T,n_k} dn_j, \tag{5-68}$$

or

$$d\mu_i = -\bar{S}_i dT + \bar{V}_i dP + \sum_{j=1}^{n} \mu_{ij}^c dn_j, \tag{5-69}$$

in which

$$\mu_{ij}^c = \left(\frac{\partial \mu_i^c}{\partial n_j}\right)_{T,P,n_k}. \tag{5-70}$$

For the cases in which μ_i^c depends only on n_i and $\mu_{ij}^c = 0$ for $i \neq j$,

$$d\mu_i = -\bar{S}_i dT + \bar{V}_i dP + \mu_{ii}^c dn_i. \tag{5-71}$$

In the ideal case,

$$\mu_i^c = \mu_i^0 + RT \ln c_i, \tag{5-72}$$

and

$$\mu_{ii}^c = RT \frac{d \ln c_i}{dn_i},$$

so that

$$d\mu_i = -\bar{S}_i dT + \bar{V}_i dP + RTd \ln c_i. \tag{5-73}$$

These remarks on chemical thermodynamics and chemical potentials conclude the first part of our treatment. In order to proceed further toward a description of nonequilibrium processes, we must supplement the conceptual framework of classical thermodynamics by developing quantitative notions of flows and forces that will enable us to construct a coordinated system of thermodynamics for flow processes.

CHAPTER 6

FLOWS AND FORCES IN THE THERMODYNAMICS OF IRREVERSIBLE PROCESSES

6.1. Formal Treatment of Flows

THE flows treated in this book belong to two groups, scalar flows, which have no direction in space, and directed flows, characterized by vectorial properties. The scalar flows that will be considered are only those of chemical reactions, while the vectorial ones vary in nature and include flows of diffusion, electric current, heat, and others. The present treatment does not consider more complex cases, such as viscous flow, which may be omitted in the study of numerous biophysical phenomena.

A quantitative description of vectorial flows requires the mastery of several theorems of differential vector analysis. We shall not present their derivation, but shall discuss the mode of their application and their physical significance in terms of a specific example, the diffusional flow of a substance i. The diffusional flow vector, $\mathbf{J}_i$, may be defined as the number of moles n_i passing a unit area per unit time in a given direction:

$$\mathbf{J}_i = \frac{1}{\mathcal{A}}\frac{dn_i}{dt}, \tag{6-1}$$

in which $\mathcal{A}$ is the area through which the flow passes. The flow vector can also be defined in an alternative way. Let the geometric translation of the ith substance be represented by a vector $\mathbf{v}_i$, the average velocity of the particles at a given point. This vector may vary in both magnitude and direction at different points in space. It is, however, always possible to consider at any point x, y, z a sufficiently small area $d\mathcal{A}$ perpendicular to $\mathbf{v}_i$ in which $\mathbf{v}_i$ is virtually constant. The volume scanned by the particles passing $d\mathcal{A}$ in unit time will then be $\mathbf{v}_i d\mathcal{A}$. If the concentration per unit volume at x, y, z is denoted by c_i, the total amount of substance i transported through the area is $c_i\mathbf{v}_i d\mathcal{A}$. The local flow is again given by the amount of material passing unit area in unit time, so that

$$\mathbf{J}_i = c_i\mathbf{v}_i. \tag{6-2}$$

In general, the three quantities $\mathbf{J}_i$, c_i, and $\mathbf{v}_i$ in Eq. (6-2) are functions of time and the space coordinates x, y, z.

In the previous paragraph we considered an area $d\mathcal{A}$ perpendicular to the flow vector, but we may also encounter areas of arbitrary orientation. To characterize the general area $d\mathcal{A}$, we shall construct a unit vector $\mathbf{n}$, perpendicular to $d\mathcal{A}$, whose direction will specify the direction of the area. The magnitude of the vector, $\mathbf{n}d\mathcal{A} = \mathbf{d\mathcal{A}}$ will be taken as the "directed area" under consideration. As indicated in Fig. 12, the scalar product $\mathbf{v}_i \cdot \mathbf{d\mathcal{A}}$ gives the volume dV scanned by the vector $\mathbf{v}_i$ upon passing an area element in any direction. Thus,

$$\mathbf{v}_i \cdot \mathbf{d\mathcal{A}} = \mathbf{v}_i \cdot \mathbf{n} d\mathcal{A} = h d\mathcal{A} = dV.$$

Multiplying $\mathbf{v}_i \cdot \mathbf{d\mathcal{A}}$ by the local concentration, we obtain

$$c_i \mathbf{v}_i \cdot \mathbf{d\mathcal{A}} = \mathbf{J}_i \cdot \mathbf{d\mathcal{A}},$$

which represents the amount of the substance passing an element of area making any angle with the velocity vector $\mathbf{v}_i$. This amount is called the differential flux, $d\Phi_i$, through the area element $\mathbf{d\mathcal{A}}$, or

$$d\Phi_i = \mathbf{J}_i \cdot \mathbf{d\mathcal{A}}. \tag{6-3}$$

If we now consider a volume V enclosed by a surface of area $\mathcal{A}$, as illustrated in Fig. 13, the total amount of substance i leaving the volume is given by

$$\Phi_i = \int_{\mathcal{A}} d\Phi_i = \int_{\mathcal{A}} \mathbf{J}_i \cdot \mathbf{d\mathcal{A}}, \tag{6-4}$$

in which $\int_{\mathcal{A}}$ indicates integration over the surface. According to the present convention for the direction of $\mathbf{J}_i$, a positive value of Φ_i indicates an overall net loss of material from the volume V, while a negative value of Φ_i means that there is a net influx and accumulation of the substance i in the volume.

In order to characterize the behavior of a flow more clearly, Gauss

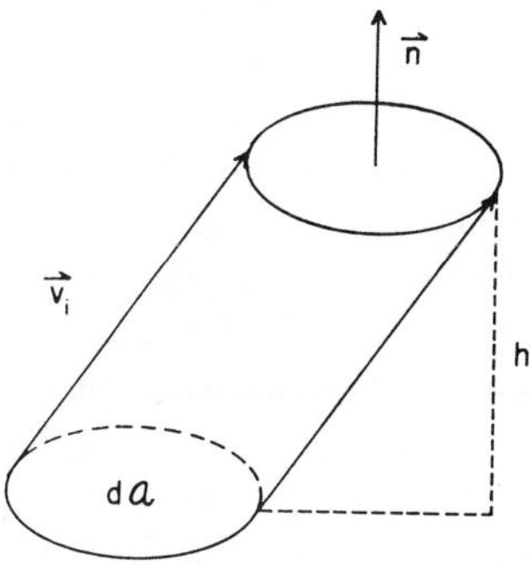

Fig. 12. Geometric representation of flow through an area element $d\mathcal{A}$ that is not perpendicular to the velocity vector $\mathbf{v}_i$.

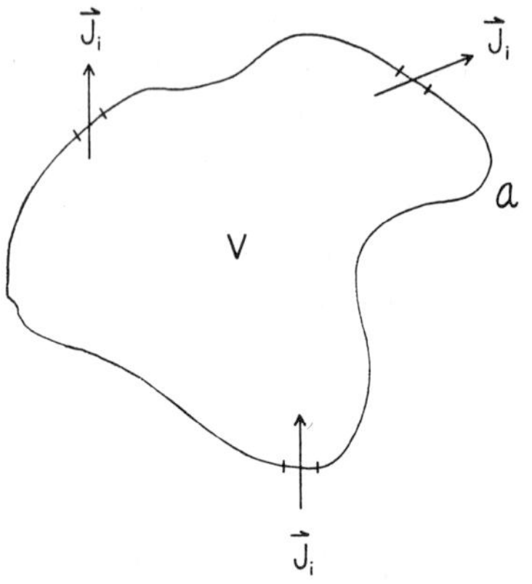

Fig. 13. Flow through a volume element V bounded by a surface $\mathcal{A}$.

considered the ratio of Φ_i to the volume and showed that the value of the flux per unit volume at a point, given by the expression

$$\lim_{V \to 0} \frac{\Phi_i}{V},$$

assumes well-defined values at all points in space. This ratio is called the divergence of the flow $\mathbf{J}_i$, and, from Eq. (6-4), may be written

$$\text{div}\,\mathbf{J}_i = \lim_{V \to 0} \frac{\Phi_i}{V} = \lim_{V \to 0} \frac{\mathbf{J}_i \cdot \mathbf{d}\mathcal{A}}{V}. \tag{6-5}$$

In cartesian coordinates, the divergence is given by

$$\text{div}\,\mathbf{J}_i = \frac{\partial J_{i(x)}}{\partial x} + \frac{\partial J_{i(y)}}{\partial y} + \frac{\partial J_{i(z)}}{\partial z}, \tag{6-6}$$

in which $J_{i(x)}$, $J_{i(y)}$, and $J_{i(z)}$ are the cartesian components of the vector $\mathbf{J}_i$. Since both the volume V and the product $\mathbf{J}_i \cdot \mathbf{d}\mathcal{A}$ are scalars, the divergence is also a scalar quantity.

The physical meaning of div $\mathbf{J}_i$ may be illustrated by consideration of the properties of the flux. A positive divergence means that at the point under consideration there is a net outflow of the ith component, or, in more descriptive language, the point of positive divergence is a "source" of component i. On the other hand, a negative divergence indicates a net inflow of the ith component; the point under consideration is a "sink." At points where div $\mathbf{J}_i = 0$, there is neither accumulation nor removal of material. These considerations suggest that the integral of the divergence over a volume should be equal to the total flow of the ith substance through the surface bounding the volume. As shown by Gauss, the divergence in the volume and the flux across the surface are related by the equation

$$\int_V \operatorname{div} \mathbf{J}_i dV = \int_{\mathcal{A}} \mathbf{J}_i \cdot d\mathbf{\mathcal{A}}, \tag{6-7}$$

in which $\int_V$ denotes the volume integral. Thus, the surface integral of a flow may be transformed into a volume integral of a divergence. The importance of this transformation in discussing systems in which flows are occurring will be illustrated in the next section.

6.2. Conservative and Nonconservative Continuous Systems

6.2.1. The concept of divergence is very useful in the consideration of local conservation laws at all points of a system. To demonstrate the utility of Eq. (6-7), we shall first consider the law of conservation of mass for a system exchanging matter with its surroundings. We shall analyze a system of volume V bounded by a surface $\mathcal{A}$ that loses mass M to the surroundings at a rate $-dM/dt$. Since the law of conservation requires that mass cannot be created or destroyed in the system, the decrease in mass must be due to flow out of the system at a rate given by the flux through $\mathcal{A}$ Thus,

$$-\frac{dM}{dt} = \int_{\mathcal{A}} \mathbf{J}_M \cdot d\mathbf{\mathcal{A}}, \tag{6-8}$$

in which $\mathbf{J}_M$ is the mass flow. The total mass of the system is given by the sum of the masses of all local volume elements, or

$$M = \int_V dM = \int_V \rho dV, \tag{6-9}$$

in which ρ is the local density in mass per unit volume. On the basis of Eq. (6-9), the loss of mass may be expressed in terms of the local change in density, $\partial\rho/\partial t$, as

$$-\frac{dM}{dt} = \int_V -\frac{\partial \rho}{\partial t} dV. \tag{6-10}$$

The use of the partial differential $\partial/\partial t$ in Eq. (6-10) and the following means that in the differentiation the geometry of the system is kept constant, and that it is the specific mass of a fixed volume element that changes with time; that is, $\partial/\partial t$ is the *local derivative* with respect to time at fixed x, y, z.

With the aid of Eq. (6-7), the surface integral of the mass flow can be transformed into a volume integral of the local divergence, so that Eq. (6-8) may be written

$$-\frac{dM}{dt} = \int_V \operatorname{div} \mathbf{J}_M dV. \tag{6-11}$$

Comparing Eqs. (6-10) and (6-11), we obtain

$$\int_V -\frac{\partial \rho}{\partial t}\,dV = \int_V \operatorname{div} \mathbf{J}_M dV, \tag{6-12}$$

which holds for any arbitrary volume so that the integrands must be equal and

$$\frac{\partial \rho}{\partial t} = -\operatorname{div} \mathbf{J}_M. \tag{6-13}$$

Equation (6-13) is the local equivalent of the law of conservation of mass. It expresses the fact that matter cannot be created or destroyed at any point of a material system and that the matter flowing out of a point ($\operatorname{div} \mathbf{J}_M$) can do so only at the expense of a decrease in the local density.

6.2.2. The same treatment may be applied to individual substances that are conserved in a flow process. Since the total number of moles n_i of the ith component is given by

$$n_i = \int_V c_i dV,$$

we may write, in exact correspondence with Eqs. (6-8), (6-10), (6-12), and (6-13),

$$-\frac{dn_i}{dt} = \int_V -\frac{\partial c_i}{\partial t}\,dV = \int_\mathfrak{a} \mathbf{J}_i \cdot \mathbf{d}\mathfrak{A} = \int_V \operatorname{div} \mathbf{J}_i dV, \tag{6-14}$$

and

$$\frac{\partial c_i}{\partial t} = -\operatorname{div} \mathbf{J}_i. \tag{6-15}$$

Components that undergo a chemical reaction and are not conserved during a flow process cannot be described by Eq. (6-15). The description of such nonconserved substances will be considered in the next section.

Other quantities that obey laws of conservation may also be treated in a similar manner. According to the first law of thermodynamics, the total energy is conserved both locally and for the system as a whole. If we assign local energy density ρ_e to each point of a system, we can obtain by similar arguments the equivalent of Eqs. (6-13) and (6-15):

$$\frac{\partial \rho_e}{\partial t} = -\operatorname{div} \mathbf{J}_e, \tag{6-16}$$

in which $\mathbf{J}_e$ is the energy flow. Thus, energy cannot be created or destroyed by any process and local energy content can change only as a result of inflow or outflow of energy.

6.2.3. Application of the concepts developed above is not limited to conservative systems. By a straightforward generalization, nonconservative cases can be included, providing local expressions for the formation of substances in a chemical reaction or for the production of entropy in irreversible processes. We shall consider first the change in the number of moles of a component that participates in a chemical reaction and that is transported into a system. According to the considerations of the previous paragraph, the total influx of the ith component into a volume V is given by

$$\frac{d_T n_i}{dt} = -\int_V \operatorname{div} \mathbf{J}_i dV,$$

in which $d_T n_i/dt$ represents a change in n_i due to transport. The amount of component i formed in a chemical reaction, $d_R n_i/dt$, depends on the rate of chemical change per unit volume which is given by $J_{\text{ch}} = d\xi/dt$. If the stoichiometric coefficient for the ith component is ν_i, the contribution of the reaction is

$$\frac{d_R n_i}{dt} = \int_V \nu_i J_{\text{ch}} dV.$$

The total change in n_i is

$$\frac{dn_i}{dt} = \frac{d_T n_i}{dt} + \frac{d_R n_i}{dt} = \int_V \frac{\partial c_i}{\partial t} dV, \tag{6-17}$$

and therefore

$$\int_V \frac{\partial c_i}{\partial t} dV = -\int_V \operatorname{div} \mathbf{J}_i dV + \int_V \nu_i J_{\text{ch}} dV. \tag{6-18}$$

The validity of this equation is independent of the geometry of the system so that the equality holds not only for the integrals but also for the integrands, and the expression for a nonconservative change in the local concentration of the ith component is

$$\frac{\partial c_i}{\partial t} = -\operatorname{div} \mathbf{J}_i + \nu_i J_{\text{ch}}. \tag{6-19}$$

If the substance does not participate in a chemical reaction, $\nu_i J_{\text{ch}} = 0$, and Eq. (6-19) reduces to the conservative expression, Eq. (6-15). For all other cases, the local change in concentration is a result of both flow and local chemical formation of the component. If the ith component participates in more than one chemical reaction, the second term on the right-hand side of Eq. (6-19) must be summed over all the reactions involved.

A similar analysis may be applied to local changes in entropy. However, this treatment requires the introduction of some concepts that have intuitive meaning but whose physical validity must be verified by experimental test. The simplest concept is that of local entropy density, defined as the entropy per unit volume, s_v. The total entropy of a system is then given by

$$S = \int_V s_v dV \tag{6-20}$$

and the change in total entropy with time is

$$\frac{dS}{dt} = \int_V \frac{\partial s_v}{\partial t} dV. \tag{6-21}$$

The second concept is that of an entropy flow, $\mathbf{J}_S$, which is related to the exchange of entropy with the surroundings by the expression

$$\frac{d_eS}{dt} = -\int_{\mathfrak{a}} \mathbf{J}_S \cdot \mathbf{d\mathfrak{a}} = -\int_V \text{div } \mathbf{J}_S dV. \tag{6-22}$$

The most intricate concept is that of local entropy production, σ. As pointed out in Sec. 4.4, the entropy produced irreversibly in any local element of the system, as well as the total entropy production for the system, is greater than zero ($\sigma > 0$). The over-all entropy production is related to the local production by the expression

$$\frac{d_iS}{dt} = \int_V \sigma dV. \tag{6-23}$$

Introducing Eqs. (6-21), (6-22), and (6-23) into the expression for the total change in entropy,

$$\frac{dS}{dt} = \frac{d_eS}{dt} + \frac{d_iS}{dt},$$

we obtain

$$\int_V \frac{\partial s_v}{\partial t} dV = -\int_V \text{div } \mathbf{J}_S dV + \int_V \sigma dV. \tag{6-24}$$

Thus, for any local change,

$$\frac{\partial s_v}{\partial t} = -\text{div } \mathbf{J}_S + \sigma. \tag{6-25}$$

Equation (6-25) is of fundamental importance for the description of irreversible processes in continuous systems. This simple expression makes possible the isolation of σ from the total change in entropy and the evaluation of the dependence of σ on flows and forces.

6.3. Flows in Stationary States

Of all the processes described by the equations derived in the last section, a special role is played by those during which all the properties of a system are independent of time. These processes are known as stationary or steady-state processes. They resemble equilibria in their invariance with time, but differ in that flows continue to occur in the system and, consequently, entropy is being produced. The time independence of all properties means that the partial differentials of ρ, c_i, ρ_e, and s_v discussed above will vanish in a steady state. If the property under consideration represents a conservative property, the divergence of the corresponding flow must vanish according to Eqs. (6-13), (6-15), and (6-16). This means that the steady flow of a conservative quantity must be "source-free." Moreover, in the cases considered below, the physical solution of the equation div $\mathbf{J}_i = 0$ is generally $\mathbf{J}_i =$ constant, so that in stationary states the flows of conservative properties are constant. At equilibrium, all flows must vanish and the constant values of the steady flows become zero.

The situation is more involved in the case of nonconservative steady flows. If we consider the change in the local entropy of a system in a steady state, $\partial s_v/\partial t$ must be zero since entropy is a single-valued function of all the parameters of the system. Thus, the local entropy density must remain constant in a steady state because the external and internal parameters do not change with time. However, upon introducing the condition

$$\frac{\partial s_v}{\partial t} = 0 \tag{6-26}$$

into Eq. (6-25) we find that the divergence of entropy flow does not vanish. We obtain, instead, the relation

$$\text{div } \mathbf{J}_S = \sigma. \tag{6-27}$$

In order to maintain a steady state, the entropy created at any point of a system must be removed by a flow of entropy taking place at that point. In the state of equilibrium, the flow of entropy vanishes together with all other flows so that the necessary and sufficient condition for equilibrium is

$$\sigma = 0. \tag{6-28}$$

As was pointed out by Meixner,[1] this criterion of equilibrium may prove a useful means of determining the state of a system. It is of interest to note that a steady state cannot be maintained in an adiabatic system, since the requirement of Eq. (6-24) together with that of Eq. (6-26) cannot be satisfied. The entropy produced by irreversible processes, $\int_V \sigma dV$, cannot be removed from an adiabatic system since it cannot be exchanged with the environment. The only time-invariant state that can be achieved by an adiabatic system is that of equilibrium.

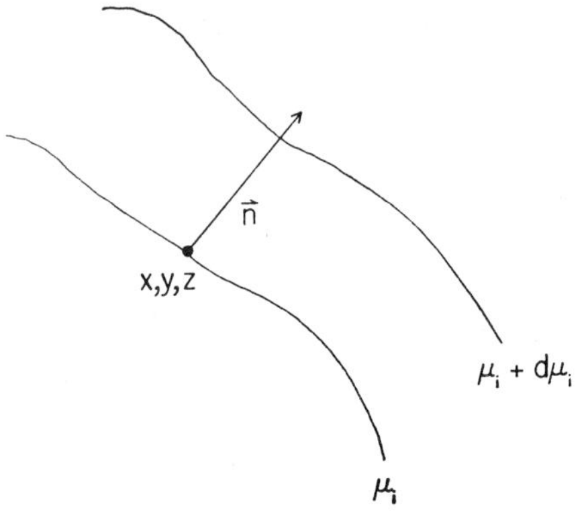

Fig. 14. Spatial relations of equipotential surfaces for the chemical potential. The unit vector **n** is perpendicular to the surface μ_i at the point x, y, z.

6.4. Treatment of Thermodynamic Forces

6.4.1. In previous sections we have mentioned briefly several forces, such as the affinity of a chemical reaction, a difference in chemical potential, or a difference in hydrostatic pressure, that cause thermodynamic flows. In this section, we shall analyze these forces in terms suitable for the description of local processes. There is no need to consider scalar forces, such as the affinity, in further detail. However, proper spatial characteristics must be assigned to vectorial forces. Since these thermodynamic forces are generally derived from scalar potentials, the first requirement is to define clearly the potential field. We may consider, for example, a region in which the chemical potential of the ith component is a function of the space coordinates. We shall assign all points of equal μ_i to equipotential surfaces and attempt to characterize the local density of these surfaces. Following the procedures of differential vector analysis, we consider two neighboring equipotential surfaces with chemical potentials μ_i and $\mu_i + d\mu_i$ as shown in Fig. 14. At a given point on the surface μ_i we construct a perpendicular unit vector with direction **n** and consider the change in μ_i with n, $\partial\mu_i/\partial n$. The direction **n** corresponds to the direction of maximal change in μ_i and the rate of change in μ_i as we move along **n**, $\partial\mu_i/\partial n$, is an adequate measure of the local density of equipotential surfaces. The vector $\mathbf{n}(\partial\mu_i/\partial n)$ is called the gradient of the field at the point x, y, z:

$$\operatorname{grad} \mu_i = \mathbf{n}\,\frac{\partial \mu_i}{\partial n}. \tag{6-29}$$

If unit vectors in the direction of the x, y, and z coordinates are denoted by **i**, **j**, and **k** respectively, the gradient of μ_i may be written in cartesian coordinates as

$$\text{grad } \mu_i = \mathbf{i}\,\frac{\partial \mu_i}{\partial x} + \mathbf{j}\,\frac{\partial \mu_i}{\partial y} + \mathbf{k}\,\frac{\partial \mu_i}{\partial z}. \tag{6-30}$$

A driving force occurs whenever a difference in potential exists and its direction is that of the maximal decrease in μ_i. Hence, at the point x, y, z the local force $\mathbf{X}_i$ driving the ith component is

$$\mathbf{X}_i = -\text{grad } \mu_i. \tag{6-31}$$

In many experimental situations, μ_i depends on a single coordinate, for example x. In this case, the force becomes

$$\mathbf{X}_i = -\mathbf{i}\,\frac{\partial \mu_i}{\partial x}. \tag{6-32}$$

Equation (6-32) is readily amenable to physical interpretation. From the definition of the chemical potential, we may write

$$-\frac{\partial \mu_i}{\partial x} = \frac{\partial}{\partial x}\left(\frac{-\partial G}{\partial n_i}\right) = \frac{\partial}{\partial n_i}\left(\frac{-\partial G}{\partial x}\right), \tag{6-33}$$

in which $-dG$ is the free energy available for the performance of useful work, dW'. The differential of work with distance, dW'/dx, is a force, f, so that

$$-\frac{\partial \mu_i}{\partial x} = \frac{\partial f}{\partial n_i}. \tag{6-34}$$

Since $\partial f/\partial n_i$ is the force per mole of substance, $\mathbf{X}_i$ is a force per mole of the ith component operating in the direction of the unit vector $\mathbf{i}$, which is the direction of the greatest change in chemical potential. In the previous chapter we considered the difference in chemical potential, $\mu_{i(1)} - \mu_{i(2)}$, as the driving force for the transport of matter from point 1 to point 2. This over-all thermodynamic force, which is applicable to *discontinuous systems*, is simply the integral of Eq. (6-32) along the x coordinate:

$$\int_1^2 \mathbf{X}_i dx = -\mathbf{i} \int_1^2 \frac{\partial \mu_i}{\partial x}\, dx = \mathbf{i}(\mu_{i(1)} - \mu_{i(2)}). \tag{6-35}$$

However, $\Delta\mu_i$ is a difference in potential while $-\partial\mu_i/\partial x$ is a force in the sense used in classical mechanics.

The same approach is applicable to the electric force that causes a current. Denoting the electric potential at the point x, y, z by ψ we may write

$$\mathbf{X}_{\text{el}} = -\text{grad } \psi, \tag{6-36}$$

in which $\mathbf{X}_{\text{el}}$ is the force per unit charge or the local intensity of the electric field. In several cases, we shall deal with the difference in electric potential between two points rather than with local electric forces. This quantity is the well-known electromotive force, which is denoted by E and is given, for the unidimensional case, by an expression equivalent to Eq. (6-35):

$$E = -\mathbf{i} \int_1^2 \frac{d\psi}{dx}\, dx = \mathbf{i}(\psi_1 - \psi_2). \tag{6-37}$$

Other types of forces will be encountered in the thermodynamics of irreversible processes, but the basic notions considered above remain the same whatever the structure of the field producing the force.

6.5. An Example of the Dependence of Flow on Force: Simple Diffusion in a Binary Solution

6.5.1. The dependence of flows on the forces operative in the system is of major importance in the study of any irreversible process and will be discussed in detail in the following chapters. Here we shall consider a simple case which will introduce this concept and will also serve to illustrate the use of the equations for flows and forces that have been discussed in this chapter. The example is that of simple diffusion in a binary system assuming only a single flow, the flow of the solute, $\mathbf{J}_s$, is involved. (A full discussion of flows and forces in diffusion is given in Chapter 9.)

It is plausible to assume that the velocity of diffusion, $\mathbf{v}_s$, is linearly proportional to the driving force for diffusion, grad $(-\mu_s)$, or

$$\mathbf{v}_s = -\omega_s \operatorname{grad} \mu_s, \tag{6-38}$$

in which ω_s is a constant proportionality factor. This factor is the velocity per unit force or the mobility of a mole of solute in the medium, and is inversely proportional to the molar frictional coefficient of the solute, f_s, or

$$\omega_s = \frac{1}{f_s}. \tag{6-39}$$

In dilute ideal solutions in which Eq. (5-72) is valid,

$$\operatorname{grad} \mu_s = \frac{RT}{c_s} \operatorname{grad} c_s,$$

providing the temperature and pressure are constant. Equation (6-38) may then be written

$$\mathbf{v}_s = -\frac{\omega_s RT}{c_s} \operatorname{grad} c_s,$$

or

$$c_s \mathbf{v}_s = -RT\omega_s \operatorname{grad} c_s.$$

However, according to Eq. (6-2), $c_s \mathbf{v}_s = \mathbf{J}_s$, so that

$$\mathbf{J}_s = -RT\omega_s \text{ grad } c_s = -D \text{ grad } c_s. \tag{6-40}$$

Equation (6-40) is the well-known diffusion law of Fick in which the diffusion constant, D, is related to the mobility by the Plank–Einstein relation,

$$D = RT\omega_s. \tag{6-41}$$

The constancy of D at a given temperature implies the constancy of ω, which underlies the hydrodynamic equation, Eq. (6-38).

In the thermodynamic treatment of the dependence of flows on forces, it is more useful to relate the flow directly to the force through a phenomenological coefficient, L, so that, for the present case,

$$\mathbf{J}_s = L\mathbf{X}_s = -L \text{ grad } \mu_s. \tag{6-42}$$

Comparison of Eqs. (6-38) and (6-42) indicates that

$$L = c_s\omega_s, \tag{6-43}$$

so that the phenomenological coefficient is not a constant but a function of concentration. The importance of the phenomenological coefficient will become clear in the subsequent discussion of systems in which coupling of flows and forces occurs. It is necessary to stress that, although L is a function of c_s, it is not a function of either the force, grad μ_s, or the flow, $\mathbf{J}_s$. In general, the phenomenological coefficients may be functions of the parameters, such as temperature and concentration, defining the state of the volume element under consideration, but should not depend on the forces defined by the gradients of these parameters.

It is of interest to note the orders of magnitude of mobilities, frictional coefficients, and diffusion constants. The coefficient of friction F of a spherical particle of radius r in a medium of viscosity η is given by the Stokes equation,

$$F = 6\pi r\eta.$$

For a particle of molecular dimensions, for example 3 Å $= 3 \times 10^{-8}$ cm, suspended in water ($\eta \approx 10^{-2}$ poise),

$$F = 5.6 \times 10^{-9} \text{ dyne sec/cm}.$$

The friction exerted on a mole of substance is N_AF, where N_A is Avogadro's number:

$$N_AF = 6.02 \times 10^{23} \times 5.6 \times 10^{-9} = 3.4 \times 10^{15} \text{ dyne sec/cm},$$

and the molar mobility per unit force, ω, is

$$\omega = \frac{1}{N_AF} = 2.9 \times 10^{-16} \text{ cm/sec dyne}.$$

The diffusion coefficient at 300°K is

$$D = RT\omega = 8.3 \times 10^7 \times 300 \times 2.9 \times 10^{-16} = 7 \times 10^{-6} \text{ cm}^2/\text{sec}.$$

6.5.2. Let us now consider the case of stationary diffusion which may be realized by connecting two large reservoirs at concentrations c_1 and c_2 by a column, as illustrated in Fig. 15. After a sufficiently long time, a steady-state distribution will be reached in the column, so that at every point

$$\frac{\partial c_s}{\partial t} = 0,$$

and according to Eq. (6-15)

$$-\text{div } \mathbf{J}_s = 0. \tag{6-44}$$

Equation (6-44) indicates that, under these steady-state conditions, the flow of solute is constant.

For the system illustrated in Fig. 15, the gradient of concentration reduces to a derivative along the x-coordinate, so that Eq. (6-40) may be written

$$\mathbf{J}_s = -D \frac{dc_s}{dx} \mathbf{i}. \tag{6-45}$$

Equation (6-45) may now be integrated along the x-coordinate, using the condition that $\mathbf{J}_s$ is constant:

$$\int_0^h \mathbf{J}_s dx = \mathbf{J}_s h = -D\mathbf{i} \int_0^h \frac{dc_s}{dx}\, dx = -D\mathbf{i} \int_{c_1}^{c_2} dc_s = D\mathbf{i}(c_1 - c_2). \tag{6-46}$$

Hence, the steady flow is given by the simple expression

$$\mathbf{J}_s = D \frac{(c_1 - c_2)}{h} \mathbf{i}. \tag{6-47}$$

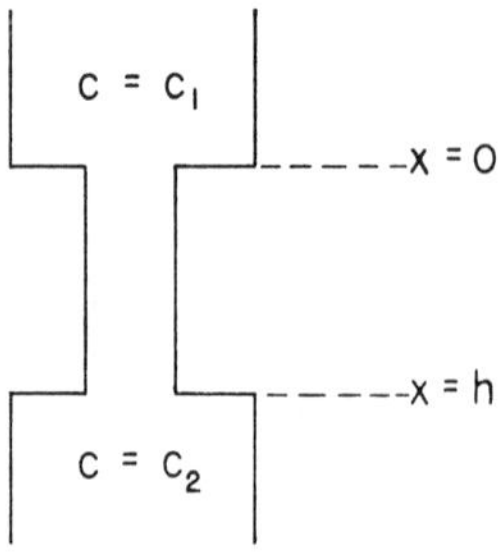

Fig. 15. An arrangement for obtaining a steady diffusion of solute between two reservoirs of constant concentration, c_1 and c_2. A diffusion column of height h is imposed between the reservoirs.

Further, the local concentration, c, at any point x of the column may be evaluated by carrying out the integration in Eq. (6-46) from 0 to x, to yield

$$\mathbf{J}_s x = D\mathrm{i}(c_1 - c).$$

Upon introducing $\mathbf{J}_s$ from Eq. (6-47) we get for c,

$$c = c_1 - \frac{x}{h}(c_1 - c_2).$$

Thus, the distribution of concentrations in a steady diffusion is linear. On the other hand, the constancy of the flow does not imply that the velocity, $\mathbf{v}_s$, is constant. Since $\mathbf{J}_s = c\mathbf{v}_s$, the velocity must change as c changes from c_1 to c_2 along the column. Furthermore, the driving force, grad μ_s, is not constant since it is directly proportional to the velocity by Eq. (6-38). However, the product of the force and the suitable coefficient must fulfill the requirements of a steady state.

Throughout much of the remainder of this book, we shall be concerned with the relations between the flows and forces that have been introduced in this chapter. The foregoing example serves as a brief introduction to the use of these concepts. However, before undertaking the detailed analysis of more interesting and complex systems, we must utilize the concepts introduced above in a calculation of the entropy production in a continuous system in which flows of matter, energy, and chemical reaction are occurring. This calculation is, as we shall see, essential for the further analysis of flow processes, since it defines the flows and forces that must be used in the thermodynamic description of any system.

CHAPTER 7

ENTROPY PRODUCTION IN CONTINUOUS SYSTEMS

THIS chapter is devoted to the evaluation of the local entropy production, σ, for a continuous system in which irreversible processes are taking place. Our aim is to express σ in terms of the flows and generalized forces considered in the previous chapter. As discussed in Chapter 4, the total change in the entropy of a system, dS, is the sum of the entropy exchanged with the surroundings, d_eS, and the entropy created by irreversible processes proceeding in the system, d_iS. The local production of entropy is related to the rate of increase in entropy within the system as a whole by a volume integral,

$$\int_V \sigma dV = \frac{d_iS}{dt}. \tag{7-1}$$

Thus, while d_iS/dt is an over-all indication of the behavior of the system, σ characterizes the local events and their contribution to the total formation of entropy.

7.1. The Gibbs Equation for Local Quantities

The calculation of σ is based on a suitable adaptation of the equation for the second law of thermodynamics to the description of local processes. For this purpose, we shall isolate, within the total volume V of a system, a small volume v, in which the entropy, internal energy, and number of moles are given by s, u, and n_i. The volume v is sufficiently small that, within it, the intensive properties T, P, and μ_i are virtually equal at all points, but large enough to make the influence of fluctuations negligible. We now assume that the Gibbs equation may be used for the description of changes taking place in v, so that we may write

$$Tds = du + Pdv - \sum_{i=1}^{n} \mu_i dn_i. \tag{7-2}$$

The use of Eq. (7-2) for the description of a system that is not in equilibrium depends on one of the basic assumptions of the thermodynamics of irreversible processes. In applying this equation, the existence of a "local" equilibrium is assumed. Even if irreversible processes are taking place within the system as a whole, we assume that it is possible to isolate a small part of the system that may be considered at equilibrium. However, the restrictions placed on this subsystem, that T, P, and μ_i are virtually constant and that fluctuations are insignificant, imply certain limitations on the processes occurring. If the gradients of the intensive parameters in the system are large, it may be impossible to isolate a subsystem that satisfies both of these requirements. Thus, Eq. (7-2) cannot be used if the system is "too far" from equilibrium. The range of applicability of the Gibbs equation cannot be specified on a priori grounds, and the justification of its use rests, in the final analysis, on the validity of the results obtained. On the basis of this criterion, many irreversible processes of interest can be treated using Eq. (7-2) as a starting point. An extensive discussion of the foundations of the thermodynamics of irreversible processes, including the validity of the Gibbs equation under nonequilibrium conditions, may be found in de Groot and Mazur.[1]

Equation (7-2) may be integrated to give

$$Ts = u + Pv - \sum_{i=1}^{n} \mu_i n_i \tag{7-3}$$

by the method discussed in Sec. 3.2 for the integration of the Gibbs equation applied to the system as a whole. Further analysis is facilitated by introducing local concentrations of entropy, energy, and matter which are defined by the expressions

$$s_v = \frac{s}{v}, \qquad u_v = \frac{u}{v}, \qquad c_i = \frac{n_i}{v}. \tag{7-4}$$

Dividing Eq. (7-3) by v and making use of Eqs. (7-4), we find that the local concentrations are related by the expression

$$Ts_v = u_v + P - \sum_{i=1}^{n} \mu_i c_i. \tag{7-5}$$

By introducing Eqs. (7-4) into Eq. (7-2), we may define an additional equation relating the changes in the respective local concentrations. Equation (7-2) then becomes

$$Td(vs_v) = d(vu_v) + Pdv - \sum_{i=1}^{n} \mu_i d(vc_i),$$

or, upon carrying out the differentiation and rearranging,

$$v\left(Tds_v - du_v + \sum_{i=1}^{n} \mu_i dc_i\right) = dv\left(-Ts_v + u_v + P - \sum_{i=1}^{n} \mu_i c_i\right). \tag{7-6}$$

The right-hand side of Eq. (7-6) is zero according to Eq. (7-5), and, since v is nonvanishing, we obtain

$$Tds_v = du_v - \sum_{i=1}^{n} \mu_i dc_i. \tag{7-7}$$

The reader should not be misled by the formal resemblance of Eqs. (7-2) and (7-7). While Eq. (7-2) correlates changes in extensive properties of the volume v, Eq. (7-7) relates the local specific properties at any point within the system. The transition from Eq. (7-2) to Eq. (7-7) is not trivial, since the volume must be taken as a variable.

At this point it is useful to consider the first law of thermodynamics as applied to the subvolume v:

$$du = dq - Pdv. \tag{7-8}$$

Since the subsystem is an open system capable of exchanging matter with its surroundings, the term dq must represent all the energy transported into the volume, including that resulting from the transfer of matter. The term Pdv represents the mechanical work done on the volume element. By a treatment similar to that given above, it may be shown that

$$du_v = dq_v, \tag{7-9}$$

in which dq_v is the total heat increment per unit volume. To do this, we consider a form of the first law that is valid for open systems,

$$du = dq' - Pdv + \sum_{i=1}^{n} \bar{H}_i dn_i, \tag{7-10}$$

in which $\bar{H}_i$ is the partial molar enthalpy of component i discussed in Chapter 5. The sum $(dq' + \sum \bar{H}_i dn_i)$ corresponds to the term dq in Eq. (7-8); $\sum \bar{H}_i dn_i$ is the heat change caused by a change in composition of the system, while dq' represents an increment of "pure" heat. Introducing Eqs. (7-4) into Eq. (7-10), we obtain

$$d(vu_v) = vdq'_v - Pdv + \sum_{i=1}^{n} \bar{H}_i d(vc_i),$$

in which dq'_v is the increment of pure heat per unit volume. Carrying out the differentiation and rearranging yields

$$v\left(du_v - dq'_v - \sum_{i=1}^{n} \bar{H}_i dc_i\right) = dv\left[-(u_v + P) + \sum_{i=1}^{n} \bar{H}_i c_i\right]. \tag{7-11}$$

The right-hand side of Eq. (7-11) is zero, since

$$-(u_v + P) = -\frac{(u + Pv)}{v} = -\frac{h}{v},$$

and

$$\sum_{i=1}^{n} \bar{H}_i c_i = \sum_{i=1}^{n} \frac{\bar{H}_i n_i}{v} = \frac{h}{v},$$

in which h is the enthalpy of the volume v. Since v is not zero,

$$du_v = dq'_v + \sum_{i=1}^{n} \bar{H}_i dc_i = dq_v,$$

as stated in Eq. (7-9).

Using Eq. (7-9), we may write Eq. (7-7) in the form

$$Tds_v = dq_v - \sum_{i=1}^{n} \mu_i dc_i. \tag{7-12}$$

The next step required is evaluation of the changes in the local concentrations with time. This is done by dividing Eq. (7-12) by dt and requiring that the space coordinates remain constant. We then obtain

$$T\frac{\partial s_v}{\partial t} = \frac{\partial q_v}{\partial t} - \sum_{i=1}^{n} \mu_i \frac{\partial c_i}{\partial t}. \tag{7-13}$$

Equation (7-13) is the final expression which may be utilized for determination of the local rate of entropy production in a continuous system.

The differentials appearing in Eq. (7-13) are local derivatives applying at a fixed point in space. The behavior of a volume element participating in a flow process may be described by the total or barycentric differential. In this case, the properties of the volume element change not only with time but also with position. The total differential of any quantity α is related to the local differential by the following equation:

$$\frac{d\alpha}{dt} = \left(\frac{\partial\alpha}{\partial t}\right)_{x,y,z} + \left(\frac{\partial\alpha}{\partial x}\right)_{t,y,z}\frac{dx}{dt} + \left(\frac{\partial\alpha}{\partial y}\right)_{t,x,z}\frac{dy}{dt} + \left(\frac{\partial\alpha}{\partial z}\right)_{t,x,y}\frac{dz}{dt}.$$

The last three terms on the right-hand side are the scalar product of the velocity of the center of mass,

$$\mathbf{v} = \mathbf{i}\frac{dx}{dt} + \mathbf{j}\frac{dy}{dt} + \mathbf{k}\frac{dz}{dt},$$

and the gradient of α,

$$\text{grad}\,\alpha = \mathbf{i}\frac{\partial\alpha}{\partial x} + \mathbf{j}\frac{\partial\alpha}{\partial y} + \mathbf{k}\frac{\partial\alpha}{\partial z},$$

so that

$$\frac{d\alpha}{dt} = \frac{\partial\alpha}{\partial t} + \mathbf{v}\cdot\text{grad}\,\alpha.$$

For change of s_v, q_v, and c_i with position at a given time, Eq. (7-12) becomes

$$T \text{ grad } s_v = \text{grad } q_v - \sum_{i=1}^{n} \mu_i \text{ grad } c_i.$$

Multiplying this expression by $\mathbf{v}$ and adding the result to Eq. (7-13), we obtain

$$T \frac{ds_v}{dt} = \frac{dq_v}{dt} - \sum_{i=1}^{n} \mu_i \frac{dc_i}{dt}.$$

7.2. The Local Entropy Production

The differentials of Eq. (7-13) are related to divergences of the corresponding flows by the laws of conservation and continuity discussed in Chapter 6. Thus, in Sec. 6.2, we showed that

$$\frac{\partial s_v}{\partial t} = -\text{div } \mathbf{J}_S + \sigma,$$

$$\frac{\partial c_i}{\partial t} = -\text{div } \mathbf{J}_i + \nu_i J_{\text{ch}}.$$

Further,

$$\frac{\partial q_v}{\partial t} = -\text{div } \mathbf{J}_q, \tag{7-14}$$

in which $\mathbf{J}_q$ is the total flow of heat across the boundaries of the volume element v. Introducing these expressions into Eq. (7-13), we obtain

$$-\text{div } \mathbf{J}_S + \sigma = -\frac{1}{T} \text{div } \mathbf{J}_q - \sum_{i=1}^{n} \frac{\mu_i}{T} (-\text{div } \mathbf{J}_i + \nu_i J_{\text{ch}}). \tag{7-15}$$

Equation (7-15) may be modified by making use of the relation obtained from differential vector analysis, that

$$\text{div } a\mathbf{b} = a \text{ div } \mathbf{b} + \mathbf{b} \cdot \text{grad } a,$$

in which a is a scalar and $\mathbf{b}$ is a vector. Thus,

$$\frac{1}{T} \text{div } \mathbf{J}_q = \text{div } \frac{\mathbf{J}_q}{T} - \mathbf{J}_q \cdot \text{grad } \frac{1}{T},$$

and

$$\frac{\mu_i}{T} \text{div } \mathbf{J}_i = \text{div } \frac{\mu_i \mathbf{J}_i}{T} - \mathbf{J}_i \cdot \text{grad } \frac{\mu_i}{T}.$$

Introducing these relations into Eq. (7-15) and rearranging gives

$$-\text{div } \mathbf{J}_S + \sigma = -\text{div } \frac{\mathbf{J}_q - \sum_{i=1}^{n} \mu_i \mathbf{J}_i}{T}$$

$$+ \mathbf{J}_q \cdot \text{grad } \frac{1}{T} + \sum_{i=1}^{n} \mathbf{J}_i \cdot \text{grad} \left(-\frac{\mu_i}{T}\right) + J_{\text{ch}} \frac{A}{T}, \tag{7-16}$$

in which $A = -\sum \nu_i \mu_i$ is the affinity of the single chemical reaction considered here. If more than one reaction is involved, the last term on the right-hand side of Eq. (7-16) will be summed over all the reactions.

The division of the terms on the right-hand side of Eq. (7-16) into a divergence and a sum of scalar products is unique and makes possible a comparison of the components of the left- and right-hand sides. We may equate the two divergence terms,

$$\text{div } \mathbf{J}_S = \text{div} \frac{\mathbf{J}_q - \sum_{i=1}^{n} \mu_i \mathbf{J}_i}{T}, \tag{7-17}$$

indicating that the external flow of entropy across the boundaries of v is

$$\mathbf{J}_S = \frac{\mathbf{J}_q - \sum_{i=1}^{n} \mu_i \mathbf{J}_i}{T}, \tag{7-18}$$

as suggested by the direct inspection of Eq. (7-2). The more important result, from our point of view, is the isolation of the local entropy production σ:

$$\sigma = \mathbf{J}_q \cdot \text{grad} \frac{1}{T} + \sum_{i=1}^{n} \mathbf{J}_i \cdot \text{grad} \left(-\frac{\mu_i}{T}\right) + J_{\text{ch}} \frac{A}{T}. \tag{7-19}$$

Equation (7-19) shows that σ may be expressed as a sum of products of flows with their conjugated forces. In the general case, σ may be written in the form

$$\sigma = \sum_{i=1}^{n} J_i X_i, \tag{7-20}$$

in which X_i is the force conjugate with the flow J_i. As discussed in more detail in the next chapter, Eq. (7-19) or (7-20) defines the flows and forces that must be employed in the thermodynamic analysis of a system. Thus the choice of the set of flows fixes the proper forces that have to be used in the thermodynamic treatment. In Eq. (7-19), the choice of $\mathbf{J}_q$ as the heat flow determines grad $(1/T)$ as the suitable force, while the flows of matter $\mathbf{J}_i$ have selected grad $(-\mu_i/T)$ as the correct driving force.

As pointed out by Meixner,[2] the choice of flows or forces is to a certain extent arbitrary. However, when one set of variables is chosen, the set of conjugate variables is determined by the following requirements: (*a*) the product of any flow and its conjugate force must have the dimensions of entropy production; (*b*) for a given system, the sum of the products must remain the same for any transformation of flows and forces. The successful choice of flows and forces plays a role in nonequilibrium thermodynamics similar to that of the choice of the right system of coordinates in the solution of problems in analytical mechanics. Only when the thermodynamic flows and forces correspond to those amenable to experimental determination will the thermodynamic formalism produce interesting correlations between observable phenomena.

As an example, we may consider a rather simple and important transformation which may be obtained by a direct treatment of Eq. (7-19). Since the operation of a gradient is carried out by the rules of ordinary differentiation, we may write

$$\operatorname{grad}\frac{1}{T} = -\frac{1}{T^2}\operatorname{grad} T$$

and

$$\operatorname{grad}\left(-\frac{\mu_i}{T}\right) = -\frac{1}{T}\operatorname{grad}\mu_i + \frac{\mu_i}{T^2}\operatorname{grad} T.$$

Introducing these expressions into Eq. (7-19), we obtain, after rearrangement,

$$\sigma = \frac{\mathbf{J}_q - \sum_{i=1}^{n}\mu_i\mathbf{J}_i}{T^2}\cdot\operatorname{grad}(-T) + \sum_{i=1}^{n}\frac{\mathbf{J}_i}{T}\cdot\operatorname{grad}(-\mu_i) + J_{\mathrm{ch}}\frac{A}{T},$$

or, in view of Eq. (7-18),

$$\sigma = \frac{\mathbf{J}_S}{T}\cdot\operatorname{grad}(-T) + \sum_{i=1}^{n}\frac{\mathbf{J}_i}{T}\cdot\operatorname{grad}(-\mu_i) + J_{\mathrm{ch}}\frac{A}{T}. \tag{7-21}$$

It is often convenient to use instead of σ another function $\Phi = T\sigma$ which was called by Lord Rayleigh the dissipation function. It has the dimensions of free energy per unit time and is a measure of the rate of local dissipation of free energy by irreversible processes. For the present case,

$$T\sigma = \mathbf{J}_S\cdot\operatorname{grad}(-T) + \sum_{i=1}^{n}\mathbf{J}_i\cdot\operatorname{grad}(-\mu_i) + J_{\mathrm{ch}}A. \tag{7-22}$$

A noteworthy feature of Eq. (7-22) is that the dissipation function is also the sum of products of flows and forces. However, instead of the heat flow we have now the flow of entropy driven by the force, grad $(-T)$. The flows of matter and chemical reaction remain unaltered, but their conjugate forces assume another and more familiar form.

The evaluation of the local entropy production has been carried out by a method different from that used by others in order to simplify the presentation. As shown in the Appendix to this chapter, the present treatment assumes that the system is in mechanical equilibrium. This assumption excludes from the full expression for σ several terms, especially those related to viscous flow under a gradient of velocities. We have also assumed that there are no external forces acting on the system. It is important to note that at mechanical equilibrium the reference velocity, to which all flows are referred, is immaterial; σ remains invariant to different choices of reference velocity.

7.3. Entropy Production in Electrochemical Systems

The entropy production and dissipation function derived above describe only systems containing uncharged solutes. For the description of systems containing electrolytes and for the treatment of electrical conductors, the extended form of the Gibbs equation, including the electrical term ψde, must be used. This leads to a generalization of the concept of chemical potential suitable for the description of electrochemical systems.

Let us assume that the system under consideration contains n_i moles of the ith charged substance. The total charge carried by a mole of this substance is $z_i\mathfrak{F}$, where z_i is the ionic valence and $\mathfrak{F}$ is the Faraday (96,500 coulombs/mole); z_i may be positive, negative, or zero, depending on the charge of the species. If the electric potential at a point is ψ, the electrical work required to increase the number of moles at this point by dn_i is evidently $z_i\mathfrak{F}\psi dn_i$. Thus, the Gibbs equation (3-2) may be written

$$dU = TdS - PdV + \sum_{i=1}^{n} \mu_i dn_i + \sum_{i=1}^{n} z_i\mathfrak{F}\psi dn_i. \tag{7-23}$$

The summations on the right-hand side go over both ionic and nonionic species. The last term obviously corresponds to the term ψde in Eq. (3-2), since $\sum z_i\mathfrak{F} dn_i$ is the total change in charge, de.

Combining the terms under the summation and rearranging, we obtain

$$TdS = dU + PdV - \sum_{i=1}^{n} (\mu_i + z_i\mathfrak{F}\psi) dn_i$$

or

$$TdS = dU + PdV - \sum_{i=1}^{n} \tilde{\mu}_i dn_i. \tag{7-24}$$

The new quantity $\tilde{\mu}_i$ appearing in Eq. (7-24) is the electrochemical potential of component i,

$$\tilde{\mu}_i = \mu_i + z_i\mathfrak{F}\psi, \tag{7-25}$$

introduced by Guggenheim.[3] As shown in standard treatises on thermodynamics, there is no general physical method of separating the chemical and electrical parts of the electrochemical potential, and $\tilde{\mu}_i$ should be regarded as a primary thermodynamic quantity for the characterization of electrochemical systems.

Equation (7-24) may now be applied to a small volume element and treated in the same manner as Eq. (7-2) to yield

$$Tds_v = dq_v - \sum_{i=1}^{n} \tilde{\mu}_i dc_i \tag{7-26}$$

and

$$T\frac{\partial s_v}{\partial t} = \frac{\partial q_v}{\partial t} - \sum_{i=1}^{n} \tilde{\mu}_i \frac{\partial c_i}{\partial t}. \tag{7-27}$$

The flow of entropy, $\mathbf{J}_S$, and the entropy production may be obtained from Eq. (7-27) by the method previously discussed:

$$\mathbf{J}_S = \frac{\mathbf{J}_q - \sum_{i=1}^{n} \tilde{\mu}_i \mathbf{J}_i}{T}, \tag{7-28}$$

$$\sigma = \mathbf{J}_q \cdot \text{grad}\,\frac{1}{T} + \sum_{i=1}^{n} \mathbf{J}_i \cdot \text{grad}\left(-\frac{\tilde{\mu}_i}{T}\right) + J_{\text{ch}}\frac{\tilde{A}}{T}. \tag{7-29}$$

The symbol $\tilde{A}$ in Eq. (7-29) denotes the electrochemical affinity of the reaction, defined as

$$\tilde{A} = -\sum \nu_i \tilde{\mu}_i = -\sum \nu_i \mu_i - \sum \nu_i z_i \mathfrak{F} \psi = A - \sum \nu_i z_i \mathfrak{F} \psi. \tag{7-30}$$

The dissipation function for the present case is derived in the same manner as previously and is

$$T\sigma = \Phi = \mathbf{J}_S \cdot \text{grad}\,(-T) + \sum_{i=1}^{n} \mathbf{J}_i \cdot \text{grad}\,(-\tilde{\mu}_i) + J_{\text{ch}}\tilde{A}. \tag{7-31}$$

The dissipation function for electrochemical systems will be discussed in more detail in Chapter 11, but for the present Eqs. (7-29) and (7-31) are sufficient. We now turn to a general consideration of the relation between the flows and forces that are defined by these functions.

7.4. Appendix

In most discussions of entropy production in continuous systems, local entropy, energy, and composition of the system are expressed in terms of amount per unit mass and Eq. (7-13) is used with total rather than local differentials. The resulting expression for σ is formally similar to Eq. (7-19) except that all the flows appearing are flows relative to the velocity of the center of mass. These are related to the absolute flows of Eq. (7-19) by the expressions

$$\begin{aligned} \mathbf{J}_q^m &= \mathbf{J}_q - q_v\mathbf{v}, \\ \mathbf{J}_i^m &= \mathbf{J}_i - c_i\mathbf{v}, \\ \mathbf{J}_S^m &= \mathbf{J}_S - s_v\mathbf{v}, \end{aligned} \tag{7-32}$$

in which $\mathbf{v}$ is the velocity of the center of mass and the superscript m indicates flow relative to $\mathbf{v}$. In order to simplify the discussion, we have used an alternative development which does not involve the less familiar mass units. Here we wish to show that the two treatments are entirely equivalent provided that the system is in a state of mechanical equilibrium.[4]

In order to demonstrate this equivalence we may utilize Eq. (7-22) and the corresponding expression with the relative flows, $\mathbf{J}_i^m$ and $\mathbf{J}_S^m$. If $T\sigma$ is invariant, the following equality must hold:

$$\mathbf{J}_S \cdot \text{grad}\,(-T) + \sum_{i=1}^{n} \mathbf{J}_i \cdot \text{grad}\,(-\mu_i) = \mathbf{J}_S^m \cdot \text{grad}\,(-T) + \sum_{i=1}^{n} \mathbf{J}_i^m \cdot \text{grad}\,(-\mu_i).$$

Introducing Eqs. (7-32) and rearranging yields

$$\mathbf{J}_S \cdot \text{grad}\,(-T) + \sum_{i=1}^{n} \mathbf{J}_i \cdot \text{grad}\,(-\mu_i) = \mathbf{J}_S \cdot \text{grad}\,(-T) + \sum_{i=1}^{n} \mathbf{J}_i \cdot \text{grad}\,(-\mu_i)$$
$$- \mathbf{v} \cdot \left[s_v \,\text{grad}\,(-T) + \sum_{i=1}^{n} c_i \,\text{grad}\,(-\mu_i)\right],$$

and the requirement that $T\sigma$ be invariant becomes

$$\mathbf{v} \cdot \left[s_v \,\text{grad}\,(-T) + \sum_{i=1}^{n} c_i \,\text{grad}\,(-\mu_i)\right] = 0.$$

Since $\mathbf{v}$ is, in general, not zero, we require that

$$s_v \,\text{grad}\, T + \sum_{i=1}^{n} c_i \,\text{grad}\, \mu_i = 0. \tag{7-33}$$

The explicit expression for grad μ_i, obtained from Eq. (5-68), is

$$\text{grad}\, \mu_i = -\bar{S}_i \,\text{grad}\, T + \bar{V}_i \,\text{grad}\, P + \text{grad}\, \mu_i^c, \tag{7-34}$$

in which μ_i^c represents the concentration-dependent part of μ_i. Introducing Eq. (7-34) into Eq. (7-33) we obtain

$$s_v \,\text{grad}\, T - \sum_{i=1}^{n} c_i \bar{S}_i \,\text{grad}\, T$$
$$+ \sum_{i=1}^{n} c_i \bar{V}_i \,\text{grad}\, P + \sum_{i=1}^{n} c_i \,\text{grad}\, \mu_i^c = 0. \tag{7-35}$$

The last term on the left-hand side is zero according to Eq. (5-47), the Gibbs–Duhem equation. Since

$$\sum_{i=1}^{n} c_i \bar{S}_i = s_v,$$

$$\sum_{i=1}^{n} c_i \bar{V}_i = \sum_{i=1}^{n} \varphi_i = 1,$$

in which φ_i is the volume fraction of component i, Eq. (7-35) reduces to

$$\text{grad } P = 0. \tag{7-36}$$

Thus, $T\sigma$ is unaltered by a transformation from flows relative to the center of mass velocity to absolute flows if grad $P = 0$. This is, however, the requirement of mechanical equilibrium in a system not subject to external forces. The condition of mechanical equilibrium requires that the velocity of the center of mass be constant or that

$$\frac{d\mathbf{v}}{dt} = 0.$$

Since, with no external forces,

$$\frac{d\mathbf{v}}{dt} = -\text{grad } P,$$

Eq. (7-36) is the expression of mechanical equilibrium. A similar analysis can be carried out if there are external forces acting on the system. Thus, we have shown that Eq. (7-22) gives the proper value of $T\sigma$ if the system is in mechanical equilibrium. Since this condition may be assumed for nearly all of the processes discussed in the following chapters, we may use Eq. (7-22) for the dissipation function rather than the more complex expression involving flows relative to the center of mass velocity.

CHAPTER 8

THE PHENOMENOLOGICAL EQUATIONS RELATING FLOWS AND FORCES; ONSAGER'S LAW

8.1. Introductory Remarks

THE description of irreversible processes in terms of the entropy production or the dissipation function is interesting from a general thermodynamic point of view but is of little direct value in the study of the processes themselves. One could even say that the dissipation function can be evaluated only when the flows and forces are known, so that no additional information is gained by writing the sum of the products of flows and forces. However, the situation changes markedly when an explicit correlation between flows and forces is known, and hence numerous attempts have been made to discover such functional relations. The first relation between flows and forces was obtained in 1811 by Fourier, who showed that the heat flow is linearly related to the gradient of temperature. During the first half of the 19th century several other laws of similar nature were established. Ohm proved that the electric current is proportional to the electromotive force and Fick showed that the rate of diffusion of matter is determined by the negative gradient of concentration. The reader familiar with classical mechanics should not be disturbed by the fact that in all these laws force is proportional to velocity and not to acceleration. Newton's first law holds only for frictionless media; in the presence of frictional forces, the mechanical relation between force f, acceleration a, and velocity v is given by

$$f = ma + hv.$$

The acceleration is usually damped out after a short time, and mechanical forces assume the form $f = hv$ implied in the laws of Fourier, Fick, and Ohm.

Even before Fourier published his studies on the conduction of heat, experimental observation had suggested that the simple dependence of a flow on its conjugated force does not always hold. In 1801, Rouss carried out his important experiments on the electrical and osmotic behavior of porous media, and found that the application of an electromotive force may produce not only a flow of charge but also a nonconjugated flow of volume. On the other hand, the application of hydrostatic pressure was found to produce a nonconjugated flow of electricity. Several years later, the thermoelectric phenomena were discovered by Seebeck, who showed that a gradient of temperature in a bimetallic system established a gradient of electric potential, and later Peltier showed that passage of electric current through the system caused an isothermal transport of heat from one junction to the other. Such phenomena are summarized by stating that there may exist coupling between forces of one type and flows of another type. For sufficiently slow processes, any flow may depend in a direct and linear manner not only on the conjugated force, but also on nonconjugated forces. The thermodynamic study of coupling phenomena was pioneered by Kelvin in 1854. Although his approach has since been modified, the consideration of coupling is one of the essential features of the new thermodynamics and will occupy much of our attention in the following chapters. Using the general relation between all flows and forces, as well as the dissipation function, we shall be able to derive useful expressions that will not only confirm known facts but will also lead to new predictions and indicate correlations between phenomena.

8.2. The Phenomenological Equations

In his famous treatise on the theory of sound, Lord Rayleigh used a set of equations that expressed, in an explicit manner, the linear dependence of all mechanical flows on all mechanical forces operating in a system. Onsager,[1] in 1931, extended this concept to include all thermodynamic flows and forces. The resulting set of equations, known as the *phenomenological equations*, may be written as follows:

$$\begin{aligned} J_1 &= L_{11}X_1 + L_{12}X_2 + L_{13}X_3 + \cdots + L_{1n}X_n, \\ J_2 &= L_{21}X_1 + L_{22}X_2 + L_{23}X_3 + \cdots + L_{2n}X_n, \\ J_3 &= L_{31}X_1 + L_{32}X_2 + L_{33}X_3 + \cdots + L_{3n}X_n, \\ &\vdots \qquad\qquad\qquad \vdots \\ J_n &= L_{n1}X_1 + L_{n2}X_2 + L_{n3}X_3 + \cdots + L_{nn}X_n, \end{aligned} \tag{8-1}$$

or

$$J_i = \sum_{k=1}^{n} L_{ik}X_k. \qquad (i = 1, 2, 3, \cdots, n) \tag{8-2}$$

In the set of equations (8-1), the vectorial notation has been dropped since in the completely general case all flows and forces need not be vectors. The meaning of these equations can be readily explained. Consider a system in which n simultaneous flows or processes $J_1, J_2, \ldots, J_n$ take place. To each flow, we may assign a conjugate force $X_1, X_2, \ldots, X_n$ by the methods outlined in the previous chapters. The choice of a force conjugate to the flow J_i is restricted by the requirement that the product J_iX_i should have the dimensions of entropy production or decrease in free energy with time. In accord with the discoveries of Fourier, Fick, Ohm, and others, we may write that each flow is linearly proportional to its conjugate force, the "straight" coefficient being L_{ii}. All the straight coefficients appear on the diagonal of the matrix of forces on the right-hand side of the set of equations (8-1). However, the equations also state that the flow J_1 may be driven by the forces $X_2, X_3, \ldots, X_n$ if the "coupling coefficients" or "cross coefficients" $L_{12}, L_{13}, \ldots, L_{1n}$ differ from zero. In general, a force X_j will contribute to a flow J_i $(i \neq j)$ if $L_{ij} \neq 0$. Finally, the equations imply that the dependence of the flows on nonconjugated forces is also linear.

We must, however, stress from the outset that this linearity holds only for sufficiently slow processes occurring when the system is not too distant from a state of equilibrium. The more general case of rapid processes is still under investigation and cannot be described by the considerations developed in the following sections. In spite of this limitation, the range of phenomena covered by the phenomenological equations is very wide and many processes of physical, chemical, biochemical, and physiological interest are included.

The linear form of Eqs. (8-1) makes possible an alternative set of expressions in which the forces are represented as linear functions of the flows,[2] so that

$$\begin{aligned} X_1 &= R_{11}J_1 + R_{12}J_2 + R_{13}J_3 + \cdots + R_{1n}J_n, \\ X_2 &= R_{21}J_1 + R_{22}J_2 + R_{23}J_3 + \cdots + R_{2n}J_n, \\ X_3 &= R_{31}J_1 + R_{32}J_2 + R_{33}J_3 + \cdots + R_{3n}J_n, \\ &\vdots \qquad\qquad\qquad \vdots \\ X_n &= R_{n1}J_1 + R_{n2}J_2 + R_{n3}J_3 + \cdots + R_{nn}J_n, \end{aligned} \tag{8-3}$$

or

$$X_i = \sum_{k=1}^{n} R_{ik}J_k. \qquad (i = 1, 2, 3, \cdots, n) \tag{8-4}$$

The set of equations (8-3) may be obtained by solving the set (8-1) for the forces. The coefficients $L_{ik} = (J_i/X_k)_{X_j}$ are flows per unit force and have the characteristics of generalized conductances or mobilities. The coefficients $R_{ik} = (X_i/J_k)_{J_j}$ have dimensions of force per unit flow and represent generalized resistances or frictions. The choice of the set (8-1) or (8-3) to describe a given system is dictated by considerations of convenience and physical clarity, but it is always possible to pass from one system of coefficients to the other by the rules of matrix algebra. For the simple case of two flows and two forces,

$$\begin{aligned} J_1 &= L_{11}X_1 + L_{12}X_2, & X_1 &= R_{11}J_1 + R_{12}J_2, \\ J_2 &= L_{21}X_1 + L_{22}X_2, & X_2 &= R_{21}J_1 + R_{22}J_2, \end{aligned} \tag{8-5}$$

the relations between the R_{ik} and the L_{ik} are given by

$$R_{11} = \frac{L_{22}}{|L|}, \quad R_{12} = \frac{-L_{12}}{|L|}, \quad R_{21} = \frac{-L_{21}}{|L|}, \quad R_{22} = \frac{L_{11}}{|L|}, \tag{8-6}$$

in which the determinant $|L| = L_{11}L_{22} - L_{12}L_{21}$. In general,

$$R_{ik} = \frac{|L|_{ik}}{|L|},$$

in which $|L|$ is the determinant of the matrix of the coefficients L_{ik} and $|L|_{ik}$ is the minor of the determinant corresponding to the term L_{ik}.

8.3. *The Curie–Prigogine Principle*[3,4,5]

In writing Eqs. (8-1) and (8-3), we have implicitly assumed the possibility of a linear coupling between all forces and all flows participating in the irreversible changes occurring in a system. This assumption requires, however, a more careful examination in view of the different nature of the various flows and forces. As pointed out in Chapter 6, the flow of chemical reaction and its associated thermodynamic force, the affinity, are scalar quantities, while flows of heat and matter as well as their conjugated forces are vectors. Viscous phenomena, omitted in this treatment, are tensors of second order. Thus, if scalar flows are denoted by J_s and the conjugate forces by X_s, and vectorial flows and forces by J_v and X_v, the dissipation function may be written

$$\Phi = \sum J_s X_s + \sum J_v X_v,$$

or more simply

$$\Phi = J_s X_s + J_v X_v, \qquad \begin{aligned} &(s = 1, 2, \cdots, k) \\ &(v = k + 1, k + 2, \cdots, n) \end{aligned}$$

where the running symbols denote the summations.

The question immediately arises whether coupling can exist between flows of one character and forces of another character. On a priori grounds the x-component of any flow can be coupled with the x-component of a force of any tensorial order. (A scalar is a tensor of zeroth order, a vector is a tensor of first order, and tensors of higher order may also occur.) For the present case, with the summation convention introduced above, we may write the phenomenological equations as

$$J_s = L_{ss}X_s + L_{sv}X_v,$$

$$J_v = L_{vs}X_s + L_{vv}X_v.$$

In this set, the coefficient L_{ss}, relating the scalar force X_s to the scalar flow J_s, is itself a scalar. The coefficient L_{sv} must be a vector in order to give a scalar flow through the inner product with the vectorial force X_v; L_{vs} must also be a vector in order to produce a vectorial resultant, J_v, when multiplied by the scalar X_s. Finally, L_{vv} is a tensor of second order, which transforms the vector X_v into the vector J_v.

The general coupling described in these equations may occur in an anisotropic system in which there is no spatial symmetry. However, in systems endowed with certain symmetry properties and especially in isotropic systems for which the properties at equilibrium are the same in all directions, not all modes of coupling are possible. It can be shown that flows and forces of different tensorial order are not coupled. This leads, in the isotropic case, to a reduction of the equations above to the simplified form

$$J_s = L_{ss}X_s,$$

$$J_v = L_{vv}X_v,$$

and the coefficient L_{vv} becomes a scalar.

The reason for this behavior is that in an isotropic system a reversal of the sign of all the coordinate axes must leave all the phenomenological coefficients invariant. Since L_{ss} is a scalar, it fulfills this requirement automatically, but the vectors L_{sv} and L_{vs} would change sign upon inversion of the coordinate system; L_{sv} and L_{vs} can remain invariant only if both are equal to zero or if no coupling exists between scalar flows and vectorial forces and between vectorial flows and scalar forces. The requirement that L_{vv} be invariant under any rotation of the coordinate system leads to the conclusion that, for isotropic systems, L_{vv} must be a scalar. This requirement that there be no coupling between scalar and vectorial quantities may be called the *Curie–Prigogine principle,* since it is based on the considerations of Curie regarding cause-and-effect relations in static systems of different symmetry, and was extended by Prigogine to irreversible systems in flow. An important conclusion from this principle is that simultaneous diffusion and chemical reaction cannot be coupled phenomenologically in an isotropic system.

8.4. Onsager's Law

Although the phenomenological equations adequately summarize the thermodynamic information about slow processes, their application presents considerable difficulties. Even in the simplest case of two flows and two forces, there are four coefficients which must be determined by four independent experimental methods. For the case of three flows and forces, the number of coefficients increases to nine, making the experimental analysis extremely difficult. However, in his fundamental papers in 1931, Onsager[1] was able to show that the matrix of phenomenological coefficients is symmetric, or that

$$L_{ik} = L_{ki}. \qquad (i \neq k) \tag{8-7}$$

Equation (8-7) is valid so long as the flows and forces appearing in the phenomenological equations are taken in such a way that

$$\sigma = \sum_{i=1}^{n} J_i X_i. \tag{8-8}$$

This condition illustrates clearly the importance of evaluating the explicit expression for the entropy production. As we shall see in subsequent chapters, the use of Eq. (8-7) plays a central role in the thermodynamics of irreversible processes. However, it can be employed only if Eq. (8-8) is utilized to choose the proper flows and forces for the phenomenological equations.

Equation (8-7) not only leads to an appreciable reduction in the number of independent coefficients but permits the prediction of correlations between flow phenomena that have proved to be of great interest and importance. Onsager's proof of the reciprocal relation between coefficients is based on statistical mechanical considerations that hold for processes close to equilibrium. However, an impressive amount of experimental material has now been analyzed critically, and generally Eq. (8-7) has been found to hold to a close approximation. (This material has recently been assembled and reviewed in detail by Miller[6] and some of it will be considered briefly in subsequent chapters.) On the basis of these findings, Onsager's reciprocal relation may be regarded as a well-established law whose experimental validity goes beyond the range of the statistical justification.

The coefficients of Eq. (8-1) are independent, but the absolute magnitude of the coupling coefficients is restricted by the magnitude of the straight coefficients because of the positive-definite nature of the entropy production. If we consider the case of two flows and two forces, the entropy production is

$$\sigma = J_1X_1 + J_2X_2. \tag{8-9}$$

Introducing the expressions for J_1 and J_2 from Eq. (8-5), we obtain

$$\sigma = L_{11}X_1^2 + (L_{12} + L_{21})X_1X_2 + L_{22}X_2^2 > 0. \tag{8-10}$$

Since either X_1 or X_2 may be made to vanish, we have the requirements that

$$L_{11}X_1^2 \geq 0, \qquad L_{22}X_2^2 \geq 0, \tag{8-11}$$

so that both straight coefficients, L_{11} and L_{22}, must be positive. Further, the quadratic form, Eq. (8-10), will remain positive-definite only if the determinant

$$\begin{vmatrix} L_{11} & L_{12} \\ L_{21} & L_{22} \end{vmatrix} = L_{11}L_{22} - L_{12}L_{21} \geq 0, \tag{8-12}$$

which provides the restriction on the possible magnitudes of the coupling coefficients L_{12} and L_{21}. In view of Eq. (8-7), this condition becomes

$$L_{11}L_{22} \geq L_{12}^2. \tag{8-13}$$

For the general case of any number of flows and forces, the requirement that $\sigma > 0$ imposes two conditions on the phenomenological coefficients:

$$L_{ii} \geq 0 \tag{8-14}$$

and

$$\begin{vmatrix} L_{11} & L_{12} & \cdots & L_{1n} \\ L_{21} & L_{22} & \cdots & L_{2n} \\ \vdots & & & \vdots \\ L_{n1} & L_{n2} & \cdots & L_{nn} \end{vmatrix} = |L| \geq 0, \tag{8-15}$$

so that

$$L_{ii}L_{jj} \geq L_{ij}^2..$$

8.5. Chemical Kinetics and Phenomenological Equations. The Principle of Detailed Balance and Its Relation to Onsager's Law

8.5.1. Considerations of chemical kinetics played a special role in the development of the ideas concerning the reciprocal relations, Eq. (8-7). Although we will not consider the statistical proof of Eq. (8-7) until a later chapter, some of the important points underlying this relation can be brought to light by consideration of chemical reactions. In order to carry out such an analysis, we must first consider the relation between the kinetic and the thermodynamic descriptions of chemical reaction rates. In the classical equations of chemical kinetics, which are known to describe chemical processes quite exactly, the reaction rates are proportional to concentrations or their powers. On the other hand, phenomenological equations require that the reaction velocity be proportional to the thermodynamic force or affinity, which is, in turn, proportional to logarithms of concentrations. To remove this inconsistency, we must consider more closely the phenomenological description in the neighborhood of equilibrium when the rate of chemical change is sufficiently slow. The analysis may be carried out for the simple example of a monomolecular transformation, such as

$$A \underset{k_{-1}}{\overset{k_1}{\rightleftharpoons}} B.$$

The rates of reaction given by kinetic theory are

$$\frac{dc_A}{dt} = -k_1 c_A + k_{-1} c_B,$$

$$\frac{dc_B}{dt} = k_1 c_A - k_{-1} c_B. \tag{8-16}$$

The chemical treatment distinguishes two reaction flows, characterized by two constants. There is, however, only one macroscopic flow of reaction from the left to the right, so that

$$J_{\mathrm{ch}} = -\frac{dc_A}{dt} = \frac{dc_B}{dt}. \tag{8-17}$$

At equilibrium, the flow vanishes and

$$k_1 \bar{c}_A = k_{-1} \bar{c}_B, \tag{8-18}$$

or

$$\frac{k_{-1}}{k_1} = \frac{\bar{c}_A}{\bar{c}_B} = K, \tag{8-19}$$

in which $\bar{c}_A$ and $\bar{c}_B$ are the equilibrium concentrations of A and B and K is the equilibrium constant of the reaction. We shall now define deviations, α_i, of the concentrations from their equilibrium values by the relations

$$\begin{aligned} \alpha_A &= c_A - \bar{c}_A, \\ \alpha_B &= c_B - \bar{c}_B, \end{aligned} \tag{8-20}$$

and restrict the range of observation to concentrations close to equilibrium, so that

$$\frac{\alpha_A}{\bar{c}_A} \ll 1, \qquad \frac{\alpha_B}{\bar{c}_B} \ll 1. \tag{8-21}$$

Since the reaction proceeds without exchange of matter with the surroundings,

$$c_A + c_B = \bar{c}_A + \bar{c}_B$$

and

$$\alpha_A + \alpha_B = 0. \tag{8-22}$$

Introducing Eqs. (8-20) into Eq. (8-16), we obtain

$$J_{\text{ch}} = k_1(\bar{c}_A + \alpha_A) - k_{-1}(\bar{c}_B + \alpha_B).$$

Using Eqs. (8-18), (8-19), and (8-22), we may write this

$$J_{\text{ch}} = \alpha_A(k_1 + k_{-1}) = k_1\alpha_A(1 + K). \tag{8-23}$$

The same problem may now be considered from the thermodynamic point of view. According to previous considerations, the driving force for the reaction is the affinity,

$$A = -\sum_{i=1}^{2} \nu_i\mu_i = \mu_A - \mu_B. \tag{8-24}$$

At equilibrium, A goes to zero so that

$$\bar{\mu}_A = \bar{\mu}_B, \tag{8-25}$$

in which the bar denotes the equilibrium values of the chemical potentials. Further, the chemical flow should be proportional to the force:

$$J_{\text{ch}} = LA = L(\mu_A - \mu_B). \tag{8-26}$$

Under the conditions of constant temperature and pressure,

$$\mu_i = \mu_i^0 + RT \ln c_i$$

for ideal solutions. Introducing this expression into Eq. (8-24) and using Eqs. (8-20), we obtain, after rearrangement,

$$A = \mu_A^0 + RT \ln \bar{c}_A + RT \ln \left(1 + \frac{\alpha_A}{\bar{c}_A}\right)$$

$$- \mu_B^0 - RT \ln \bar{c}_B - RT \ln \left(1 + \frac{\alpha_B}{\bar{c}_B}\right), \tag{8-27}$$

or, in view of Eq. (8-25),

$$A = RT\left[\ln \left(1 + \frac{\alpha_A}{\bar{c}_A}\right) - \ln \left(1 + \frac{\alpha_B}{\bar{c}_B}\right)\right]. \tag{8-28}$$

If $\alpha_A/\bar{c}_A$, $\alpha_B/\bar{c}_B \ll 1$, the logarithms may be expanded in series, only the first term being retained, so that Eq. (8-28) becomes

$$A = RT\left(\frac{\alpha_A}{\bar{c}_A} - \frac{\alpha_B}{\bar{c}_B}\right) = RT \frac{\alpha_A}{\bar{c}_A}(1 + K), \tag{8-29}$$

in which Eqs. (8-19) and (8-22) have been used. Insertion of this result into Eq. (8-26) yields

$$J_{\text{ch}} = \frac{LRT}{\bar{c}_A}\alpha_A(1 + K). \tag{8-30}$$

However, in order to obtain Eq. (8-30), we have had to assume that the reaction is close to equilibrium so that the terms α_A and α_B, the deviations of concentrations from their equilibrium values, are small. Thus, in the limit of slow reactions near equilibrium, the two methods of representation, the kinetic and the thermodynamic, give the same results. To make the expressions identical, the coefficient L of Eq. (8-30) must fulfill the condition

$$L = \frac{k_1 \bar{c}_A}{RT}. \tag{8-31}$$

This expression shows that for chemical reactions the coefficient L is a variable, dependent on the equilibrium concentration $\bar{c}_A$. Thus, as in the case considered in Sec. 6.6, the phenomenological coefficient is not a constant but is a function of the characteristic parameters of the system. In all cases, however, the coefficients must be independent of the rates of change of the parameters, the flows and forces that they relate.

The discussion in this section has also illustrated that the phenomenological description of chemical reactions in terms of a linear relation between flow and force (the affinity) has a limited range of validity. The other phenomena that will be discussed may be described by a linear relation over a relatively wide range of flows and forces, but in the case of reactions large deviations from linearity may be easily observed. As pointed out by Prigogine *et al.*,[7] the phenomenological equation of the form given by Eq. (8-26) will be valid only in the limit when $A/RT \ll 1$, and this requires that the reaction be quite close to equilibrium. In experimental practice, values of A much greater than RT can occur.

8.5.2. Using considerations of the previous section we may now analyze a more complicated reaction system, which was used by Onsager to disclose the principle from which the symmetry of phenomenological coefficients may be derived. We wish to consider a cyclic reaction of the type

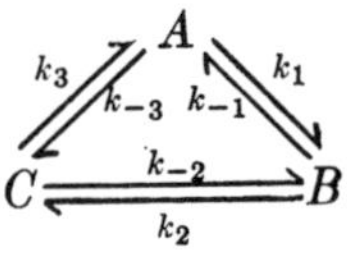

The reaction scheme is characterized by six kinetic coefficients and the rates of the three reactions will be given by

$$\begin{aligned} J_1 &= k_1 c_A - k_{-1} c_B, \\ J_2 &= k_2 c_B - k_{-2} c_C, \\ J_3 &= k_3 c_C - k_{-3} c_A. \end{aligned} \tag{8-32}$$

However, according to the phenomenological description, there are only

two independent flows that define the reaction rate. The affinities of the three reactions are

$$\begin{aligned} A_1 &= \mu_A - \mu_B, \\ A_2 &= \mu_B - \mu_C, \\ A_3 &= \mu_C - \mu_A; \end{aligned} \tag{8-33}$$

but these are not all independent since

$$A_3 = -(A_1 + A_2). \tag{8-34}$$

Consideration of the dissipation function for the reaction system indicates that there are also two independent flows:

$$T\sigma = J_1A_1 + J_2A_2 + J_3A_3 = (J_1 - J_3)A_1 + (J_2 - J_3)A_2. \tag{8-35}$$

On the basis of the considerations of Secs. 8.2 and 8.3, the phenomenological equations corresponding to Eq. (8-35) are

$$\begin{aligned} J_1 - J_3 &= L_{11}A_1 + L_{12}A_2, \\ J_2 - J_3 &= L_{21}A_1 + L_{22}A_2. \end{aligned} \tag{8-36}$$

The thermodynamic condition of equilibrium is the equality of the chemical potentials, $\bar{\mu}_A = \bar{\mu}_B = \bar{\mu}_C$, and hence, by Eq. (8-33),

$$\begin{aligned} A_1 &= 0, \\ A_2 &= 0 \end{aligned} \tag{8-37}$$

at equilibrium, and

$$\begin{aligned} J_1 - J_3 &= 0, \\ J_2 - J_3 &= 0, \end{aligned} \tag{8-38}$$

or

$$J_1 = J_2 = J_3. \tag{8-39}$$

Thus, the thermodynamic condition of equilibrium does not require that all the flows vanish, only that they all be equal. The reaction may, therefore, circulate indefinitely without producing entropy and without violating any of the classical laws of thermodynamics. However, in physical-chemical terms, we require not only that the over-all independent flows vanish, but also that the individual flows of every reaction become zero at true equilibrium. This requirement is not based on any previous notion, and constitutes an additional principle of physical chemistry, which is referred to as the *principle of detailed balance.* This concept is closely related to one of the fundamental principles of statistical mechanics, the principle of *microscopic reversibility*, which was formulated by Tolman as follows: "Under equilibrium conditions, any molecular process and the reverse of that process will be taking place, on the average, at the same rate. We may expect on the average, for a system at equilibrium, the same frequency of transition from the condition κ to ν as from ν to κ; the transition from ν to κ does not have to be thought of as balanced with the help of some indirect route such as ν to λ and λ to κ."[8]

In the present case, the principle of detailed balance requires that

$$J_1 = J_2 = J_3 = 0, \tag{8-40}$$

and we may show immediately that this condition for equilibrium requires that the coefficients L_{12} and L_{21} in Eq. (8-36) be equal. Applying Eq. (8-40) to Eqs. (8-32) we find that, at equilibrium,

$$\begin{aligned} k_1\bar{c}_A &= k_{-1}\bar{c}_B, \\ k_2\bar{c}_B &= k_{-2}\bar{c}_C, \\ k_3\bar{c}_C &= k_{-3}\bar{c}_A. \end{aligned} \tag{8-41}$$

Introducing deviations from equilibrium α_i, defined in the manner illustrated by Eqs. (8-20), into Eqs. (8-32), we find, with the aid of Eqs. (8-41), that

$$J_1 = k_1\alpha_A - k_{-1}\alpha_B, \tag{8-42.1}$$

$$J_2 = k_2\alpha_B - k_{-2}\alpha_C, \tag{8-42.2}$$

$$J_3 = k_3\alpha_C - k_{-3}\alpha_A. \tag{8-42.3}$$

Following the procedure used in Sec. 8.5.1, the affinity A_1 may be represented in terms of the deviations from equilibrium:

$$A_1 = RT\left(\frac{\alpha_A}{\bar{c}_A} - \frac{\alpha_B}{\bar{c}_B}\right). \tag{8-43}$$

Using Eqs. (8-41), which are based on the principle of detailed balance, we find for Eq. (8-43)

$$A_1 = \frac{RT}{k_1\bar{c}_A}\,(k_1\alpha_A - k_{-1}\alpha_B), \tag{8-44}$$

or, in view of Eq. (8-42.1),

$$J_1 = \frac{k_1\bar{c}_A}{RT}\,A_1. \tag{8-45}$$

By applying similar reasoning to A_2 and A_3, we can show that

$$J_2 = \frac{k_2\bar{c}_B}{RT}\,A_2, \tag{8-46}$$

$$J_3 = -\frac{k_3\bar{c}_C}{RT}\,(A_1 + A_2), \tag{8-47}$$

in which Eqs. (8-33) have been used. Equations (8-36) can then be written

$$
\begin{aligned}
J_1 - J_3 &= \frac{k_1\bar{c}_A + k_3\bar{c}_C}{RT} A_1 + \frac{k_3\bar{c}_C}{RT} A_2, \\
J_2 - J_3 &= \frac{k_3\bar{c}_C}{RT} A_1 + \frac{k_2\bar{c}_B + k_3\bar{c}_C}{RT} A_2.
\end{aligned}
\tag{8-48}
$$

Thus, the principle of detailed balance allows us to express the phenomenological coefficients as explicit functions of the constant rate coefficients, k_1, k_2, and k_3, and the equilibrium concentrations of A, B, and C:

$$
\begin{aligned}
L_{11} &= \frac{k_1\bar{c}_A + k_3\bar{c}_C}{RT}, \\
L_{12} &= \frac{k_3\bar{c}_C}{RT} = L_{21}, \\
L_{22} &= \frac{k_2\bar{c}_B + k_3\bar{c}_C}{RT},
\end{aligned}
$$

and to show that $L_{12} = L_{21}$. This simple analysis suggests that the general law $L_{ik} = L_{ki}$ could be derived from the principle of microscopic reversibility by applying the more powerful methods of statistical mechanics. However, before considering the statistical proof for the symmetry of the coefficient matrix, we shall analyze in detail several types of phenomena using the set of equations (8-1).

CHAPTER 9

ISOTHERMAL DIFFUSION AND SEDIMENTATION

9.1. General Considerations

THE first example to which the formal tools developed in the previous chapters will be applied is that of isothermal diffusion in a continuous system. An elementary treatment of diffusion was given in Chapter 6, but its aim was mainly to introduce the concepts without sufficient justification for the procedure. The theoretical concepts now available may also be used to reconsider this simple case of diffusion in a binary system of nonreacting components.

According to the considerations of Chapter 7, the over-all dissipation function for the system is

$$\Phi = \mathbf{J}_S \cdot \operatorname{grad}(-T) + \sum_{i=1}^{n} \mathbf{J}_i \cdot \operatorname{grad}(-\mu_i) + J_{\mathrm{ch}} A.$$

For the present case we assume that the system is isothermal (grad $(-T)=0$) and that no chemical reaction takes place between the components ($J_{\mathrm{ch}}=0$), so that the dissipation function reduces to

$$\Phi = \sum_{i=1}^{n} \mathbf{J}_i \cdot \operatorname{grad}(-\mu_i). \tag{9-1}$$

The gradient of the chemical potential in an isothermal system is given by

$$\operatorname{grad}(-\mu_i) = \bar{V}_i \operatorname{grad}(-P) + \operatorname{grad}(-\mu_i^c),$$

in which μ_i^c is the concentration-dependent part of the chemical potential, P is the hydrostatic pressure, and $\bar{V}_i$ is the partial molar volume of the ith component. The diffusional processes under consideration are relatively slow, so that mechanical equilibrium prevails in the system throughout the period of observation. Under these conditions, Prigogine's[1] theorem states that

$$-\operatorname{grad} P + \sum_{i=1}^{n} \mathbf{F}_i \rho_i = 0,$$

where ρ_i is the total weight concentration of the ith component and $\mathbf{F}_i$ is the external force operating on unit weight of this component. In our case there are no external forces and $\mathbf{F}_i = 0$, so that

$$-\text{grad } P = 0. \tag{9-2}$$

Introducing Eq. (9-2) into Eq. (9-1) we obtain a reduced form for the dissipation function of a diffusion system:

$$\Phi = \sum_{i=1}^{n} \mathbf{J}_i \cdot \text{grad } (-\mu_i^c). \tag{9-3}$$

The forces grad $(-\mu_i^c)$ appearing in Eq. (9-3) are not independent, since the gradients are related by the Gibbs-Duhem equation which requires that

$$\sum_{i=1}^{n} c_i \text{ grad } (-\mu_i^c) = 0. \tag{9-4}$$

Using Eq. (9-4), one of the forces may be isolated and expressed as a linear function of all the others. It is preferable to consider the component in excess as solvent, w, and to express its driving force, grad $(-\mu_w)$, in terms of those operating on the solutes, i:

$$\text{grad } (-\mu_w) = -\frac{1}{c_w} \sum_{i=1}^{n-1} c_i \text{ grad } (-\mu_i^c). \tag{9-5}$$

The introduction of Eq. (9-5) into Eq. (9-3) and rearrangement of the terms gives

$$\Phi = \sum_{i=1}^{n-1} \left(\mathbf{J}_i - \frac{c_i \mathbf{J}_w}{c_w}\right) \cdot \text{grad } (-\mu_i^c) = \sum_{i=1}^{n-1} \mathbf{J}_i^d \cdot \text{grad } (-\mu_i^c). \tag{9-6}$$

Thus, for an n-component system, there are only $n - 1$ independent diffusional forces, grad $(-\mu_i^c)$, and $n - 1$ corresponding diffusional flows, which are given by

$$\mathbf{J}_i^d = \mathbf{J}_i - \frac{c_i \mathbf{J}_w}{c_w}. \tag{9-7}$$

The physical significance of these flows may be readily seen as follows:

$$\mathbf{J}_i^d = c_i\left(\frac{\mathbf{J}_i}{c_i} - \frac{\mathbf{J}_w}{c_w}\right),$$

but $\mathbf{J}_i = c_i \mathbf{v}_i$ and $\mathbf{J}_w = c_w \mathbf{v}_w$, so that

$$\mathbf{J}_i^d = c_i(\mathbf{v}_i - \mathbf{v}_w). \tag{9-8}$$

Thus, the diffusional flows, $\mathbf{J}_i^d$, are determined by the velocities of the solutes *relative* to that of the solvent, $\mathbf{v}_i - \mathbf{v}_w$. The *absolute* flows, $\mathbf{J}_i$, are relative to the diffusion vessel, and are not independent. It is the relative flows that are independent and amenable to further theoretical treatment by phenomenological equations. In general, the absolute flows are measured experimentally and, before a consistent calculation can be carried out, a suitable correction must be made for the difference between $\mathbf{J}_i$ and $\mathbf{J}_i^d$.

In dilute solutions, the difference is negligible and the experimentally determined value $\mathbf{J}_i$ may often be used. A comprehensive analysis of the treatment of experimental data is given by Fujita.[2] The theory of transformation of flows to different frames of reference is discussed in detail by Kirkwood, *et al.*[3] as well as by de Groot and Mazur[4] and by Fitts.[5]

9.2. Binary Solutions

From the foregoing considerations it should be clear that in a binary solution containing solvent and a single solute there is only one independent flow, say that of the solute, and Eq. (9-1) for the dissipation function reduces to

$$\Phi = \mathbf{J}_s^d \cdot \text{grad}\,(-\mu_s^c),$$

in which the subscript s indicates the solute. Thus, the phenomenological description of diffusion in a binary solution contains only a single equation,

$$\mathbf{J}_s^d = -L_s \text{ grad } \mu_s^c. \tag{9-9}$$

The mutual diffusion of two components is a single phenomenon and no cross coefficients are involved. This analysis provides the fundamental justification for our use of an expression identical to Eq. (9-9) in Chapter 6. The chemical potential, μ_s^c, changes with location only because the concentration is a function of position, so that

$$\text{grad } \mu_s^c = \frac{\partial \mu_s^c}{\partial c_s} \text{ grad } c_s.$$

Introducing the notation

$$\mu_{ss} = \frac{\partial \mu_s^c}{\partial c_s},$$

we may then write Eq. (9-9) as

$$\mathbf{J}_s^d = -L_s\mu_{ss} \text{ grad } c_s. \tag{9-10}$$

Equation (9-10) is the correct diffusion equation for the solute flow referred to the flow of the solvent. In a more conventional form, Eq. (9-10) may be written

$$\mathbf{J}_s^d = -D \text{ grad } c_s, \tag{9-11}$$

where D is the diffusion coefficient. Comparison of Eqs. (9-10) and (9-11) shows that D is related to the Onsager coefficient L_s by the expression

$$D = L_s\mu_{ss}. \tag{9-12}$$

If the solute is a nonelectrolyte exhibiting an ideal behavior in aqueous solution,

$$\mu_s^c = RT \ln c_s$$

and

$$\mu_{ss} = \frac{\partial \mu_s^c}{\partial c_s} = \frac{RT}{c_s},$$

so that

$$D = \frac{L_s RT}{c_s}.$$

If D obeys Einstein's equation, $D = RT\omega_s$, where ω_s is the solute mobility,

$$L_s = c_s \omega_s,$$

as shown in more detail in Chapter 6.

As discussed above, the usual experimental procedure is to determine the diffusional flow relative to the walls of the diffusion cell, not relative to the velocity of the solvent. The ordinary Fick equation is then written

$$\mathbf{J}_s = -D' \operatorname{grad} c_s, \tag{9-13}$$

where $\mathbf{J}_s$ is the absolute solute flow and D' is the diffusion coefficient in this frame of reference. Our next step is, therefore, to find the relation between D of Eq. (9-11) and D' of Eq. (9-13).

An additional relation between $\mathbf{J}_s$ and $\mathbf{J}_s^d$ can be obtained by considering the volume flow of the solution $\mathbf{J}_v$. The total volume V of a solution is given by the expression

$$V = \sum_{i=1}^{n} n_i \bar{V}_i,$$

which can be cast in several other forms:

$$1 = \sum_{i=1}^{n} \frac{n_i \bar{V}_i}{V} = \sum_{i=1}^{n} c_i \bar{V}_i = \sum_{i=1}^{n} \varphi_i, \tag{9-14}$$

in which φ_i $(= c_i \bar{V}_i)$ is the volume fraction of the ith component. The rate of volume change with time, for a system in which the $\bar{V}_i$ are constant, is

$$\frac{dV}{dt} = \sum_{i=1}^{n} \bar{V}_i \frac{dn_i}{dt}. \tag{9-15}$$

The rates dn_i/dt are, however, the absolute flows $\mathbf{J}_i$, and dV/dt is the total volume flow $\mathbf{J}_v$, so that

$$\mathbf{J}_v = \sum_{i=1}^{n} \mathbf{J}_i \bar{V}_i, \tag{9-16}$$

or, for a binary solution,

$$\mathbf{J}_v = \mathbf{J}_s \bar{V}_s + \mathbf{J}_w \bar{V}_w. \tag{9-17}$$

In the case of ordinary diffusion the total volume flow is zero ($\mathbf{J}_v = 0$) so that Eq. (9-17) provides a relation between solute and solvent flows:

$$\mathbf{J}_w = -\frac{\bar{V}_s}{\bar{V}_w}\mathbf{J}_s. \tag{9-18}$$

Introducing Eq. (9-18) into Eq. (9-7) we obtain an expression relating the absolute and diffusional solute flows:

$$\mathbf{J}_s^d = \mathbf{J}_s - \frac{c_s}{c_w}\mathbf{J}_w = \mathbf{J}_s\left(1 + \frac{c_s\bar{V}_s}{c_w\bar{V}_w}\right) = \mathbf{J}_s\frac{\varphi_w + \varphi_s}{\varphi_w}.$$

Since $\varphi_w + \varphi_s = 1$,

$$\mathbf{J}_s^d = \frac{\mathbf{J}_s}{\varphi_w}. \tag{9-19}$$

Dividing Eq. (9-13) by Eq. (9-11) yields

$$\frac{\mathbf{J}_s}{\mathbf{J}_s^d} = \frac{D'}{D}.$$

Making use of Eq. (9-19), we find that

$$D' = D\varphi_w. \tag{9-20}$$

Thus, the experimentally determined diffusion coefficient D' is related to the thermodynamic coefficient D through the volume fraction of the solvent. In dilute solutions φ_w is generally close to unity, so that Eqs. (9-19) and (9-20) provide the justification for the statement that the two modes of representation are nearly identical under these conditions.

9.3. Ternary Solutions

In a system of two solutes and one solvent, there exist two diffusional flows that may exhibit coupling phenomena. This is, therefore, the first case in which the cross coefficients L_{ik} play a significant role and which allows an experimental investigation of Onsager's law.

Denoting the two solutes by the subscripts 1 and 2, we may write for the dissipation function, Eq. (9-6),

$$\Phi = \mathbf{J}_1^d\cdot\text{grad}\,(-\mu_1^c) + \mathbf{J}_2^d\cdot\text{grad}\,(-\mu_2^c). \tag{9-21}$$

According to the considerations of Chapter 8, the phenomenological equations will be

$$\begin{aligned} \mathbf{J}_1^d &= -L_{11}\,\text{grad}\,\mu_1^c - L_{12}\,\text{grad}\,\mu_2^c, \\ \mathbf{J}_2^d &= -L_{21}\,\text{grad}\,\mu_1^c - L_{22}\,\text{grad}\,\mu_2^c, \end{aligned} \tag{9-22}$$

and the single reciprocal relation is

$$L_{12} = L_{21}.$$

Here again the dependence of chemical potential on position is due to the local changes of the solute concentrations c_1 and c_2, so that

$$\text{grad } \mu_1^c = \frac{\partial \mu_1^c}{\partial c_1} \text{ grad } c_1 + \frac{\partial \mu_1^c}{\partial c_2} \text{ grad } c_2$$
$$= \mu_{11} \text{ grad } c_1 + \mu_{12} \text{ grad } c_2 \quad (9\text{-}23)$$

and

$$\text{grad } \mu_2^c = \frac{\partial \mu_2^c}{\partial c_1} \text{ grad } c_1 + \frac{\partial \mu_2^c}{\partial c_2} \text{ grad } c_2$$
$$= \mu_{21} \text{ grad } c_1 + \mu_{22} \text{ grad } c_2, \quad (9\text{-}24)$$

in which

$$\mu_{ij} = \frac{\partial \mu_i^c}{\partial c_j}.$$

Introducing Eqs. (9-23) and (9-24) into Eqs. (9-22) and rearranging, we obtain

$$\mathbf{J}_1^d = -(L_{11}\mu_{11} + L_{12}\mu_{21}) \text{ grad } c_1 - (L_{11}\mu_{12} + L_{12}\mu_{22}) \text{ grad } c_2,$$
$$\mathbf{J}_2^d = -(L_{21}\mu_{11} + L_{22}\mu_{21}) \text{ grad } c_1 - (L_{21}\mu_{12} + L_{22}\mu_{22}) \text{ grad } c_2,$$

or, in terms of diffusion coefficients,

$$\mathbf{J}_1^d = -D_{11} \text{ grad } c_1 - D_{12} \text{ grad } c_2,$$
$$\mathbf{J}_2^d = -D_{21} \text{ grad } c_1 - D_{22} \text{ grad } c_2. \quad (9\text{-}25)$$

Equations (9-25) are a generalization of Fick's equation for two independent diffusional flows.[6] The flows are related to the gradients of concentration of both solutes by four diffusion coefficients, two straight coefficients, D_{11} and D_{22}, and two cross coefficients, D_{12} and D_{21}. Comparison of the two sets of equations for $\mathbf{J}_1^d$ and $\mathbf{J}_2^d$ indicates that

$$D_{11} = L_{11}\mu_{11} + L_{12}\mu_{21}, \qquad D_{12} = L_{11}\mu_{12} + L_{12}\mu_{22},$$
$$D_{21} = L_{21}\mu_{11} + L_{22}\mu_{21}, \qquad D_{22} = L_{21}\mu_{12} + L_{22}\mu_{22}. \quad (9\text{-}26)$$

It will be observed that the thermodynamic requirement $L_{12} = L_{21}$ does not lead to equality of the coefficients D_{12} and D_{21}. Neither does the vanishing of the hydrodynamic coupling ($L_{12} = 0$) lead to D_{12} becoming zero. Only when both hydrodynamic and thermodynamic coupling vanish, that is, when $\mu_{12} = \mu_{21} = 0$ and $L_{12} = 0$, will the cross diffusion coefficients vanish. The relation between the diffusion coefficients D_{ij}, the Onsager coefficients L_{ij}, and the thermodynamic coupling coefficients μ_{ij} is conveniently expressed as a product of matrices:

$$\begin{vmatrix} D_{11} & D_{12} \\ D_{21} & D_{22} \end{vmatrix} = \begin{vmatrix} L_{11} & L_{12} \\ L_{21} & L_{22} \end{vmatrix} \cdot \begin{vmatrix} \mu_{11} & \mu_{12} \\ \mu_{21} & \mu_{22} \end{vmatrix}.$$

This expression is equivalent to Eq. (9-12), the role of the single diffusion constant being played by the matrix $|D_{ij}|$ and the roles of the single Onsager coefficient L_s and the single thermodynamic coefficient μ_{ss} by the corresponding matrices $|L_{ij}|$ and $|\mu_{ij}|$.

Equations (9-26) can be solved for the L_{ij} in terms of the D_{ij} and μ_{ij}, yielding

$$L_{12} = \frac{D_{12}\mu_{11} - D_{11}\mu_{12}}{|\mu_{ij}|},$$
$$L_{21} = \frac{D_{21}\mu_{22} - D_{22}\mu_{21}}{|\mu_{ij}|}, \qquad (9\text{-}27)$$

in which $|\mu_{ij}| = \mu_{11}\mu_{22} - \mu_{12}\mu_{21}$. Thus, an experimental determination of the D_{ij}, with due correction for the difference between absolute and diffusional flows of both solutes, permits evaluation of L_{12} and L_{21} provided data are available for the μ_{ij}. Careful determinations of the four diffusion coefficients have been carried out by Gosting and his co-workers[7] for several three-component systems. The results of their study on the system NaCl–KCl–water are summarized in Table 1. The data show that $L_{12} = L_{21}$ within 3 percent for all combinations of concentrations studied lending experimental support to the validity of Onsager's law for the case of isothermal diffusion. It is of interest to note that the cross coefficients L_{12} and L_{21} are appreciable and cannot be neglected relative to the straight coefficients L_{11} and L_{22}.

9.4. Sedimentation in a Centrifugal Field

9.4.1. The movement of matter in a gravitational field is so similar to that caused by a gradient of chemical potential that it is advantageous to treat diffusion and sedimentation from a unified point of view. The main tool for the production of large gravitational fields is the ultracentrifuge, which has been one of the major instruments of modern biophysics

Table 1. Phenomenological coefficients for the system NaCl–KCl–water.[a]

C_{NaCl} (M)	0.25	0.5	0.25	0.5
C_{KCl} (M)	0.25	0.25	0.5	0.5
$L_{11} \times 10^9\, RT$	2.61	4.77	2.79	5.15
$L_{12} \times 10^9\, RT$	−0.750	−1.03	−0.99	−1.52
$L_{21} \times 10^9\, RT$	−0.729	−1.02	−0.97	−1.55
$L_{22} \times 10^9\, RT$	3.50	3.38	6.36	7.02
L_{12}/L_{21}	1.03	1.01	1.02	0.98

[a] From H. Fujita and L. J. Gosting, *J. Phys. Chem. 64* (1960), 1256 and P. J. Dunlop and L. J. Gosting, *J. Phys. Chem. 63* (1959), 86.

and biochemistry since its invention by Svedberg in 1923. Recent developments in sedimentation techniques permit a fine characterization of single macromolecules and biological mixtures and lend new insights into biocolloidal interactions.[8] A clear theoretical grasp of the flows and forces in the centrifugal cell is required if a quantitative analysis of the measurements is attempted, and the following discussion will serve as an introductory step for this purpose. For a fuller analysis of sedimentation the reader is advised to consult the articles of Hooyman[9] or the recent book of Fujita.[2] The cases treated here are only those of nonelectrolytes in convection-free flow and in cells maintained at constant temperature.

We shall consider a sedimentation cell of the type shown in Fig. 16, rotating with an angular velocity ω. The linear velocity at a distance r from the center of rotation is ωr, and the kinetic energy lost per gram of matter in the rotation is $(\omega r)^2/2$. A mole of the ith component whose molecular weight is M_i will have an effective mass in solution of $M_i - \rho \bar{V}_i$, where ρ is the density of the solution and $\rho \bar{V}_i$ is the Archimedean loss due to buoyancy. The work of rotation per mole of component i is $(M_i - \rho \bar{V}_i)\omega^2 r^2/2$, and it may be stated that the chemical potential of the substance will be lowered by the part converted into kinetic energy. Thus,

$$\mu_i = \mu_i^0(T) + \mu_i^c - (M_i - \rho \bar{V}_i)\omega^2 r^2/2. \tag{9-28}$$

The partial molar volume $\bar{V}_i$ can be written as $M_i v_i$, where v_i is the partial specific volume (volume per gram), so that

$$\mu_i = \mu_i^0 + \mu_i^c - M_i(1 - \rho v_i)\omega^2 r^2/2. \tag{9-29}$$

For the present case, the dissipation function has the same form as for a diffusion system,

$$\Phi = \sum_{i=1}^{n} \mathbf{J}_i \cdot \operatorname{grad}(-\mu_i),$$

except that the forces, grad $(-\mu_i)$, must be evaluated from Eq. (9-29) for μ_i. For the system shown in Fig. 16, grad $(-\mu_i)$ reduces to the simple expression $-d\mu_i/dr$. Differentiating Eq. (9-29) with respect to r, we obtain for the total force acting on component i

$$-\frac{d\mu_i}{dr} = -\frac{d\mu_i^c}{dr} + M_i(1 - \rho v_i)\omega^2 r. \tag{9-30}$$

Equation (9-30) may also be obtained by means of an alternative approach. We may assume that, in addition to the ordinary diffusional forces, the ith component is affected by the centrifugal force $M_i\omega^2 r$, so that

$$-\frac{d\mu_i}{dr} = -\bar{V}_i \frac{dP}{dr} - \frac{d\mu_i^c}{dr} + M_i\omega^2 r.$$

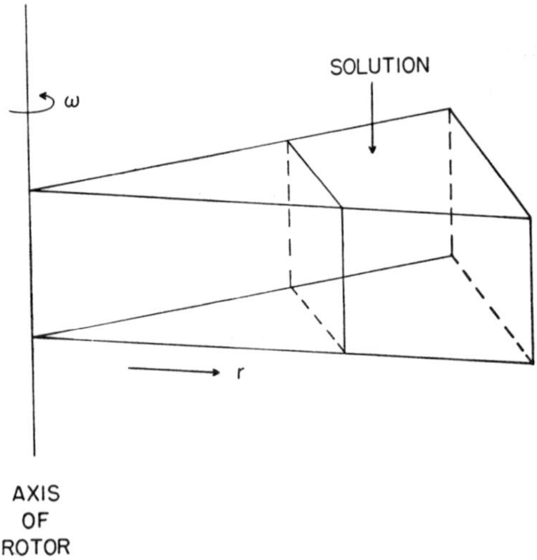

Fig. 16. Schematic illustration of a centrifuge cell.

However, the condition of mechanical equilibrium, which will be attained quickly if ω is constant, is

$$-\frac{dP}{dr} + \rho\omega^2 r = 0.$$

Therefore,

$$-\frac{d\mu_i}{dr} = -\frac{d\mu_i^c}{dr} + (M_i - \rho\bar{V}_i)\omega^2 r = -\frac{d\mu_i^c}{dr} + M_i(1 - \rho v_i)\omega^2 r.$$

9.4.2. If sedimentation is carried out for sufficiently long times, a state of sedimentation equilibrium may be attained. At equilibrium, all local forces vanish and

$$\frac{d\mu_i}{dr} = 0$$

for all components at every point of the solution. From Eq. (9-30) we see immediately that the condition of equilibrium is

$$\frac{d\mu_i^c}{dr} = M_i(1 - \rho v_i)\omega^2 r, \tag{9-31}$$

which expresses mathematically the physical requirement of exact balance of the diffusional forces, $-d\mu_i^c/dr$, and the centrifugal forces, $M_i(1 - \rho v_i)\omega^2 r$. If v_i is assumed to be independent of concentration, Eq. (9-31) may be integrated from a point r_1 to a point r_2 in the sedimentation cell:

$$\int_1^2 \frac{d\mu_i^c}{dr}\, dr = (\mu_i^c)_2 - (\mu_i^c)_1 = \frac{M_i(1 - \rho v_i)\omega^2}{2}(r_2^2 - r_1^2). \tag{9-32}$$

If the chemical potential is assumed to follow ideal rules,

$$(\mu_i^c)_2 - (\mu_i^c)_1 = RT \ln \frac{c_{i2}}{c_{i1}} = M_i(1 - \rho v_i)\omega^2 \frac{r_2^2 - r_1^2}{2},$$

and the molecular weight of the substance can be determined from observation of c_i as a function of r under conditions of sedimentation equilibrium:

$$M_i = \frac{2RT \ln (c_{i2}/c_{i1})}{\omega^2(1 - \rho v_i)(r_2^2 - r_1^2)}. \tag{9-34}$$

Sedimentation equilibrium could also be used to study the dependence of chemical potential on concentration by using macromolecules of known molecular weight since, in the absence of ideal behavior, $d\mu_i^c/dr = \sum (\partial\mu_i/\partial c_j)(dc_j/dr)$.

9.4.3. We may now turn to a consideration of the nonequilibrium state of the system, and examine the dissipation function in more detail. For an n-component system,

$$\Phi = \sum_{i=1}^{n} \mathbf{J}_i \cdot \left(-\frac{d\mu_i}{dr}\right). \tag{9-35}$$

However, as in the case of diffusion, the forces appearing in Eq. (9-35) are not independent; they are related by an expression similar to the Gibbs–Duhem relation,

$$\sum_{i=1}^{n} c_i \frac{d\mu_i}{dr} = 0. \tag{9-36}$$

This equation may be verified by introducing Eq. (9-30) for $d\mu_i/dr$:

$$\sum_{i=1}^{n} c_i \frac{d\mu_i}{dr} = \sum_{i=1}^{n} c_i \frac{d\mu_i^c}{dr} + \omega^2 r\left(\sum_{i=1}^{n} c_i M_i - \rho \sum_{i=1}^{n} c_i M_i v_i\right).$$

The first term on the right-hand side is zero according to the Gibbs–Duhem relation. The second term may be evaluated as follows:

$$\sum_{i=1}^{n} c_i M_i = \frac{1}{V} \sum_{i=1}^{n} n_i M_i = \rho$$

and

$$\sum_{i=1}^{n} c_i M_i v_i = \sum_{i=1}^{n} c_i \bar{V}_i = 1$$

according to Eq. (9-14). Thus,

$$\sum_{i=1}^{n} c_i M_i - \rho \sum_{i=1}^{n} c_i M_i v_i = \rho - \rho = 0,$$

which proves Eq. (9-36).

Equation (9-36) may be utilized to express the force acting on the solvent in terms of the forces on the solutes:

$$\frac{d\mu_w}{dr} = -\sum_{i=1}^{n-1} \frac{c_i}{c_w} \frac{d\mu_i}{dr}. \tag{9-37}$$

Introducing Eq. (9-37) into Eq. (9-35) yields

$$\Phi = \sum_{i=1}^{n-1} \left(\mathbf{J}_i - \frac{c_i}{c_w} \mathbf{J}_w\right) \cdot \left(-\frac{d\mu_i}{dr}\right) = \sum_{i=1}^{n-1} \mathbf{J}_i^d \cdot \left(-\frac{d\mu_i}{dr}\right), \tag{9-38}$$

in which the diffusional flows $\mathbf{J}_i^d$ are relative to the solvent. Thus, as in the case of diffusion, the dissipation function for an n-component system in a centrifugal field may be expressed in terms of $n - 1$ independent flows and forces. In the present case also it is only for the independent diffusional flows that meaningful phenomenological equations can be written and that Onsager's law holds for the cross coefficients. On the other hand, the measured flows are "absolute" or referred to the wall of the sedimentation cell. The way of passing from one set of flows to the other was outlined in Sec. 9.2 and will not be considered further here.

9.4.4. The simplest case described by Eq. (9-38) is that of a binary solution in a centrifugal field. In this case, there is only one independent flow, driven by a single force, and the phenomenological equations reduce to the simple form

$$\mathbf{J}_s^d = -L_s \frac{d\mu_s}{dr} = L_s M_s (1 - \rho v_s)\omega^2 r - L_s \frac{d\mu_s^c}{dr}. \tag{9-39}$$

Equation (9-39) may be simplified by making use of the sedimentation coefficient $\mathcal{S}$, first introduced by Svedberg. For the case of a binary solution $\mathcal{S}$ is defined as

$$\mathcal{S} = \frac{L_s M_s (1 - \rho v_s)}{c_s}. \tag{9-40}$$

Further, the term $L_s d\mu_s^c/dr$ may be transformed following the considerations introduced in Sec. 9.2:

$$L_s \frac{d\mu_s^c}{dr} = L_s \frac{\partial \mu_s}{\partial c_s} \frac{dc_s}{dr} = L_s \mu_{ss} \frac{dc_s}{dr} = D \frac{dc_s}{dr}.$$

Thus, Eq. (9-39) may be cast in the form

$$\mathbf{J}_s^d = \mathcal{S} c_s \omega^2 r - D \frac{dc_s}{dr}. \tag{9-41}$$

The study of the rate of sedimentation in a binary system shows that during the centrifugation the solute concentration in the cell will attain a form similar to that illustrated schematically in Fig. 17. There is a change in concentration in a boundary region, which is followed by a plateau in which $dc_s/dr = 0$. Moreover, the movement of the boundary will be equal to the flow within the plateau region. Hence, within this region, we may write for $\mathbf{J}_s^d$:

$$\mathbf{J}_s^d = \mathcal{S}c_s\omega^2 r. \tag{9-42}$$

This expression also serves to make clear the physical meaning of the sedimentation coefficient. Recalling that

$$\mathbf{J}_s^d = c_s(\mathbf{v}_s - \mathbf{v}_w),$$

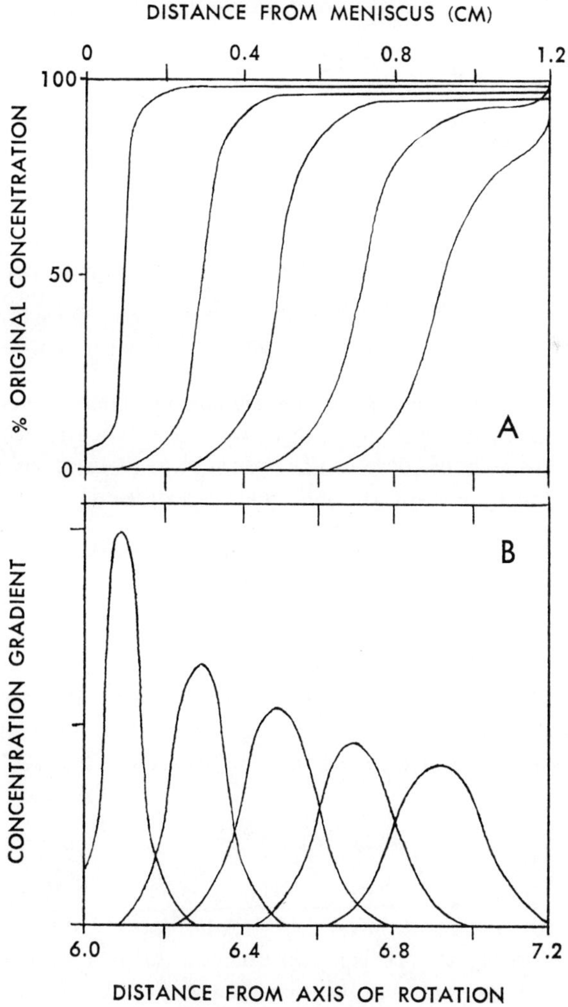

Fig. 17. Concentration and concentration gradient as a function of distance during a sedimentation velocity experiment. Reproduced by permission from H. K. Schachman, *Ultracentrifugation in Biochemistry* (Academic Press, New York, 1959).

we find that

$$\mathcal{S} = \frac{\mathbf{v}_s - \mathbf{v}_w}{\omega^2 r}. \tag{9-43}$$

Thus, $\mathcal{S}$ is the relative velocity of the solute per unit centrifugal force, or the mobility of the solute. It may be determined by observing the rate of migration of the boundary region depicted in Fig. 17.

It is further possible to determine D in independent diffusion experiments and obtain the ratio of $\mathcal{S}$ to D, which from Eqs. (9-40) and (9-12) is

$$\frac{\mathcal{S}}{D} = \frac{L_s M_s(1 - \rho v_s)}{c_s L_s \mu_{ss}} = \frac{M_s(1 - \rho v_s)}{c_s \mu_{ss}}. \tag{9-44}$$

If the solute behaves in an ideal manner,

$$\mu_{ss} = \frac{RT}{c_s},$$

and we obtain from Eq. (9-44) the well-known equation of Svedberg:

$$\frac{\mathcal{S}}{D} = \frac{M_s(1 - \rho v_s)}{RT}. \tag{9-45}$$

This relation can be utilized for determination of the molecular weight of the solute from measurements of $\mathcal{S}$, D, and v_s. On the other hand, for nonideal solutes of known molecular weight, Eq. (9-44) permits the determination of the important thermodynamic coefficient μ_{ss}, since

$$\mu_{ss} = \frac{M_s(1 - \rho v_s)D}{\mathcal{S} c_s}.$$

The ratio $\mathcal{S}/D$ is sufficiently important that an independent method for its evaluation should be available. This determination may be carried out by the method developed by Archibald,[10] who pointed out that at the bottom of the sedimentation cell (at $r = r_b$) the diffusional flow of the solute has to be zero. Introducing this condition into Eq. (9-41), we obtain

$$\frac{\mathcal{S}}{D} = \frac{(dc_s/dr)_{r=r_b}}{c_s^b \omega^2 r_b}, \tag{9-46}$$

which makes possible the determination of $\mathcal{S}/D$ from the measured concentration and concentration gradient at the bottom of the cell.

Before concluding this section, an estimate may be given of the order of magnitude of the sedimentation coefficient encountered in the study of macromolecules. We shall consider a protein of molecular weight 70,000. The order of magnitude of v_s is 0.75, while ρ is approximately unity. A reasonable value for the diffusion coefficient is 6.1×10^{-7} cm^2/sec and RT

is $8.3 \times 10^7 \times 293 = 24.3 \times 10^9$ ergs. Introducing these values into the Svedberg equation (9-45), we obtain

$$\mathcal{S} = \frac{70{,}000(1 - 0.75)6.1 \times 10^{-7}}{24.3 \times 10^9} = 4.4 \times 10^{-13} \text{ cm/sec dyne.}$$

As previously discussed, the units of $\mathcal{S}$ are those of a mobility or velocity per unit force. This may also be seen directly from Eq. (9-45) if we introduce the relation $D = RT\omega_s$, where ω_s is the solute mobility in molar units:

$$\mathcal{S} = M_s(1 - \rho v_s)\omega_s. \tag{9-47}$$

The usual unit employed in sedimentation studies is the Svedberg unit, defined as 1×10^{-13} cm/sec dyne; thus proteins are characterized by $\mathcal{S}$ values lying between 1 and 150 Svedberg units.

9.4.5. As a final example, sedimentation in a ternary mixture may be considered briefly. Such a system is characterized by two independent diffusional flows and we may write directly the phenomenological equations,

$$\begin{aligned} J_1^d &= -L_{11}\frac{d\mu_1}{dr} - L_{12}\frac{d\mu_2}{dr}, \\ J_2^d &= -L_{21}\frac{d\mu_1}{dr} - L_{22}\frac{d\mu_2}{dr}, \end{aligned} \tag{9-48}$$

in which the subscripts 1 and 2 denote the two solutes. Introducing the forces from Eq. (9-30), rearranging terms, and making use of Eqs. (9-26) defining the diffusion coefficients, we obtain

$$\begin{aligned} J_1^d &= \mathcal{S}_1 c_1 \omega^2 r - D_{11}\frac{dc_1}{dr} - D_{12}\frac{dc_2}{dr}, \\ J_2^d &= \mathcal{S}_2 c_2 \omega^2 r - D_{21}\frac{dc_1}{dr} - D_{22}\frac{dc_2}{dr}. \end{aligned} \tag{9-49}$$

The sedimentation coefficients $\mathcal{S}_1$ and $\mathcal{S}_2$ are again the relative velocities of the solutes per unit force under conditions of uniform composition. For the present case, these coefficients have the form

$$\begin{aligned} \mathcal{S}_1 &= \frac{1}{c_1}[L_{11}M_1(1 - \rho v_1) + L_{12}M_2(1 - \rho v_2)], \\ \mathcal{S}_2 &= \frac{1}{c_2}[L_{21}M_1(1 - \rho v_1) + L_{22}M_2(1 - \rho v_2)]. \end{aligned} \tag{9-50}$$

If the rates of sedimentation can be measured under conditions such that distinct plateaus develop for both solutes, so that $dc_1/dr = dc_2/dr = 0$, the flow equations reduce to the simpler forms

$$J_1^d = \mathcal{S}_1 c_1 \omega^2 r,$$
$$J_2^d = \mathcal{S}_2 c_2 \omega^2 r,$$

which permit evaluation of $\mathcal{S}_1$ and $\mathcal{S}_2$. By the Archibald technique, it is possible to determine c_1, c_2, dc_1/dr, dc_2/dr at the bottom of the sedimentation cell where both $\mathbf{J}_1^d$ and $\mathbf{J}_2^d$ must vanish. Under these conditions Eqs. (9-49) may be written

$$\mathcal{S}_1 c_1^b \omega^2 r_b = D_{11}\left(\frac{dc_1}{dr}\right)_{r=r_b} + D_{12}\left(\frac{dc_2}{dr}\right)_{r=r_b},$$

$$\mathcal{S}_2 c_2^b \omega^2 r_b = D_{21}\left(\frac{dc_1}{dr}\right)_{r=r_b} + D_{22}\left(\frac{dc_2}{dr}\right)_{r=r_b}.$$

Evaluation of $\mathcal{S}_1$ and $\mathcal{S}_2$ from these expressions requires knowledge of the four D_{ij} or the assumption that D_{12} and D_{21} may be neglected. Investigation of the expressions for $\mathcal{S}_1$ and $\mathcal{S}_2$ indicates that, even if D_{12} and D_{21} are taken as zero, the values of the two sedimentation coefficients are dependent on properties of both solutes. It is only in an ideal mixture, in which $\mu_{ij} = 0$ and $\mu_{ii} = RT/c_i$ and in which $D_{ij} = 0$ for $i \neq j$, that the relation between $\mathcal{S}_i$ and M_i assumes the simple form discussed for binary systems. Since Eqs. (9-48) are governed by the same set of Onsager coefficients L_{ij} and the same set of thermodynamic coefficients μ_{ij} as required for characterization of isothermal diffusion in ternary mixtures, a simultaneous study of diffusion and sedimentation should provide fuller information on both thermodynamic and hydrodynamic interactions in biocolloid mixtures. Such investigations encounter, however, great technical difficulties and, to date, no experimental data are available.

CHAPTER 10

MEMBRANE PERMEABILITY TO NONELECTROLYTES: DISCONTINUOUS SYSTEMS

10.1. Transition to Discontinuous Systems

THE study of isothermal diffusion leads naturally to the consideration of diffusion across membranes. Membrane permeability plays such an important role in the life of cells and tissues that it deserves a closer consideration from the point of view of the thermodynamics of irreversible systems. The simplest arrangement for the consideration of transport across membranes is represented in Fig. 18. The system consists of two compartments separated by a membrane of thickness Δx. The compartments may contain different concentrations of substances that can penetrate the membrane, as well as components to which the membrane is impermeable but which contribute to a difference in osmotic pressure across the membrane. Moreover, although each compartment is well stirred and there are no gradients of hydrostatic pressure within either compartment, we may impose different pressures on the left- and right-hand sides of the membrane and maintain a constant pressure difference ΔP in the system. By symmetry requirements, the flows $\mathbf{J}_i$ passing the membrane will be perpendicular to its surface and, for a homogeneous membrane, will have the same value at all points of the surface.

A cursory inspection of this experimental arrangement shows that, in spite of the fact that we are dealing with diffusion processes, the conditions differ appreciably from those encountered in the continuous system discussed in Chapter 9. The most conspicuous differences are (*a*) that there are no concentration gradients in the external solutions, all the gradients in chemical potential being found within the membrane, where no experimental study of the forces is possible, and (*b*) that the flows from one compartment to another have to cross a boundary between the solution phase and the membrane phase. In other words, the case of membrane permeability involves a discontinuous transition, and our first task is to adapt the formalism developed in the previous chapter to the description of flows and forces in a multiphase system.

Great simplification is achieved if one studies discontinuous systems

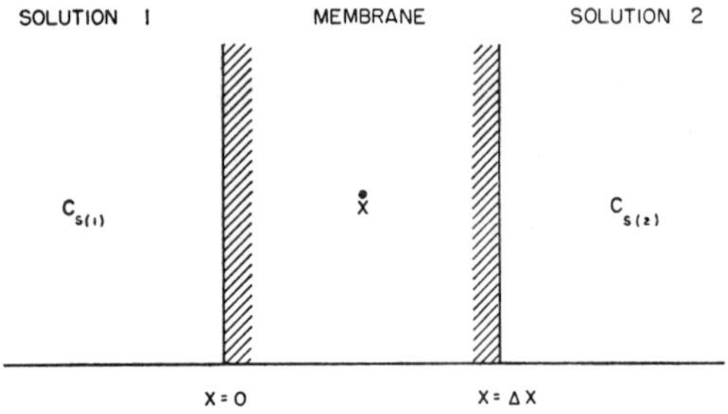

Fig. 18. Illustration of a membrane of thickness Δx bathed by solutions of a single nonelectrolyte at different concentrations, $c_{s(1)}$ and $c_{s(2)}$. Analysis of the system is begun by considering flows and forces at a point x within the membrane phase.

in a state of stationary flow. As discussed in Chapter 6 the parameters of state are independent of time during stationary flow, so that at any point of the system, whether in the compartments or in the membrane,

$$\left(\frac{\partial c_i}{\partial t}\right)_{x,y,z} = 0.$$

For substances undergoing transfer without participation in any chemical reaction, the equation of continuity, Eq. (6-15), states that

$$\frac{\partial c_i}{\partial t} = -\text{div}\ \mathbf{J}_i,$$

so that in a stationary state

$$\text{div}\ \mathbf{J}_i = 0,$$

or, for the unidimensional case considered here,

$$\mathbf{J}_i = \text{constant}, \tag{10-1}$$

at any point in the system. The physical significance of Eq. (10-1) is that the same flow will pass a unit area whether the ith component moves in a single phase or across the boundaries of different phases. For the system illustrated in Fig. 18, the flows under consideration start on one side of the membrane, pass through the membrane, and continue on the other side. However, the condition expressed by Eq. (10-1) holds for the system as a whole and the same constant flow must pass all the phases.

We shall now isolate within the membrane a volume element of unit area and of thickness dx and evaluate the dissipation function within the element. Since the element is thin we may assume it to be homogeneous and shall apply to it the equation obtained for the case of isothermal diffusion in a continuous phase, Eq. (9-1):

$$\Phi = \sum_{i=1}^{n} \mathbf{J}_i \cdot \text{grad} (-\mu_i). \tag{10-2}$$

Since the flows are constant in a stationary state it is possible, under these conditions, to integrate Eq. (10-2) across the membrane from surface 0 to surface Δx and evaluate the dissipation per unit area of the membrane as a whole:

$$\int_0^{\Delta x} \Phi \, dx = \mathbf{\Phi} = \int_0^{\Delta x} \sum_{i=1}^{n} J_i \text{ grad} (-\mu_i)$$
$$= \sum_{i=1}^{n} J_i \int_0^{\Delta x} - \frac{d\mu_i}{dx} dx = \sum_{i=1}^{n} J_i(\mu_i^0 - \mu_i^{\Delta x}),$$

or

$$\mathbf{\Phi} = \sum_{i=1}^{n} J_i \Delta\mu_i, \tag{10-3}$$

where $\mathbf{\Phi}$ represents the dissipation function for the membrane. In discussing discontinuous systems, we shall assume that all gradients are along the x-coordinate and dispense with vector notation. Thus, flows will be denoted by J_i, forces by X_i, and velocities by v_i.

By means of the integration we have replaced the unknown local forces in the membrane, grad $(-\mu_i)$, by new "forces," the differences in chemical potential, $\Delta\mu_i$. Although these forces have different dimensions from the gradients, they are proper members of the family of thermodynamic affinities. The only difficulty with the use of the $\Delta\mu_i$ is that these quantities represent a difference between the chemical potentials of the ith component in the membrane at the points 0 and Δx; these values of μ_i are unknown, and not available to experimental determination. However, following Kirkwood,[1] we shall make the assumption that the chemical potentials at the surface are the same as the corresponding potentials in the adjacent solution. Thus, μ_i^0 (membrane) $=$ μ_i^0 (solution) and $\mu_i^{\Delta x}$ (membrane) $=$ $\mu_i^{\Delta x}$ (solution), and $\Delta\mu_i$ is equal to the difference of the chemical potentials of the ith component in the left- and right-hand compartments. The considerations underlying Kirkwood's statement may be clarified by examining a thin transition layer of thickness dx between the membrane surface and the adjacent solution, as illustrated in Fig. 19. The layer may be partially in the solution and partially in the membrane. The chemical potential of the ith component at the point x in the solution is μ_i^x, while its value at the point $x + dx$ in the membrane is μ_i^{x+dx}. Expanding μ_i^{x+dx} in a Taylor series and taking only the first term, we may write

$$\mu_i^{x+dx} = \mu_i^x + \frac{d\mu_i}{dx} dx.$$

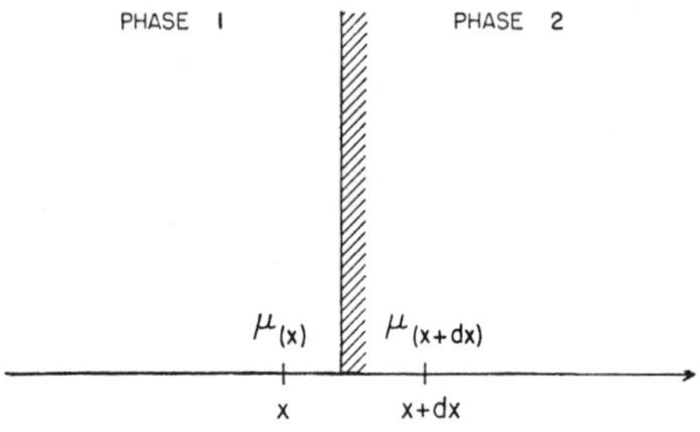

Fig. 19. The chemical potential at a phase boundary.

As dx approaches zero, μ_i^{x+dx} will approach μ_i^x unless $d\mu_i/dx$ becomes infinite. However, an infinite value of $d\mu_i/dx$ would mean that the local force would become infinite and this is not possible in a state of stationary flow. Thus, the chemical potential will be the same on both sides of the boundary separating the two phases.

The continuity of the chemical potentials across a dividing surface does not imply continuity of the forces $d\mu_i/dx$ at the surface. This point can be demonstrated easily for the simple case of a stationary flow of a single component across the boundary between phases 1 and 2. The flow is characterized by a single phenomenological coefficient, L, which may have a different value in each phase. Since the flow remains constant throughout the system,

$$J = -L_1(d\mu/dx)_1 = -L_2(d\mu/dx)_2.$$

If L_1 and L_2 are not identical, $(d\mu/dx)_1$ must differ from $(d\mu/dx)_2$ and there will exist a discontinuity in the force at the surface of separation of the phases. Both the continuity in chemical potential and the discontinuity in its gradient are illustrated in Fig. 20.

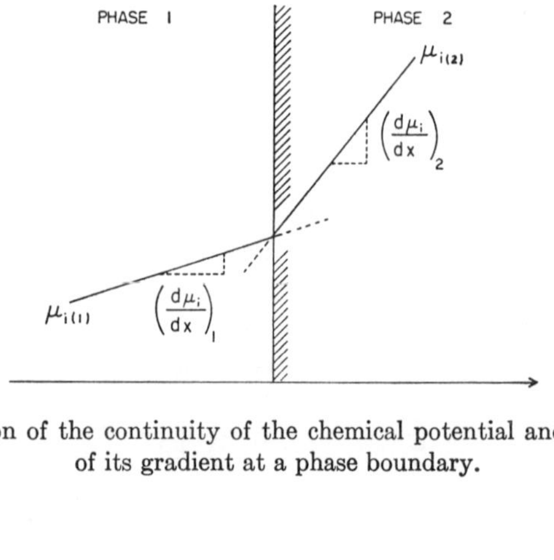

Fig. 20. Illustration of the continuity of the chemical potential and the discontinuity of its gradient at a phase boundary.

10.2. Flows and Forces

Equation (10-3) will form the basis of our treatment of irreversible processes in discontinuous systems under isothermal conditions. We shall begin the analysis of membrane permeability with a discussion of the transport of a binary solution of nonelectrolytes across a simple membrane. The dissipation function for this case is

$$\mathbf{\Phi} = J_s \Delta\mu_s + J_w \Delta\mu_w, \tag{10-4}$$

in which the subscripts s and w denote, respectively, the solute and the solvent. Phenomenological relations can be constructed between the flows and forces defined by Eq. (10-4). In the present case, however, it is advantageous to transform the thermodynamic forces into simpler quantities according to the considerations of Kedem and Katchalsky.[2] As discussed in Chapter 8, such transformations are possible provided that the products of the transformed flows and forces have the dimensions of entropy production and that $\mathbf{\Phi}$ remains invariant under the transformation. The transformation properties of the thermodynamic equations are discussed in detail by de Groot[3] and de Groot and Mazur.[4] The transformation to new sets of flows and forces leads to the introduction of new sets of phenomenological coefficients. However, it is possible to show that in most transformations of physical interest the Onsager reciprocal relations remain valid for the new coefficients provided the entropy production is maintained invariant.

The desired transformation for the membrane system can be obtained by considering the explicit expression for the chemical potentials μ_s and μ_w. According to Eq. (5-58), under isothermal conditions

$$\mu_w = \mu_w^0 + \bar{V}_w P + \mu_w^c,$$

where μ_w^c is the concentration-dependent part of μ_w, and

$$\begin{aligned} \Delta\mu_w &= (\mu_w)_0 - (\mu_w)_{\Delta x} \\ &= \bar{V}_w(P_0 - P_{\Delta x}) + (\mu_w^c)_0 - (\mu_w^c)_{\Delta x} \\ &= \bar{V}_w \Delta P + \Delta\mu_w^c. \end{aligned}$$

From the consideration of Sec. 5.4.2 concerning osmotic pressure, we note that

$$\Delta\mu_w^c = -\bar{V}_w \Delta\pi = -\bar{V}_w RT(c_s^0 - c_s^{\Delta x}).$$

Thus,

$$\Delta\mu_w = \bar{V}_w(\Delta P - \Delta\pi). \tag{10-5}$$

By entirely similar arguments,

$$\Delta\mu_s = \bar{V}_s \Delta P + \Delta\mu_s^c. \tag{10-6}$$

Equation (10-6) may be cast in a more useful form by defining an "average concentration" $\bar{c}_s$ such that

$$\Delta\mu_s^c = \frac{\Delta\pi}{\bar{c}_s}. \tag{10-7}$$

Upon introducing Eq. (10-7) into Eq. (10-6), we obtain

$$\Delta\mu_s = \bar{V}_s\Delta P + \frac{\Delta\pi}{\bar{c}_s}. \tag{10-8}$$

For ideal solutions, the value of $\bar{c}_s$ is readily evaluated:

$$\Delta\mu_s^c = RT\,(\ln c_s^0 - \ln c_s^{\Delta x})$$

and

$$\Delta\pi = RT\,(c_s^0 - c_s^{\Delta x}).$$

Since $\bar{c}_s = \Delta\pi/\Delta\mu_s^c$,

$$\bar{c}_s = \frac{c_s^0 - c_s^{\Delta x}}{\ln\,(c_s^0/c_s^{\Delta x})}.$$

The logarithm may be expanded by means of the series

$$\ln x = 2\left(\frac{x-1}{x+1}\right) + \frac{1}{3}\left(\frac{x-1}{x+1}\right)^3 + \cdots.$$

Assuming that the concentration difference is small, so that $c_s^0/c_s^{\Delta x}$ is close to unity, we may use only the first term in the expansion and obtain

$$\bar{c}_s = \frac{c_s^0 + c_s^{\Delta x}}{2}.$$

Thus, for ideal solutions under conditions of small concentration differences, $\bar{c}_s$ is the numerical average of the concentrations on the two sides of the membrane.

Introducing explicit expressions for $\Delta\mu_s$ and $\Delta\mu_w$ from Eqs. (10-8) and (10-5) into Eq. (10-4) and rearranging yields

$$\Phi = (J_w\bar{V}_w + J_s\bar{V}_s)\Delta P + \left(\frac{J_s}{\bar{c}_s} - \bar{V}_wJ_w\right)\Delta\pi. \tag{10-9}$$

The first term in parentheses is, according to Eq. (9-15), the total volume flow J_v across the membrane:

$$J_v = J_w\bar{V}_w + J_s\bar{V}_s.$$

The significance of the second term in parentheses becomes clear if we recall that the average volume fraction of water in the two compartments, $\bar{c}_w\bar{V}_w$, is very close to unity, so that $\bar{V}_w \cong 1/\bar{c}_w$. Using this condition, we have

$$\frac{J_s}{\bar{c}_s} - J_w\bar{V}_w \cong \frac{J_s}{\bar{c}_s} - \frac{J_w}{\bar{c}_w} = \frac{\bar{c}_s v_s}{\bar{c}_s} - \frac{\bar{c}_w v_w}{\bar{c}_w} = v_s - v_w.$$

Thus, the new flow conjugate to the force $\Delta\pi$ is simply the velocity of the solute relative to that of the solvent. Because of its similarity to the ordinary diffusion flow, it will be denoted by J_D. Introducing the volume flow and the diffusional velocity into Eq. (10-9), we obtain the transformed dissipation function,

$$\Phi = J_v\Delta P + J_D\Delta\pi, \tag{10-10}$$

in which the new forces are the difference in hydrostatic pressure ΔP and the difference is osmotic pressure $\Delta\pi$ across the membrane.

It is of interest to note that the volume flow may also be regarded as a velocity, the external velocity of the solvent, v_w. This may be demonstrated by writing the explicit expression for J_v and introducing the volume fractions of solute and solvent:

$$J_v = J_w\bar{V}_w + J_s\bar{V}_s = \bar{c}_w\bar{V}_w v_w + \bar{c}_s\bar{V}_s v_s = \varphi_w v_w + \varphi_s v_s.$$

Since $\varphi_w \gg \varphi_s$ and $\varphi_w \cong 1$,

$$J_v \cong v_w. \tag{10-11}$$

10.3. Membrane Properties

10.3.1. The phenomenological equations relating the flows and forces defined by Eq. (10-10) are

$$\begin{aligned} J_v &= L_P\Delta P + L_{PD}\Delta\pi, \\ J_D &= L_{DP}\Delta P + L_D\Delta\pi. \end{aligned} \tag{10-12}$$

For this system, the Onsager reciprocal relation is

$$L_{PD} = L_{DP}.$$

The significance of Eqs. (10-12) may be clarified by examination of several common physical situations. Let us first consider an experiment in which the concentration of the solute is the same on both sides of the membrane, so that $\Delta\pi = 0$. If a pressure difference is maintained, there will exist a volume flow J_v, which is a linear function of ΔP. The proportionality coefficient relating J_v to ΔP is L_P, which is the mechanical filtration capacity of the membrane. The filtration coefficient has the character of a mobility and represents the velocity of fluid per unit pressure difference. A closer inspection of Eqs. (10-12) shows, however, that a hydrostatic pressure at $\Delta\pi = 0$ can produce not only a volume flow but also a diffusional flow:

$$(J_D)_{\Delta\pi=0} = L_{DP}\Delta P. \tag{10-13}$$

Movement of solute relative to solvent, J_D, induced by a mechanical pressure is a well-known phenomenon in colloid chemistry and is called ultrafiltration. Thus, the coupling coefficient L_{DP} is a measure of the ultrafiltration properties of the membrane.

An alternative experimental arrangement is one in which different solute concentrations exist in the two compartments ($\Delta\pi \neq 0$) and the pressure is uniform ($\Delta P = 0$). As expected, the difference in osmotic pressure causes a diffusional flow characterized by the coefficient L_D, which represents a diffusional mobility per unit osmotic pressure:

$$(J_D)_{\Delta P=0} = L_D \Delta\pi.$$

There is, however, another effect implied in Eqs. (10-12), a volume flow caused by an osmotic pressure difference at zero hydrostatic-pressure difference:

$$(J_v)_{\Delta P=0} = L_{PD} \Delta\pi. \tag{10-14}$$

This well-known phenomenon is the osmotic flow and L_{PD} is readily identified as the coefficient of osmotic flow.

Thus we see that the phenomenological equations give an adequate description of the phenomena of membrane transport and correlate, in a consistent manner, different experimental observations. Moreover, Onsager's law provides a quantitative relation between the phenomena of ultrafiltration and osmotic flow. A combination of Eqs. (10-13) and (10-14) gives

$$\left(\frac{J_v}{\Delta\pi}\right)_{\Delta P=0} = L_{PD} = L_{DP} = \left(\frac{J_D}{\Delta P}\right)_{\Delta\pi=0}, \tag{10-15}$$

indicating that the volume flow per unit osmotic pressure should be equal to the diffusional velocity per unit pressure difference. The introduction of the cross coefficients is not arbitrary but is required by the very nature of the phenomena taking place in the membrane. Moreover, if we disregarded the existence of cross relations, we would miss one of the most interesting aspects of membrane function, the selectivity. The use of L_P alone would lead to prediction of mechanical filtration but would make no distinction between a membrane so selective as to give rise to a maximal flow under the action of an osmotic gradient and one so coarse as to make the establishment of an osmotic flow impossible. In the same way, a diffusional or exchange flow will take place in a free solution without the presence of a membrane. It is, however, the coefficient L_{DP} that introduces membrane characteristics and takes into account the phenomenon of ultrafiltration.

The importance of the cross coefficient L_{PD} warrants consideration of an additional experiment, the measurement of osmotic pressure with a membrane that is permeable to the solute. The experiment is carried out in a manner similar to that discussed in Chapter 5 and illustrated in Fig. 11. The height of the liquid in the capillary provides a measure of both the change in volume in the compartment and the ultimate pressure difference ΔP attained "at equilibrium." The time course of the volume change is illustrated in Fig. 21. It is generally assumed that, when a plateau is reached and $J_v = 0$, a state of equilibrium is attained and that ΔP measures the osmotic-pressure difference between the two solutions. That this assumption is not necessarily correct may be illustrated by introducing the condition $J_v = 0$ into Eq. (10-12). We find that

$$(\Delta P)_{J_v=0} = -\frac{L_{PD}}{L_P}\,\Delta\pi, \tag{10-16}$$

or that $\Delta P = \Delta\pi$ only if $-L_{PD} = L_P$. This condition will be satisfied for an ideal semipermeable membrane that prevents the transport of solute whatever ΔP or $\Delta\pi$ may be, so that $J_s = 0$ for all values of the forces. J_s may be evaluated by adding the expressions defining J_v and J_D. Thus,

$$J_D + J_v = \frac{J_s}{\bar{c}_s} - \bar{V}_w J_w + \bar{V}_w J_w + \bar{V}_s J_s = \frac{J_s}{\bar{c}_s}(1 + \varphi_s).$$

Assuming that $\varphi_s \ll 1$ and introducing Eqs. (10-12) for J_v and J_D, we obtain

$$\frac{J_s}{\bar{c}_s} = (L_P + L_{DP})\Delta P + (L_{PD} + L_D)\Delta\pi. \tag{10-17}$$

The requirement that $J_s = 0$ for all values of ΔP and $\Delta\pi$ means that

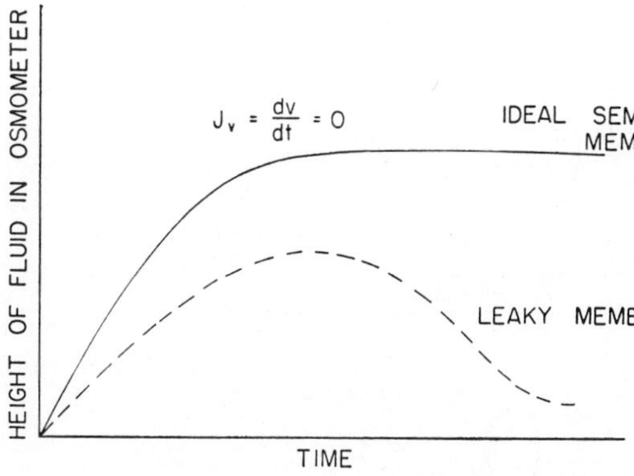

Fig. 21. Illustration of the height (or volume) of fluid in an osmometer as a function of time for a semipermeable membrane and a membrane permeable to the solute.

both terms in parentheses in Eq. (10-17) must be zero. Thus, for an ideal semipermeable membrane

$$-L_{PD} = L_P = L_D. \tag{10-18}$$

Under these conditions, Eq. (10-16) takes the form required for a true osmotic equilibrium,

$$(\Delta P)_{J_v=0} = \Delta\pi.$$

In cases in which the membrane permits passage of the solute,

$$-\frac{L_{PD}}{L_P} < 1,$$

and for a nonselective membrane, such as a porous glass filter, L_{PD} approaches zero. Staverman[5] recognized that the ratio $-L_{PD}/L_P$ is an adequate measure of membrane selectivity. He has called it the *reflection coefficient*,

$$\sigma = -\frac{L_{PD}}{L_P}, \tag{10-19}$$

to indicate that when $\sigma = 1$ all the solute is "reflected" from the membrane, while $\sigma < 1$ means that part of the solute penetrates and is not "reflected." It is important to realize that the value of σ depends on the properties of both the membrane and the solute, as indicated by the data given in Table 2. In a system containing more than one solute, there will be, in general, a different value of the reflection coefficient for each solute and the notation σ_i, where i refers to the solute, should be employed. Since we shall consider only systems with a single solute, we shall not use a subscript.

In order to clarify the concept of membrane selectivity, let us consider again the behavior of the system when $\Delta\pi = 0$. From Eq. (10-12), we find that

$$\left(\frac{J_D}{J_v}\right)_{\Delta\pi=0} = \frac{L_{PD}}{L_P} = -\sigma,$$

or, introducing the values of J_D and J_v in terms of velocities,

$$\left(\frac{v_s - v_w}{v_w}\right)_{\Delta\pi=0} = -\sigma$$

or

$$\left(\frac{v_s}{v_w}\right)_{\Delta\pi=0} = 1 - \sigma. \tag{10-20}$$

Equation (10-20) shows that for an ideal semipermeable membrane ($\sigma = 1$), $v_s = 0$ and no solute can cross the membrane. With decreas-

Table 2. Properties of membranes.

Membrane	Solute	Solute permeability, ω $\left[10^{-15}\dfrac{\text{mole}}{\text{dyne sec}}\right]$	Reflection coefficient, σ	Filtration coefficient, L_p $\left[10^{-11}\dfrac{\text{cm}^3}{\text{dyne sec}}\right]$
Toad skin[a]	Acetamide	0.0041	0.89	0.4
	Thiourea	0.00057	0.98	
Nitella translucens[b]	Methanol	11	0.50	1.1
	Ethanol	11	0.44	
	Isopropanol	7	0.40	
	Urea	0.008	1	
Human red blood cell[c]	Urea	17	0.62	0.92
	Ethylene glycol	8	0.63	
	Malonamide	0.04	0.83	
	Methanol	122	—	
Visking dialysis tubing[d]	Urea	20.8	0.013	3.2
	Glucose	7.2	0.123	
	Sucrose	3.9	0.163	
Dupont "wet gel"[d]	Urea	31.6	0.0016	9.7
	Glucose	12.2	0.024	
	Sucrose	7.7	0.036	

[a] B. Andersen and H. H. Ussing, *Acta Physiol. Scand.* *39* (1957), 228.

[b] J. Dainty and B. Z. Ginzburg, *Biochim. Biophys. Acta* *79* (1964), 102, 112, 122, 129.

[c] Values of ω from unpublished data of D. Savitz and A. K. Solomon: σ from D. G. Goldstein and A. K. Solomon, *J. Gen. Physiol.* *44* (1960), 1: L_p from V. W. Sidel and A. K. Solomon, *J. Gen. Physiol.* *41* (1957), 243.

[d] B. Z. Ginzburg and A. Katchalsky, *J. Gen. Physiol.* *47* (1963), 403.

ing selectivity or diminishing σ, v_s increases and solute is transferred. When $\sigma = 0$, $v_s = v_w$ so that for a nonselective membrane solute and solvent move at equal velocities and there is no ultrafiltration. There is also the possibility of σ being negative, and in this case $1 - \sigma > 1$. This would mean that the transfer of solute is more rapid than that of solvent or $v_s > v_w$. Such cases are known and are called *negative anomalous osmosis*; they are of special interest in transport of electrolytes through charged membranes and will be discussed in more detail in Sec. 10.4.2.

The introduction of σ into Eq. (10-12) yields, for the volume flow,

$$J_v = L_P(\Delta P - \sigma\Delta\pi). \tag{10-21}$$

or, for a system containing n solutes,

$$J_v = L_p\left(\Delta P - \sum_{i=1}^{n} \sigma_i \Delta\pi_i\right).$$

An equation similar in form to Eq. (10-21) was proposed earlier by physiological workers, assuming $\sigma = 1$. The use of the correct equation (10-21) is particularly important in consideration of substances to which the membrane is only slightly selective ($\sigma \ll 1$), such as isotopic forms of water. It is often advantageous to study the total solute flow J_s, rather than the relative velocity J_D. To do this, Eq. (10-12) is solved for ΔP in terms of J_v and $\Delta\pi$ to yield

$$\Delta P = \frac{J_v - L_{PD}\Delta\pi}{L_P}.$$

Introducing this expression into Eq. (10-17) and using also Eq. (10-19), we obtain, after rearrangement,

$$J_s = \bar{c}_s(1 - \sigma)J_v + \omega\Delta\pi, \tag{10-22}$$

in which

$$\omega = \frac{\bar{c}_s(L_P L_D - L_{PD}^2)}{L_P}. \tag{10-23}$$

The new coefficient, ω, is the coefficient of solute permeability at zero volume flow, or

$$\omega = \left(\frac{J_s}{\Delta\pi}\right)_{J_v=0}. \tag{10-24}$$

It is an important characteristic parameter of both synthetic and natural membranes. As expected, for ideally semipermeable membranes obeying Eq. (10-18), $\omega = 0$, while for nonselective membranes in which the solute diffuses freely and $L_{PD} = 0$, $\omega = \bar{c}_s L_D$. The set of coefficients L_P, σ, and ω is more convenient for description of membrane systems than the set L_P, σ, and L_D, since ω can be easily determined experimentally.

10.3.2. There is sufficient biophysical interest in the description of membrane phenonena to justify illustrating the use of Eqs. (10-21) and (10-22) by some examples. Andersen and Ussing[6] have examined the influence of volume flow on the movement of nonelectrolytes across isolated toad skin. In their experiments, the solute to be examined was placed on both sides of the skin at the same concentration ($\Delta\pi = 0$) and an osmotic flow was induced by a concentration difference of NaCl, an impermeant solute. Equation (10-22) thus becomes

$$J_s = \bar{c}_s(1 - \sigma)J_v.$$

The experiments showed that a solute flow could be induced by the volume flow and the results can be used to evaluate σ for the two solutes investigated, acetamide and thiourea. The data may also be used to estimate L_P and ω for the solutes. Andersen and Ussing refer to this induced solute movement as "solvent drag," and the experiments suggest that it could be important in biological systems. The phenomenon can be described adequately in thermodynamic terms.

The experiments of Andersen and Ussing were not designed specifically to determine the coefficients L_P, σ, and ω, so that the values are estimates only. Recently, these coefficients have been determined, with several solutes, for human red blood cells by Solomon and his coworkers,[7] for the large plant cell of *Nitella translucens* by Dainty and Ginzburg,[8] and for two artificial membranes by Ginzburg and Katchalsky.[9] The resulting values together with those estimated for toad skin are given in Table 2. (Throughout this development, we have assumed that the solutions bathing the membrane are perfectly strirred. However, experimental measurements may be significantly influenced by unstrirred layers at the membrane boundaries, particularly if the membrane is relatively permeable to the solute.[10,11] Dainty and Ginzburg and Ginzburg and Katchalsky have attempted to take this effect into account in their experiments, but the correction is difficult because of considerable uncertainty in estimating the thickness of the unstirred layer.)

The values of L_P have been obtained, for the natural membranes, by observing the volume flow caused by a concentration difference of an impermeant solute ($\sigma = 1$), and for the artificial membranes, by observing the volume flow caused by a pressure difference. Permeability coefficients ω were measured by using radioactive solutes. Two basic methods, which can be illustrated with Eq. (10-21), have been employed to measure σ. In the absence of a pressure difference, Eq. (10-21) can be written

$$J_v = -L_P\sigma\Delta\pi_s$$

for a permeant solute and

$$J_v = -L_P\Delta\pi_i$$

for an impermeant solute i. Thus σ can be estimated by observing the initial volume flow caused by a known solute concentration difference if L_P is known. An alternative method makes use of a comparison of the effects of concentration differences of permeant and impermeant solutes. If both solutes are present simultaneously, the volume flow is given by

$$J_v = -L_P(\Delta\pi_i + \sigma\Delta\pi_s).$$

Determination of the combination of $\Delta\pi_i$ and $\Delta\pi_s$ that gives an initial volume flow of zero provides an estimate of σ, since

$$\left(\frac{\Delta\pi_i}{\Delta\pi_s}\right)_{J_v=0} = -\sigma.$$

Inspection of Table 2 indicates that there are some striking differences among the various membranes. Although there are as yet insufficient data available to attempt an explanation of these differences, such measurements may be useful in obtaining a better understanding of membrane properties. For example, Solomon has utilized measurements of σ, coupled with a kinetic model of the events in the membrane, to estimate the size of equivalent aqueous channels in the membrane. A further consideration of possible interpretations of these phenomenological coefficients is given in the following section.

10.4. Frictional Interpretation of Phenomenological Coefficients

10.4.1. Correlations such as those discussed in the previous section, and many others, may be derived from the symmetry properties of phenomenological coefficients without explicit consideration of the possible physical meaning of the coefficients. Thus, this general macroscopic theory of irreversible processes is not based on any specific kinetic or statistical model of the processes. However, all the phenomenological coefficients may be evaluated in some cases, and it may be of interest to examine the possibility that additional information can be derived from a more detailed interpretation of their nature. As an example of such an analysis, we shall consider further the coefficients used in the last section to describe membrane phenomena. On the basis of Einstein's treatment of Brownian movement, diffusion coefficients, and colloid viscosity, these coefficients may be translated into more tangible physical parameters without committing ourselves to a detailed model. We shall analyze the problem of membrane permeability in terms of a generalized frictional treatment and attempt to express the phenomenological coefficients in terms of frictional coefficients.

The explicit treatment of frictional forces may be approached by considering the simple case of water filtration through a membrane, assuming that the experiment is carried out under steady-state conditions with grad $T = 0$. Pure water is placed on both sides of the membrane and the driving force is provided by a difference in pressure. Let us consider a point x in the membrane where the force driving the water is

$$X_w = -\frac{d\mu_w}{dx}. \tag{10-25}$$

Under conditions of steady flow, the driving force must be balanced by a mechanical frictional force, X_{wm}, between the water and the membrane matrix. This frictional force is given by

$$X_{wm} = f_{wm}(v_w - v_m), \tag{10-26}$$

in which f_{wm} is the coefficient of friction between water and the membrane and v_m is the geometric velocity of the membrane. If the membrane is considered as the reference for all flows, v_m may be taken as zero and, equating X_w and X_{wm}, we obtain

$$-\frac{d\mu_w}{dx} = f_{wm}v_w. \tag{10-27}$$

The flow of water at the point x is given by $J_w = C_{w(x)}v_w$. For the sake of simplicity, we shall assume that the water concentration in the membrane is the same throughout the cross section and is given by the thermodynamic distribution coefficient of water between membrane and adjoining medium:

$$\frac{C_w}{c_w} = K_w, \tag{10-28}$$

in which C_w is water concentration in the membrane, c_w is water concentration in the medium, and K_w is the distribution coefficient. The value of the distribution coefficient may be obtained by multiplying the numerator and denominator in Eq. (10-28) by $\bar{V}_w$:

$$\frac{C_w\bar{V}_w}{c_w\bar{V}_w} = \frac{\varphi_w}{1} = K_w, \tag{10-29}$$

in which φ_w is the volume fraction of water in the membrane. With these relations, Eq. (10-27) becomes

$$-\frac{d\mu_w}{dx} = \frac{f_{wm}C_wv_w}{C_w} = \frac{J_wf_{wm}}{C_w} = \frac{J_w\bar{V}_wf_{wm}}{\varphi_w}. \tag{10-30}$$

Equation (10-30) may be readily integrated across the membrane. The integral of the left-hand side is

$$\int_0^{\Delta x} -\frac{d\mu_w}{dx}\,dx = \mu_{w(0)} - \mu_{w(\Delta x)} = \Delta\mu_w = \bar{V}_w\Delta P. \tag{10-31}$$

In integrating the right-hand side, we shall assume that f_{wm} and φ_w are constant (or, alternatively, that reasonable mean values can be taken). The flow J_w is constant as a result of the assumption of steady-state conditions, and $\bar{V}_wJ_w$ is equal to the total volume flow J_v across the membrane. Thus,

$$\int_0^{\Delta x} \frac{J_w\bar{V}_wf_{wm}}{\varphi_w}\,dx = \frac{J_vf_{wm}}{\varphi_w}\,\Delta x. \tag{10-32}$$

Combining Eqs. (10-31) and (10-32) yields the integrated form,

$$\bar{V}_w\Delta P = \frac{J_vf_{wm}}{\varphi_w}\,\Delta x, \tag{10-33}$$

or, solving for J_v,

$$J_v = \frac{\varphi_w \bar{V}_w}{f_{wm}\Delta x}\,\Delta P. \tag{10-34}$$

Comparison of Eq. (10-34) with Eq. (10-12) under the condition $\Delta\pi = 0$ shows that

$$L_P = \frac{\varphi_w \bar{V}_w}{f_{wm}\Delta x}. \tag{10-35}$$

Equation (10-35) is a very simple case of translation of thermodynamic into frictional coefficients. It shows that the filtration will be directly proportional to the water content of the membrane and inversely proportional to the thickness of the membrane and to the coefficient of friction between water and the membrane matrix.

10.4.2. The reasoning of the previous section may be extended to include the transport of a single solute and solvent through a membrane.[12] The fundamental assumption underlying this more general treatment is that the frictional forces that counterbalance the thermodynamic driving forces are additive. Thus according to Spiegler,[13] the force driving the solute, X_s, is balanced by the sum of the force of interaction of solute with the membrane matrix, X_{sm}, and the force of interaction between solute and solvent in the membrane, X_{sw}. The formal hydrodynamic description of these frictional forces is

$$\begin{aligned} X_{sm} &= f_{sm}(v_s - v_m), \\ X_{sw} &= f_{sw}(v_s - v_w), \end{aligned} \tag{10-36}$$

in which f_{sw} is the frictional coefficient between a mole of solute and an infinite amount of water. We shall again regard the membrane velocity as the reference and take $v_m = 0$. Thus,

$$X_s = X_{sm} + X_{sw} = v_s(f_{sw} + f_{sm}) - v_w f_{sw}. \tag{10-37}$$

In the same manner, we may obtain the force acting on the water at any point in the membrane:

$$X_w = X_{wm} + X_{ws} = v_w(f_{wm} + f_{ws}) - v_s f_{ws}. \tag{10-38}$$

The coefficient f_{ws} is different from f_{sw} since f_{ws} is the friction between a mole of water and an infinite amount of solute. We shall see below how the two are related through the phenomenological equations. In a very loose membrane, the coefficient f_{sw} approaches the value for free solution, f_{sw}^0, which is related to the diffusion coefficient by the expression

$$D = \frac{RT}{f_{sw}^0}. \tag{10-39}$$

By means of Eq. (6-2), Eqs. (10-37) and (10-38) may be transformed as follows:

$$X_w = -\frac{d\mu_w}{dx} = -\frac{f_{ws}J_s}{C_{s(x)}} + \frac{(f_{ws} + f_{wm})J_w}{C_{w(x)}}, \tag{10-40}$$

$$X_s = -\frac{d\mu_s}{dx} = \frac{(f_{sw} + f_{sm})J_s}{C_{s(x)}} - \frac{f_{sw}J_w}{C_{w(x)}}, \tag{10-41}$$

in which $C_{s(x)}$ and $C_{w(x)}$ are concentrations of solute and water respectively at the point x in the membrane. Equations (10-40) and (10-41) have the form of the inverted phenomenological equations, illustrated by Eq. (8-3),

$$\begin{aligned} X_w &= R_{11}J_w + R_{12}J_s, \\ X_s &= R_{21}J_w + R_{22}J_s, \end{aligned} \tag{10-42}$$

and hence the translation of the R_{ik} into frictional coefficients is effected by equating the coefficients of the flows in Eqs. (10-40) and (10-41) with those in Eqs. (10-42):

$$\begin{aligned} R_{11} &= \frac{f_{ws} + f_{wm}}{C_{w(x)}}, \qquad & R_{21} &= \frac{-f_{sw}}{C_{w(x)}}, \\ R_{12} &= \frac{-f_{ws}}{C_{s(x)}}, \qquad & R_{22} &= \frac{f_{sw} + f_{sm}}{C_{s(x)}}. \end{aligned} \tag{10-44}$$

The requirement $R_{12} = R_{21}$ gives immediately the relation between the frictional coefficients f_{sw} and f_{ws}:

$$f_{ws} = \frac{C_{s(x)}f_{sw}}{C_{w(x)}}. \tag{10-45}$$

For integration across the membrane, we must express the local concentrations $C_{s(x)}$ and $C_{w(x)}$ at the point x in the membrane in terms of the external concentrations which are accessible to experimental determination. The concentration $C_{w(x)}$ can be approximated satisfactorily by the same expression as was used for pure water, Eq. (10-28). For evaluation of $C_{s(x)}$, we must use a more complex method. Imagine that at the point x a small hole is created in the membrane and filled with pure water. Under conditions of steady flow, the hole will fill up, in a short while, with solute of concentration $c'_{s(x)}$. As shown above, the chemical potential of the solute in the hole should be equal to that in the membrane so that in the case of a homogeneous membrane the ratio of the concentration at the point x in the membrane to the concentration in the equivalent aqueous phase $c'_{s(x)}$ should be given by a distribution coefficient K_s,

$$\frac{C_{s(x)}}{c'_{s(x)}} = K_s. \tag{10-46}$$

The value of K_s will be assumed to be approximately constant throughout the membrane. The advantage of this device is that, instead of the chemical potential in the membrane, we may use the equivalent potential in the aqueous phase of the small hole, and instead of the unknown concentration $C_{s(x)}$ we may use $K_s c'_{s(x)}$, which can be determined experimentally by independent measurement on solute distribution between the membrane and the external solution.

The integration is simplified appreciably if we take into consideration the fact that the permeability coefficient ω and the reflection coefficient σ may be determined at zero volume flow. Since $J_v = 0$ is, in most cases, very nearly equivalent to $J_w = 0$, we may use the latter condition. Equation (10-41) then becomes

$$\left(-\frac{d\mu_s}{dx}\right)_{J_w=0} = \frac{J_s}{K_s c'_{s(x)}}(f_{sw} + f_{sm}). \tag{10-47}$$

We may now regard the values of $d\mu_s$ as those of the chemical potential in the equivalent aqueous solution. As shown previously, $d\mu_s = d\pi/c'_{s(x)}$, so that Eq. (10-47) may be rewritten as

$$-\frac{d\pi}{dx} = \frac{J_s(f_{sw} + f_{sm})}{K_s}. \tag{10-48}$$

Equation (10-48) may be readily integrated across the membrane:

$$\int_0^{\Delta x} -\frac{d\pi}{dx}\,dx = J_s \frac{f_{sw} + f_{sm}}{K_s} \int_0^x dx,$$

or

$$(\Delta\pi)_{J_w=0} = \frac{(f_{sw} + f_{sm})\Delta x}{K_s} J_s. \tag{10-49}$$

The permeability coefficient ω has been defined as

$$\omega = \left(\frac{J_s}{\Delta\pi}\right)_{J_v=0} \cong \left(\frac{J_s}{\Delta\pi}\right)_{J_w=0} = \frac{K_s}{\Delta x(f_{sw} + f_{sm})}. \tag{10-50}$$

Equation (10-50) has a simple physical meaning. First, it shows that the permeability decreases with the thickness of the membrane. Second, it demonstrates that the permeability is inversely proportional to the over-all friction of the solute with the water and with the membrane. Finally, it introduces the distribution coefficient of the solute between membrane and solution. An increase in K_s will lead to an increased permeability.

The next coefficient to be evaluated in frictional terms is the reflection coefficient σ. We again impose the condition $J_w = 0$ and transcribe Eqs. (10-40) and (10-41) using Eq. (10-45) and $C_{w(x)}\bar{V}_w = \varphi_w$:

$$-\frac{d\mu_w}{dx} = -\frac{\bar{V}_w f_{sw}}{\varphi_w} J_s,$$
$$-\frac{d\mu_s}{dx} = \frac{f_{sw} + f_{sm}}{K_s c'_{s(x)}} J_s. \tag{10-51}$$

Eliminating J_s from these equations, we obtain

$$-c'_{s(x)} \frac{d\mu_s}{dx} = -\frac{f_{sw} + f_{sm}}{K_s f_{sw} \bar{V}_w} \varphi_w \left(-\frac{d\mu_w}{dx}\right). \tag{10-52}$$

Since $c'_{s(x)}$ and $d\mu_s$ are now regarded as the properties of the equivalent aqueous solution, we may introduce the relationship $c'_{s(x)}(d\mu_s/dx) = d\pi/dx$ and integrate Eq. (10-52) across the membrane:

$$\int_0^{\Delta x} -\frac{d\pi}{dx}\,dx = -\frac{f_{sw} + f_{sm}}{K_s f_{sw} \bar{V}_w} \varphi_w \int_0^{\Delta x} -\frac{d\mu_w}{dx}\,dx.$$

With Eq. (10-5) this becomes

$$\Delta\pi = -\varphi_w \frac{f_{sw} + f_{sm}}{K_s f_{sw}} (\Delta P - \Delta\pi),$$

or

$$\left(\frac{\Delta P}{\Delta\pi}\right)_{J_w=0} = 1 - \frac{K_s f_{sw}}{(f_{sw} + f_{sm})\varphi_w} \cong \sigma. \tag{10-53}$$

Although the difference between $J_w = 0$ and $J_v = 0$ is usually small, a correction term may be introduced since it may be shown that

$$\left(\frac{\Delta P}{\Delta\pi}\right)_{J_w=0} = \left(\frac{\Delta P}{\Delta\pi}\right)_{J_v=0} + \frac{\omega \bar{V}_s}{L_P}, \tag{10-54}$$

and thus

$$\sigma = 1 - \frac{\omega \bar{V}_s}{L_P} - \frac{K_s f_{sw}}{\varphi_w (f_{sw} + f_{sm})}. \tag{10-55}$$

Introducing the value of ω from Eq. (10-50) into the last term of Eq. (10-55), we may also write

$$\sigma = 1 - \frac{\omega \bar{V}_s}{L_P} - \frac{\omega f_{sw} \Delta x}{\varphi_w}. \tag{10-56}$$

Equation (10-56) shows that, when the membrane is impermeable to the solute and $\omega = 0$, the coefficient $\sigma = 1$, as expected for an ideal semipermeable membrane. When ω increases σ decreases and for sufficiently large values of ω may assume negative values. Negative values of σ mean that in an osmotic experiment, at zero volume flow when $\Delta P = \sigma\Delta\pi$, we have to apply a negative pressure to the solution in order to maintain

Table 3. Frictional coefficients for cellulose membranes.[a]

Membrane	Solute[b]	f_{sw} $\left[10^{16}\ \frac{\text{dyne sec}}{\text{mole cm}}\right]$	f_{sm} $\left[10^{16}\ \frac{\text{dyne sec}}{\text{mole cm}}\right]$	f_{wm} $\left[10^{13}\ \frac{\text{dyne sec}}{\text{mole cm}}\right]$
Visking dialysis tubing	Urea	0.66	0.065	8.30
	Glucose	1.89	0.23	8.52
	Sucrose	3.25	0.65	8.55
Dupont "wet Gel"	Urea	0.28	0.0046	1.68
	Glucose	0.78	0.030	1.71
	Sucrose	1.12	0.066	1.72

[a] B. Z. Ginzburg and A. Katchalsky, *J. Gen. Physiol.* *47* (1963), 403.
[b] Solute concentrations; urea 0.5 M, glucose 0.050 M, sucrose 0.025 M.

a steady state. This phenomena was observed some 130 years ago by Dutrochet and called negative anomalous osmosis. It is usually observed in electrolyte solutions with charged membranes whose behavior may be described by a reflection coefficient similar to tha given in Eq. (10-56) but for which it is easier to increase ω by raising the electrolyte concentration. This problem has been discussed in detail by Kedem and Katchalsky[12] and by Schlögl.[14]

It may be instructive to consider briefly some experimentally determined values of the frictional coefficients discussed in this section. Ginzburg and Katchalsky[9] have used measurements of ω, σ, and L_p (see Table 2) to evaluate frictional coefficients from the expressions derived above. Some of their data, obtained for three different solutes, are summarized in Table 3. For these membranes, which have a high water content, the friction between solute and water is appreciably greater than that between solute and membrane. The value of f_{sm} becomes greater the larger the molecule, as might be expected, but f_{wm}, the friction between water and membrane, is virtually independent of the nature of the solute. Investigations such as this, particularly with less permeable membranes, should lead to further information concerning the nature of both synthetic and biological membranes and of the interactions between solvent, solutes, and the membrane.

CHAPTER 11

TRANSPORT PROCESSES IN CONTINUOUS SYSTEMS CONTAINING ELECTROLYTES: IONIC CONDUCTANCE AND DIFFUSION

THROUGHOUT the previous chapters we have dealt mainly with solutions containing nonelectrolytes. These analyses provide a good theoretical introduction to the treatment of systems containing ionic species and conducting electric current. Because of the importance of electrolyte solutions in biophysics, we shall devote some space to the development of the thermodynamic description of them before considering the extensions of the theory to nonequilibrium processes.

11.1. Chemical Thermodynamics of Electrolyte Solutions

11.1.1. In many instances, it is possible to describe solutions of electrolytes in the same manner as those of nonelectrolytes. This will generally be the case if there is no electric current in the system or if electrostatic potentials are not considered. Without the application of an electric current, there is no way to introduce single ion components into the system, and the only possibility of changing the composition is by addition or removal of electrically neutral components whose behavior is adequately represented by the thermodynamic equations for nonelectrolytes. Indeed, the condition of electrical neutrality is of primary importance for the description of the macroscopic behavior of electrolyte systems. This condition derives from recognition of the fact that the electrostatic energies required to bring about a macroscopic separation of charge are much larger than those customarily used in chemical or biological laboratories.

The requirement of electroneutrality, which will be used frequently in the following analysis, may be written in different equivalent forms. Thus, if the ith ionic species has a valence z_i, a mole of this ion carries $z_i\mathfrak{F}$ coulombs of charge ($\mathfrak{F}$ is the faraday, equal to 96,500 coulombs per equivalent). Electroneutrality then means that

$$\sum_{i=1}^{n} z_i \mathfrak{F} c_i = 0, \tag{11-1}$$

in which c_i is the concentration of the ith ion. In an alternative manner, we may consider an electroneutral salt, $A_{\nu_A}B_{\nu_B}$, of concentration c_s, which dissociates into ν_A ions of type A having valence z_A and ν_B ions of type B of valence z_B;

$$A_{\nu_A}B_{\nu_B} \rightleftharpoons \nu_A A^{z_A} + \nu_B B^{z_B}.$$

Then

$$c_A = \nu_A c_s \quad \text{and} \quad c_B = \nu_B c_s,$$

and Eq. (11-1) becomes

$$c_s \mathfrak{F}(z_A \nu_A + z_B \nu_B) = 0,$$

or

$$z_A \nu_A + z_B \nu_B = 0.$$

In the general case of a solution containing a salt dissociating into n ionic species,

$$\sum_{i=1}^{n} z_i \nu_i = 0. \tag{11-2}$$

In order to extend the thermodynamic formalism to deal explicitly with charged ionic species and to permit treatment of electrostatic potentials and electric current, we return to the fundamental Gibbs equation,

$$dU = TdS - dW, \tag{11-3}$$

and reconsider the work term, dW. As usual, dW includes the work of compression, PdV, and the work involved in changing the number of moles of the components, $-\sum \mu_i dn_i$. As discussed briefly in Chapter 3, if the region under consideration has an electrostatic potential ψ, a change in charge de will result in the performance of electrostatic work given by $-\psi de$. Thus, Eq. (11-3) may be written in explicit form as

$$dU = TdS - PdV + \sum_{i=1}^{n} \mu_i dn_i + \psi de. \tag{11-4}$$

Assuming that the change in charge in the system is due to changes in the number of moles of ionic species

$$de = \sum_{i=1}^{n} z_i \mathfrak{F} dn_i, \tag{11-5}$$

and Eq. (11-4) becomes

$$dU = TdS - PdV + \sum_{i=1}^{n} \mu_i dn_i + \sum_{i=1}^{n} z_i \mathfrak{F} \psi dn_i$$

or

$$dU = TdS - PdV + \sum_{i=1}^{n} (\mu_i + z_i \mathfrak{F} \psi) dn_i. \tag{11-6}$$

Equation (11-6) demonstrates the important fact that the work performed in changing the number of moles of species i by dn_i is composed of two parts, a chemical term, $\mu_i dn_i$, and an electrical term, $z_i\mathfrak{F}\psi dn_i$. In reality, we cannot distinguish physically between these two terms and only the sum can be determined experimentally. This fact was recognized by Gibbs and considered carefully in recent years by Guggenheim,[1] who has defined the sum $\mu_i + z_i\mathfrak{F}\psi$ as the electrochemical potential, $\tilde{\mu}_i$, of the ith ionic constituent:

$$\tilde{\mu}_i = \mu_i + z_i\mathfrak{F}\psi. \tag{11-7}$$

Only under special conditions is it possible to treat μ_i and $z_i\mathfrak{F}\psi$ separately. Thus, if we consider two points in the same phase, we may encounter cases in which the composition is identical at points 1 and 2 but ψ_1 differs from ψ_2, since negligible differences in amount of charge suffice to produce significant potential differences. In this case,

$$\mu_{i(1)} = \mu_{i(2)}$$

and

$$\tilde{\mu}_{i(1)} - \tilde{\mu}_{i(2)} = z_i\mathfrak{F}(\psi_1 - \psi_2). \tag{11-8}$$

Making use of Eq. (11-7), Eq. (11-6) may be written

$$dU = TdS - PdV + \sum_{i=1}^{n} \tilde{\mu}_i dn_i. \tag{11-9}$$

This expression may be used for the construction of thermodynamic potentials and thermodynamic relations in the same manner as Eq. (3-3) has been used earlier. Thus, we may write, for the change in the Gibbs free energy,

$$dG = -SdT + VdP + \sum_{i=1}^{n} \tilde{\mu}_i dn_i, \tag{11-10}$$

or for the Gibbs–Duhem relation

$$SdT - VdP + \sum_{i=1}^{n} n_i d\tilde{\mu}_i = 0, \tag{11-11}$$

which under isothermal, isobaric conditions reduces to

$$\sum_{i=1}^{n} n_i d\tilde{\mu}_i = 0. \tag{11-12}$$

It is often useful to express the electrochemical potential as a sum of explicit terms as we have done for the chemical potential in previous chapters. Thus,

$$\tilde{\mu}_i = \mu_i^0(T) + \bar{V}_i P + \mu_i^c + z_i\mathfrak{F}\psi. \tag{11-13}$$

As previously discussed, μ_i^c, the concentration-dependent part of μ_i, is usually written

$$\mu_i^c = RT \ln \gamma_i c_i = RT \ln a_i,$$

or, in the case of ideal solutions,

$$\mu_i^c = RT \ln c_i. \tag{11-14}$$

Thus, in the case of an ion distributed between two phases, α and β, the condition of thermodynamic equilibrium is

$$\tilde{\mu}_i^\alpha = \tilde{\mu}_i^\beta, \tag{11-15}$$

which upon introduction of Eq. (11-13) becomes

$$\Delta\mu_i^0 + (\bar{V}_i^\alpha P^\alpha - \bar{V}_i^\beta P^\beta) + \Delta\mu_i^c + z_i \mathfrak{F} \Delta\psi = 0. \tag{11-16}$$

If α and β are aqueous phases separated by a membrane, $(\mu_i^0)^\alpha = (\mu_i^0)^\beta$ and $\bar{V}_i^\alpha = \bar{V}_i^\beta$, so that Eq. (11-16) becomes

$$\bar{V}_i \Delta P + \Delta\mu_i^c + z_i \mathfrak{F} \Delta\psi = 0. \tag{11-17}$$

In most cases of interest, $\bar{V}_i \Delta P$ may be neglected in comparison with the other terms, so that the condition of phase equilibrium across a membrane is

$$\Delta\mu_i^c = -z_i \mathfrak{F} \Delta\psi. \tag{11-18}$$

Equation (11-18) is often written in terms of activities as

$$\Delta\mu_i^c = RT \ln \frac{a_i^\alpha}{a_i^\beta} = -z_i \mathfrak{F} \Delta\psi,$$

or, in the case of ideal solutions,

$$RT \ln \frac{c_i^\alpha}{c_i^\beta} = -z_i \mathfrak{F} \Delta\psi. \tag{11-19}$$

For practical applications of Eq. (11-19), one usually converts to base 10 logarithms, to obtain

$$-\Delta\psi = \frac{2.303\, RT}{z_i \mathfrak{F}} \log \frac{c_i^\alpha}{c_i^\beta} = \frac{58}{z_i} \log \frac{c_i^\alpha}{c_i^\beta} \text{ (millivolts at 20°C).}$$

11.1.2. Let us now consider the changes in Eq. (11-9) introduced by an explicit application of the requirement of electroneutrality according to Eqs. (11-1) and (11-2). Instead of treating the general case, we shall analyze a definite example. The generalization presents no difficulties. The aqueous solution to be considered contains n_1 moles of sodium chloride and n_2 moles of calcium chloride. An increase in concentrations of both salts by amounts dn_1 and dn_2 will cause the following changes in ionic concentrations:

$$dn_{\text{Na}} = dn_1, \quad dn_{\text{Ca}} = dn_2, \quad dn_{\text{Cl}} = dn_1 + 2dn_2. \tag{11-20}$$

Introducing these expressions into Eq. (11-9), we obtain

$$dU = TdS - PdV + \tilde{\mu}_{\text{Na}}dn_{\text{Na}} + \tilde{\mu}_{\text{Ca}}dn_{\text{Ca}} + \tilde{\mu}_{\text{Cl}}dn_{\text{Cl}}$$

or

$$dU = TdS - PdV + (\tilde{\mu}_{\text{Na}} + \tilde{\mu}_{\text{Cl}})dn_1 + (\tilde{\mu}_{\text{Ca}} + 2\tilde{\mu}_{\text{Cl}})dn_2. \tag{11-21}$$

The variables in Eq. (11-21) are not changes in amounts of ions but rather changes in amounts of neutral salts, sodium chloride and calcium chloride. Moreover, the corresponding chemical potentials are the electroneutral combinations,

$$\tilde{\mu}_{\text{Na}} + \tilde{\mu}_{\text{Cl}} = \mu_{\text{Na}} + \mathfrak{F}\psi + \mu_{\text{Cl}} - \mathfrak{F}\psi = \mu_{\text{Na}} + \mu_{\text{Cl}} \tag{11-22}$$

and

$$\tilde{\mu}_{\text{Ca}} + 2\tilde{\mu}_{\text{Cl}} = \mu_{\text{Ca}} + 2\mathfrak{F}\psi + 2\mu_{\text{Cl}} - 2\mathfrak{F}\psi = \mu_{\text{Ca}} + 2\mu_{\text{Cl}}. \tag{11-23}$$

The physical significance of these combinations is readily seen by consideration of the dissociation equilibria,

$$\text{NaCl} \rightleftharpoons \text{Na}^+ + \text{Cl}^-,$$

$$\text{CaCl}_2 \rightleftharpoons \text{Ca}^{++} + 2\text{Cl}^-,$$

which are characterized thermodynamically by the equations

$$\begin{aligned} \mu_{\text{NaCl}} &= \tilde{\mu}_{\text{Na}} + \tilde{\mu}_{\text{Cl}}; \\ \mu_{\text{CaCl}_2} &= \tilde{\mu}_{\text{Ca}} + 2\tilde{\mu}_{\text{Cl}}. \end{aligned} \tag{11-24}$$

Equation (11-21) may, therefore, be written in terms of electrically neutral species:

$$dU = TdS - PdV + \mu_{\text{NaCl}}dn_1 + \mu_{\text{CaCl}_2}dn_2. \tag{11-25}$$

The definition of the chemical potential of the neutral salts is nontrivial since, by writing Eqs. (11-22) and (11-24) in an explicit form according to Eq. (11-13), we obtain the following interesting result for NaCl:

$$\begin{aligned} \mu_{\text{NaCl}} &= \mu_{\text{Na}} + \mu_{\text{Cl}} = \overset{0}{\mu}_{\text{Na}} + \overset{0}{\mu}_{\text{Cl}} + (\bar{V}_{\text{Na}} + \bar{V}_{\text{Cl}})P \\ &\qquad + RT \ln a_{\text{Na}} + RT \ln a_{\text{Cl}}, \\ \mu_{\text{NaCl}} &= \overset{0}{\mu}_{\text{NaCl}} + \bar{V}_{\text{NaCl}}P + RT \ln a_{\text{Na}}a_{\text{Cl}}; \end{aligned} \tag{11-26}$$

or, in the case of ideal solutions,

$$\mu_{\text{NaCl}} = \overset{0}{\mu}_{\text{NaCl}} + \bar{V}_{\text{NaCl}}P + RT \ln c_{\text{Na}}c_{\text{Cl}}. \tag{11-27}$$

Similarly, for $CaCl_2$,

$$\mu_{CaCl_2} = \overset{0}{\mu}_{Ca} + 2\overset{0}{\mu}_{Cl} + (\bar{V}_{Ca} + 2\bar{V}_{Cl})P + RT \ln a_{Ca} + 2RT \ln a_{Cl}, \tag{11-28}$$

$$\mu_{CaCl_2} = \overset{0}{\mu}_{CaCl_2} + \bar{V}_{CaCl_2}P + RT \ln a_{Ca}a_{Cl}^2,$$

and in the ideal case,

$$\mu_{CaCl_2} = \overset{0}{\mu}_{CaCl_2} + \bar{V}_{CaCl_2}P + RT \ln c_{Ca}c_{Cl}^2. \tag{11-29}$$

11.1.3. The importance of these results may be illustrated by investigation of phase equilibria of the salts across a membrane separating two solutions, α and β. The thermodynamic conditions for equilibrium of permeable components are, again,

$$\overset{\alpha}{\mu}_{NaCl} = \overset{\beta}{\mu}_{NaCl}, \quad \overset{\alpha}{\mu}_{CaCl_2} = \overset{\beta}{\mu}_{CaCl_2}. \tag{11-30}$$

Let us assume that on one side of the membrane barrier there is, in an aqueous solution of $CaCl_2$, a chloride salt of a macromolecule to which the membrane is impermeable, and on the other side a solution of $CaCl_2$ alone. The concentration of the macromolecule is c_m and the number of charged groups per molecule is ν, so that the concentration of chloride counter ions is νc_m. Further, let the concentration of $CaCl_2$ in the phase containing the macromolecule be c_s^α and the concentration in the other phase be c_s^β. On the basis of Eqs. (11-29) and (11-30), we may write for the equilibrium case,

$$\begin{aligned}\overset{\alpha}{\mu}_{CaCl_2} &= \overset{0}{\mu}_{CaCl_2} + \bar{V}_{CaCl_2}P^\alpha + RT \ln c_{Ca}^\alpha(c_{Cl}^\alpha)^2 \\ &= \overset{0}{\mu}_{CaCl_2} + \bar{V}_{CaCl_2}P^\beta + RT \ln c_{Ca}^\beta(c_{Cl}^\beta)^2 = \overset{\beta}{\mu}_{CaCl_2}.\end{aligned}$$

Generally, the pressure term may be neglected, so that the expression reduces to

$$c_{Ca}^\alpha(c_{Cl}^\alpha)^2 = c_{Ca}^\beta(c_{Cl}^\beta)^2.$$

Now

$$c_{Ca}^\alpha = c_s^\alpha \quad \text{and} \quad c_{Cl}^\alpha = \nu c_m + 2c_s^\alpha,$$

while

$$c_{Ca}^\beta = c_s^\beta \quad \text{and} \quad c_{Cl}^\beta = 2c_s^\beta,$$

and hence,

$$c_s^\alpha(\nu c_m + 2c_s^\alpha)^2 = c_s^\beta(2c_s^\beta)^2 = 4(c_s^\beta)^3.$$

This equation defines a typical example of the well-known Donnan equilibrium of salt across a membrane in the presence of a polyelectrolyte to which the membrane is impermeable. It demonstrates the characteristic properties of chemical potentials of neutral salts and indicates the mode of their utilization. We are now in a position to proceed with the next step in our investigation, development of the thermodynamic formalism for the description of irreversible processes in systems containing ionic species.

11.2. Irreversible Processes in Electrolyte Solutions

11.2.1. The local dissipation function for systems containing charged components has been derived in Chapter 7. It takes the general form

$$\Phi = \mathbf{J}_S \cdot \text{grad}\,(-T) + \sum_{i=1}^{n} \mathbf{J}_i \cdot \text{grad}\,(-\tilde{\mu}_i) + J_{\text{ch}}\tilde{A}. \tag{11-33}$$

The summation includes the flows and forces for nonelectrolytes as well as those for each ionic species, but for the nonelectrolytes the electrochemical and chemical potentials are identical. Moreover, the electrochemical affinity $\tilde{A}$ is readily shown to be equal to the chemical affinity A, since

$$\tilde{A} = -\sum \nu_i \tilde{\mu}_i = -\sum \nu_i(\mu_i + z_i \mathfrak{F}\psi) = -\sum \nu_i \mu_i - \mathfrak{F}\psi \sum \nu_i z_i.$$

However, since charge is conserved in the reaction, $\sum \nu_i z_i = 0$, so that

$$\tilde{A} = -\sum \nu_i \mu_i = A.$$

For the present, we are interested in an isothermal system in which the diffusing components do not undergo chemical reaction, so that Eq. (11-33) reduces to the simpler form

$$\Phi = \sum_{i=1}^{n} \mathbf{J}_i \cdot \text{grad}\,(-\tilde{\mu}_i). \tag{11-34}$$

Since the gradients of electrochemical potential also obey the Gibbs-Duhem equation,

$$\sum_{i=1}^{n} c_i \,\text{grad}\, \tilde{\mu}_i = 0, \tag{11-35}$$

there are, again, only $n - 1$ independent forces grad $(-\tilde{\mu}_i)$ in an n-component system. As discussed in Chapter 9, it is most convenient to make use of Eq. (11-35) to eliminate the force on the solvent from Eq. (11-34) yielding

$$\Phi = \sum_{i=1}^{n-1} \left(\mathbf{J}_i - \frac{c_i}{c_w}\mathbf{J}_w\right) \cdot \text{grad}\,(-\tilde{\mu}_i) = \sum_{i=1}^{n-1} \mathbf{J}_i^d \cdot \text{grad}\,(-\tilde{\mu}_i), \tag{11-36}$$

in which the $\mathbf{J}_i^d$ are, once again, the flows of solutes relative to that of the solvent. However, in the present case, at least some of the flows may be those of charged substances.

For the remainder of this chapter, we shall consider only solutions of a single electrolyte dissociating into two ions, so that Eq. (11-36) becomes

$$\Phi = \mathbf{J}_1^d \cdot \text{grad}\,(-\tilde{\mu}_1) + \mathbf{J}_2^d \cdot \text{grad}\,(-\tilde{\mu}_2), \tag{11-37}$$

in which

$$\mathbf{J}_1^d = \mathbf{J}_1 - \frac{c_1}{c_w}\mathbf{J}_w \quad \text{and} \quad \mathbf{J}_2^d = \mathbf{J}_2 - \frac{c_2}{c_w}\mathbf{J}_w \tag{11-38}$$

are the diffusional flows of cation and anion respectively. The phenomenological equations relating the flows and forces defined by Eq. (11-37) are

$$\begin{aligned} \mathbf{J}_1^d &= -L_{11}\,\text{grad}\,\tilde{\mu}_1 - L_{12}\,\text{grad}\,\tilde{\mu}_2, \\ \mathbf{J}_2^d &= -L_{21}\,\text{grad}\,\tilde{\mu}_1 - L_{22}\,\text{grad}\,\tilde{\mu}_2. \end{aligned} \tag{11-39}$$

The data reviewed by Miller[2] show that the Onsager reciprocal relation holds very well for transport processes in electrolyte solutions, and we may assume that

$$L_{12} = L_{21}$$

is valid within a deviation of a few percent.

11.2.2. The physical meaning of Eqs. (11-39) can be clarified by making one of the forces vanish. This represents a purely hypothetical experiment which cannot actually be carried out but is of theoretical interest since it gives a deeper insight into the interactions between ionic species in flow. If grad $\tilde{\mu}_2 = 0$, $\mathbf{J}_1^d = -L_{11}$ grad $\tilde{\mu}_1$, indicating that L_{11} has the properties of a generalized mobility of the cation, since it is the proportionality coefficient relating the flow to its conjugate force. In this case, $\mathbf{J}_2^d$ is not zero but is given by $\mathbf{J}_2^d = -L_{12}$ grad $\tilde{\mu}_1$, indicating that the movement of the cations causes a drag effect on the anions and that the interaction between the ions is determined by the coefficient L_{12}. From a thermodynamic point of view, the classical work of Debye and his colleagues[3] and, in particular, the work of Onsager and Fouss[4] is devoted to the kinetic interpretation of L_{12} in terms of electrophoretic and relaxation effects. The discussion of the kinetic theory of transport phenomena is outside the realm of this book, but we shall show how the combination of experimental results permits evaluation of the coefficients L_{11}, L_{12}, and L_{22} which serve as a starting point for a deeper insight into the properties of electrolyte solutions.

As a first step in this analysis, Eqs. (11-39) may be adapted to the special case of an electrical-conductance measurement. This determination is usually carried out under isothermal, isobaric conditions with uniform concentration throughout the cell, so that

$$\text{grad}\,\mu_i = 0 \tag{11-40}$$

for all components. The electric current $\mathbf{I}$ in the cell is driven by a potential difference between two nonpolarizable electrodes, and the local field intensity,

$$\boldsymbol{\mathcal{E}} = -\text{grad } \psi, \tag{11-41}$$

is readily evaluated from the geometry of the electrode system. With Eqs. (11-40) and (11-41), we find that the forces acting on a z_1-valent cation and a z_2-valent anion reduce to

$$\begin{aligned} \text{grad } \tilde{\mu}_1 &= \text{grad } \mu_1 + z_1\mathfrak{F} \text{ grad } \psi = -z_1\mathfrak{F}\boldsymbol{\mathcal{E}}, \\ \text{grad } \tilde{\mu}_2 &= \text{grad } \mu_2 + z_2\mathfrak{F} \text{ grad } \psi = -z_2\mathfrak{F}\boldsymbol{\mathcal{E}}, \end{aligned} \tag{11-42}$$

so that Eqs. (11-39) become

$$\begin{aligned} \mathbf{J}_1^d &= (z_1L_{11} + z_2L_{12})\mathfrak{F}\boldsymbol{\mathcal{E}}, \\ \mathbf{J}_2^d &= (z_1L_{12} + z_2L_{22})\mathfrak{F}\boldsymbol{\mathcal{E}}. \end{aligned} \tag{11-43}$$

In the case of a monomonovalent salt such as NaCl or KCl, for which $z_1 = -z_2 = 1$, we have

$$\begin{aligned} \mathbf{J}_1^d &= (L_{11} - L_{12})\mathfrak{F}\boldsymbol{\mathcal{E}}, \\ \mathbf{J}_2^d &= (L_{12} - L_{22})\mathfrak{F}\boldsymbol{\mathcal{E}}. \end{aligned} \tag{11-44}$$

The electric current due to the transport of all ionic species is given by the sum over all the charges carried by the ionic flows,

$$\mathbf{I} = \sum_{i=1}^{n-1} z_i\mathfrak{F}\mathbf{J}_i^d,$$

or, in the case of a single electrolyte,

$$\mathbf{I} = z_1\mathfrak{F}\mathbf{J}_1^d + z_2\mathfrak{F}\mathbf{J}_2^d = (z_1^2L_{11} + 2z_1z_2L_{12} + z_2^2L_{22})\mathfrak{F}^2\boldsymbol{\mathcal{E}}. \tag{11-45}$$

It is worth noting that, owing to the condition of electroneutrality, it is immaterial whether absolute or diffusional flows are used in Eq. (11-45). The diffusional flows may be written

$$\mathbf{J}_1^d = c_1(\mathbf{v}_1 - \mathbf{v}_w) \quad \text{and} \quad \mathbf{J}_2^d = c_2(\mathbf{v}_2 - \mathbf{v}_w).$$

Further, as previously discussed, $c_1 = \nu_1c_s$ and $c_2 = \nu_2c_s$, so that

$$\mathbf{J}_1^d = \nu_1c_s(\mathbf{v}_1 - \mathbf{v}_w) \quad \text{and} \quad \mathbf{J}_2^d = \nu_2c_s(\mathbf{v}_2 - \mathbf{v}_w).$$

Hence, Eq. (11-45) may be written

$$\mathbf{I} = z_1\mathfrak{F}\nu_1c_s(\mathbf{v}_1 - \mathbf{v}_w) + z_2\mathfrak{F}\nu_2c_s(\mathbf{v}_2 - \mathbf{v}_w),$$

or

$$\mathbf{I} = z_1\mathfrak{F}\nu_1c_s\mathbf{v}_1 + z_2\mathfrak{F}\nu_2c_s\mathbf{v}_2 - \mathbf{v}_w\mathfrak{F}c_s(\nu_1z_1 + \nu_2z_2).$$

However, $\nu_1 z_1 + \nu_2 z_2 = 0$ by the condition of electroneutrality so that

$$\mathbf{I} = z_1 \mathfrak{F} \mathbf{J}_1 + z_2 \mathfrak{F} \mathbf{J}_2,$$

in which the absolute flows $\mathbf{J}_1$ and $\mathbf{J}_2$ are given by

$$\mathbf{J}_1 = c_1 \mathbf{v}_1 = \nu_1 c_s \mathbf{v}_1 \quad \text{and} \quad \mathbf{J}_2 = c_2 \mathbf{v}_2 = \nu_2 c_s \mathbf{v}_2.$$

It is well known that Ohm's law holds for homogeneous, isothermal salt solutions, so that the relation between the current and the electric field intensity may also be written

$$I = \kappa \mathbf{\mathcal{E}}, \tag{11-46}$$

in which κ is the electrical conductance of the solution. Comparison of Eqs. (11-45) and (11-46) indicates that

$$\kappa = (z_1^2 L_{11} + 2 z_1 z_2 L_{12} + z_2^2 L_{22}) \mathfrak{F}^2. \tag{11-47}$$

Thus, the determination of conductance gives one relation for the Onsager coefficients.

Another expression of this relation is obtained by measuring the fraction of the total current that is carried by each ion, also under conditions in which all grad $\mu_i = 0$. This fraction is called the Hittorf transference number t_i, and is defined by the expression

$$t_i = \left(\frac{z_i \mathfrak{F} \mathbf{J}_i^d}{\mathbf{I}} \right)_{\text{grad } \mu_i = 0}. \tag{11-48}$$

For the present case of a single electrolyte, t_1 and t_2 may be evaluated by introducing Eqs. (11-43) and (11-45) in Eq. (11-48), to yield

$$t_1 = \frac{z_1 \mathfrak{F} \mathbf{J}_1^d}{\mathbf{I}} = \frac{z_1 (z_1 L_{11} + z_2 L_{12})}{z_1^2 L_{11} + 2 z_1 z_2 L_{12} + z_2^2 L_{22}} \tag{11-49}$$

and

$$t_2 = \frac{z_2 \mathfrak{F} \mathbf{J}_2^d}{\mathbf{I}} = \frac{z_2 (z_1 L_{12} + z_2 L_{22})}{z_1^2 L_{11} + 2 z_1 z_2 L_{12} + z_2^2 L_{22}}.$$

It is apparent that the two transference numbers are not independent, since

$$t_1 + t_2 = 1.$$

An additional expression is therefore required for evaluation of the three coefficients L_{ij}.

This third relation may be obtained from a consideration of the diffusion of the electrolyte. In this case, there is no electric current in the system and the total transport of charge must vanish, so that

$$z_1 \mathbf{J}_1^d + z_2 \mathbf{J}_2^d = \mathbf{I}/\mathfrak{F} = 0. \tag{11-50}$$

Introducing the values of $\mathbf{J}_1^d$ and $\mathbf{J}_2^d$ from Eqs. (11-39), we obtain a relation between the forces acting on the two ions,

$$-z_1(L_{11} \text{ grad } \tilde{\mu}_1 + L_{12} \text{ grad } \tilde{\mu}_2) - z_2(L_{12} \text{ grad } \tilde{\mu}_1 + L_{22} \text{ grad } \tilde{\mu}_2) = 0$$

or

$$\text{grad } \tilde{\mu}_1 = -\frac{z_1 L_{12} + z_2 L_{22}}{z_1 L_{11} + z_2 L_{12}} \text{ grad } \tilde{\mu}_2. \tag{11-51}$$

We know, however, from the general form of Eqs. (11-24) that

$$\nu_1 \text{ grad } \tilde{\mu}_1 + \nu_2 \text{ grad } \tilde{\mu}_2 = \text{grad } \mu_s, \tag{11-52}$$

where μ_s is the chemical potential of the salt. Equations (11-51) and (11-52) can be utilized to obtain expressions for grad $\tilde{\mu}_1$ and grad $\tilde{\mu}_2$ in terms of grad μ_s. Thus, using $\nu_1 z_1 + \nu_2 z_2 = 0$, we obtain

$$\begin{aligned} \text{grad } \tilde{\mu}_1 &= \frac{z_2}{\nu_1}\left(\frac{z_1 L_{12} + z_2 L_{22}}{z_1^2 L_{11} + 2z_1 z_2 L_{12} + z_2^2 L_{22}}\right) \text{grad } \mu_s, \\ \text{grad } \tilde{\mu}_2 &= \frac{z_1}{\nu_2}\left(\frac{z_1 L_{11} + z_2 L_{12}}{z_1^2 L_{11} + 2z_1 z_2 L_{12} + z_2^2 L_{22}}\right) \text{grad } \mu_s. \end{aligned} \tag{11-53}$$

Introducing Eqs. (11-53) into Eqs. (11-39) and rearranging yields

$$\mathbf{J}_1^d = \frac{z_1 z_2}{\nu_2}\left(\frac{L_{11}L_{22} - L_{12}^2}{z_1^2 L_{11} + 2z_1 z_2 L_{12} + z_2^2 L_{22}}\right) \text{grad } \mu_s,$$

$$\mathbf{J}_2^d = \frac{z_1 z_2}{\nu_1}\left(\frac{L_{11}L_{22} - L_{12}^2}{z_1^2 L_{11} + 2z_1 z_2 L_{12} + z_2^2 L_{22}}\right) \text{grad } \mu_s.$$

The flow $\mathbf{J}_s^d$ of the neutral salt is given by

$$\mathbf{J}_s^d = \frac{\mathbf{J}_1^d}{\nu_1} = \frac{\mathbf{J}_2^d}{\nu_2} = \frac{z_1 z_2}{\nu_1 \nu_2}\left(\frac{L_{11}L_{22} - L_{12}^2}{z_1^2 L_{11} + 2z_1 z_2 L_{12} + z_2^2 L_{22}}\right) \text{grad } \mu_s. \tag{11-54}$$

Following the discussion of Chapter 9, the diffusional flow of the neutral salt in binary solution may also be written

$$\mathbf{J}_s^d = -D \text{ grad } c_s. \tag{11-55}$$

Introducing the relation grad $\mu_s = \mu_{ss}$ grad c_s into Eq. (11-54) and comparing the resulting expression for $\mathbf{J}_s^d$ with Eq. (11-55), we find that the diffusion coefficient may be expressed in terms of the L_{ij} as

$$D = \frac{-z_1 z_2 (L_{11}L_{22} - L_{12}^2)\mu_{ss}}{\nu_1 \nu_2 (z_1^2 L_{11} + 2z_1 z_2 L_{12} + z_2^2 L_{22})}. \tag{11-56}$$

The equations for electrical conductance, the transference number, and the diffusion coefficient provide the required three relations from which the values of L_{11}, L_{12}, and L_{22} can be determined. Solving Eqs. (11-47), (11-49), and (11-56) simultaneously for these coefficients yields

$$L_{11} = \frac{\nu_1^2 D}{\mu_{ss}} + \kappa\left(\frac{t_1}{z_1\mathfrak{F}}\right)^2,$$

$$L_{22} = \frac{\nu_2^2 D}{\mu_{ss}} + \kappa\left(\frac{t_2}{z_2\mathfrak{F}}\right)^2,$$

$$L_{12} = \frac{\nu_1\nu_2 D}{\mu_{ss}} + \frac{\kappa t_1 t_2}{z_1 z_2 \mathfrak{F}^2},$$

or for a monomonovalent salt,

$$L_{11} = \frac{D}{\mu_{ss}} + \frac{\kappa t_1^2}{\mathfrak{F}^2},$$

$$L_{22} = \frac{D}{\mu_{ss}} + \frac{\kappa t_2^2}{\mathfrak{F}^2}, \tag{11-57}$$

$$L_{12} = \frac{D}{\mu_{ss}} - \frac{\kappa t_1 t_2}{\mathfrak{F}^2}.$$

The use of Eqs. (11-57) may be demonstrated by calculating the coefficients at several concentrations of NaCl, making use of the known values of D, t, κ, and μ_{ss}. The results of this analysis are summarized in Table 4. We see, in accord with our previous considerations, that the straight coefficients, L_{11} and L_{22}, are nearly linear functions of concentration, while L_{12} is more markedly concentration dependent and becomes quite small at high dilutions, where the interactions between the ions are minimal.

11.2.3. For a closer inspection of the trends of L_{11}, L_{12}, and L_{22}, it is advantageous to pass from the formal thermodynamic description to

Table 4. Phenomenological coefficients for NaCl solutions.[a]

Coefficient $\left[10^{-21}\dfrac{\text{mole}^2}{\text{dyne sec cm}^2}\right]$	Concentration (M)						
	0.01	0.02	0.05	0.10	0.20	0.50	1.00
L_{11}	5.2	10.4	25.4	49.8	97.3	232.9	440.2
L_{22}	8.0	15.8	38.9	76.2	148.9	356.0	669.3
L_{12}	0.2	0.6	2.3	5.5	13.6	42.4	93.1

[a] The data for D, t_1, κ, and μ_{ss} used in calculating L_{ij} were obtained from R. A. Robinson and R. H. Stokes, *Electrolyte Solutions* (Academic Press, New York, 1959) and from H. S. Harned and B. B. Owen, *The Physical Chemistry of Electrolytic Solutions* (Reinhold, New York, 1958).

mobilities which convey ideas on the behavior of ions in solution similar to those gained by consideration of frictional coefficients in the case of membrane permeability. The mobility may be defined by making use of the explicit expressions for flows under conditions of uniform chemical potential,

$$\mathbf{J}_1^d = c_1(\mathbf{v}_1 - \mathbf{v}_w) = \nu_1 c_s \omega_1 z_1 \mathfrak{F} \mathcal{E}, \tag{11-58}$$

in which $\nu_1 c_s = c_1$ is the concentration of ion 1 and ω_1 is the ionic mobility. Similarly,

$$\mathbf{J}_2^d = \nu_2 c_s \omega_2 z_2 \mathfrak{F} \mathcal{E}. \tag{11-59}$$

Inspection of Eq. (11-58) indicates that ω_1 is the relative velocity of the ion per unit electrical force, the velocity acquired as a result of the operation of a force of 1 dyne. However, in practice, we are usually not concerned with these absolute mobilities ω_i, but with the practical mobilities, defined as the velocity of the ions acquired in a field of $\mathcal{E} = 1$ volt/cm. Thus, the practical mobilities u_1 and u_2 of the cation and anion respectively are

$$u_1 = z_1 \omega_1 \mathfrak{F} \quad \text{and} \quad -u_2 = z_2 \omega_2 \mathfrak{F}, \tag{11-60}$$

where we have taken account of the fact that, in a given field, the direction of motion of the anion is opposite to that of the cation. With Eq. (11-60), Eqs. (11-58) and (11-59) may be written

$$\begin{aligned} \mathbf{J}_1^d &= \nu_1 c_s u_1 \mathcal{E}, \\ \mathbf{J}_2^d &= -\nu_2 c_s u_2 \mathcal{E}, \end{aligned} \tag{11-61}$$

and the total electric current becomes

$$\mathbf{I} = z_1 \mathfrak{F} \mathbf{J}_1^d + z_2 \mathfrak{F} \mathbf{J}_2^d = \nu_1 z_1 c_s \mathfrak{F}(u_1 + u_2)\mathcal{E}, \tag{11-62}$$

in which the condition of electroneutrality, $\nu_1 z_1 + \nu_2 z_2 = 0$, has been used. Thus, in terms of mobilities, the electrical conductance is given by

$$\kappa = \nu_1 z_1 c_s \mathfrak{F}(u_1 + u_2). \tag{11-63}$$

It is often convenient to consider, instead of κ, the equivalent conductance λ_{eq}, defined as

$$\lambda_{\text{eq}} = \frac{\kappa}{\nu_1 z_1 c_s} = \mathfrak{F}(u_1 + u_2). \tag{11-64}$$

Similarly, conductances of single ions can be defined by the expressions

$$\begin{aligned} \lambda_1 &= \mathfrak{F} u_1, \\ \lambda_2 &= \mathfrak{F} u_2, \end{aligned} \tag{11-65}$$

so that

$$\lambda_{eq} = \lambda_1 + \lambda_2,$$

which is the well-known expression of Kohlrausch.

Let us now return to the thermodynamic treatment of conductance and modify the expressions by introducing the mobilities defined by Eq. (11-61) into Eq. (11-43) to yield, for the cation,

$$\mathbf{J}_1^d = \nu_1 c_s u_1 \mathcal{E} = (z_1 L_{11} + z_2 L_{22}) \mathfrak{F} \mathcal{E}.$$

Therefore,

$$u_1 = \frac{(z_1 L_{11} + z_2 L_{12})\mathfrak{F}}{\nu_1 c_s} = \frac{z_1^2 L_{11} \mathfrak{F}}{\nu_1 z_1 c_s} + \frac{z_1 z_2 L_{12} \mathfrak{F}}{\nu_1 z_1 c_s}.$$

We now call

$$u_{11} = \frac{z_1^2 L_{11} \mathfrak{F}}{\nu_1 z_1 c_s}$$

the reduced phenomenological mobility of ion 1 and take the negative term

$$-u_{12} = \frac{z_1 z_2 L_{12} \mathfrak{F}}{\nu_1 z_1 c_s}$$

as a measure of the interaction of ions 1 and 2, so that

$$u_1 = u_{11} - u_{12}. \tag{11-66}$$

In an equivalent manner,

$$\mathbf{J}_2^d = -\nu_2 c_s u_2 \mathcal{E} = (z_1 L_{12} + z_2 L_{22}) \mathfrak{F} \mathcal{E},$$

so that

$$u_2 = u_{22} - u_{12}, \tag{11-67}$$

in which $u_{22} = z_2^2 L_{22} \mathfrak{F} / \nu_1 z_1 c_s$. The condition $\nu_1 z_1 + \nu_2 z_2 = 0$ has been used.

Introduction of Eqs. (11-66) and (11-67) into Eq. (11-63) gives, for the conductance,

$$\kappa = \nu_1 z_1 c_s \mathfrak{F}(u_{11} - 2u_{12} + u_{22}) = \mathfrak{F}^2 (z_1^2 L_{11} + 2 z_1 z_2 L_{12} + z_2^2 L_{22}). \tag{11-68}$$

The equivalent conductances become

$$\begin{aligned} \lambda_{eq} &= \mathfrak{F}(u_{11} - 2u_{12} + u_{22}), \\ \lambda_1 &= \mathfrak{F}(u_{11} - u_{12}), \\ \lambda_2 &= \mathfrak{F}(u_{22} - u_{12}). \end{aligned} \tag{11-69}$$

The transference numbers can be obtained immediately by making use of Eqs. (11-61), (11-62), (11-66), and (11-67):

$$t_1 = \frac{u_{11} - u_{12}}{u_{11} - 2u_{12} + u_{22}},$$
$$t_2 = \frac{u_{22} - u_{12}}{u_{11} - 2u_{12} + u_{22}}. \tag{11-70}$$

Finally, the diffusion coefficient of the salt can be expressed in terms of the mobilities from Eq. (11-56) together with the definitions of u_{11}, u_{12}, and u_{22} as well as Eq. (11-68). The resulting expression is

$$D = \frac{(u_{11}u_{22} - u_{12}^2)\mu_{ss}c_s}{\mathfrak{F}(u_{11} - 2u_{12} + u_{22})\nu_1 z_1} = \frac{c_s\mu_{ss}}{\nu_1 z_1}\left(\frac{u_{11}u_{22} - u_{12}^2}{\lambda_{\text{eq}}}\right). \tag{11-71}$$

For the ideal case in which no thermodynamic interactions exist and the pressure term may be neglected, the chemical potential of the salt is given by

$$\mu_s = \mu_s^0 + \nu_1 RT \ln \nu_1 c_s + \nu_2 RT \ln \nu_2 c_s,$$

and

$$\mu_{ss} = \frac{\partial \mu_s}{\partial c_s} = \frac{\nu_1 RT}{c_s} + \frac{\nu_2 RT}{c_s},$$

so that

$$\frac{c_s\mu_{ss}}{\nu_1 z_1} = RT\left(\frac{1}{z_1} - \frac{1}{z_2}\right).$$

If we further assume that $u_{12} = 0$, Eq. (11-71) then reduces to the classical expression of Nernst for the diffusion coefficient:

$$D = \frac{RT(z_2 - z_1)}{\mathfrak{F}z_1 z_2}\frac{u_{11}u_{22}}{u_{11} + u_{22}}.$$

For a monomonovalent salt, $z_1 = -z_2 = 1$, so that

$$\frac{c_s\mu_{ss}}{\nu_1 z_1} = 2RT,$$

and

$$D = \frac{2RTu_{11}u_{22}}{(u_{11} + u_{22})\mathfrak{F}}.$$

It is plausible to assume that u_{11} and u_{22}, which represent the reduced phenomenological mobilities of the ions, would remain approximately constant over a relatively wide range of concentrations, while u_{12}, which brings to light the interaction of the ion atmosphere with the central ion, will change appreciably. In order to evaluate these mobility factors,

Table 5. Ionic mobilities for NaCl solutions.

Mobility $\left[10^{-4}\frac{\text{cm}^2}{\text{sec volt}}\right]$	Concentration (M)						
	0.01	0.02	0.05	0.10	0.20	0.50	1.00
u_{11}	5.06	5.06	4.93	4.84	4.72	4.50	4.25
u_{22}	7.75	7.65	7.55	7.35	7.19	6.91	6.46
u_{12}	0.23	0.29	0.44	0.53	0.66	0.82	0.90

we make use of Eqs. (11-69) and (11-71) and obtain by straightforward calculation

$$\begin{aligned} u_{11} &= \mathfrak{F}\frac{\nu_1 z_1 D}{c_s\mu_{ss}} + \frac{\lambda_1^2}{\lambda_{\text{eq}}\mathfrak{F}}, \\ u_{22} &= \mathfrak{F}\frac{\nu_1 z_1 D}{c_s\mu_{ss}} + \frac{\lambda_2^2}{\lambda_{\text{eq}}\mathfrak{F}}, \\ u_{12} &= \mathfrak{F}\frac{\nu_1 z_1 D}{c_s\mu_{ss}} - \frac{\lambda_1\lambda_2}{\lambda_{\text{eq}}\mathfrak{F}}. \end{aligned} \tag{11-72}$$

The expressions can be used to calculate u_{11}, u_{12}, and u_{22} from known values of the other parameters. The results of such a calculation for NaCl are summarized in Table 5. These considerations complete our analysis of the behavior of continuous systems of electrolyte solutions. We shall now pass to an examination of the penetration of electrolytes through membranes, making use of many of the concepts developed in this chapter.

CHAPTER 12

ELECTROCHEMICAL PROCESSES IN DISCONTINUOUS SYSTEMS

12.1. The Dissipation Function

12.1.1. Having developed the fundamental concepts of electrochemistry and considered their use in the study of ionic transport in isothermal continuous systems, we shall turn our attention to electrochemical processes in discontinuous systems. The case under consideration will again involve solutions of a single salt dissociating into ν_1 z_1-valent cations and ν_2 z_2-valent anions. Solutions of different concentrations will be maintained in two compartments separated by a charged membrane. In a certain sense, the membrane may also be considered as a transition layer of aqueous solution with variable concentration, merging on one side with the solution of the left-hand compartment and on the other side with that of the right-hand compartment. Generally speaking, there is no requirement of equality of pressure throughout the system, so that a pressure difference ΔP may be imposed across the membrane and volume flow may take place from one side to the other. Ionic flows may proceed by diffusion and may be incorporated in a net electric flow driven by an electromotive force established between electrodes inserted on both sides of the membrane or liquid junction.

The simplest manner of creating a reproducible and well-defined system is by using electrodes that undergo a reversible reaction with one of the ions in solution. Thus the well-investigated silver–silver chloride electrode reacts reversibly with chloride ion according to the scheme

$$\mathrm{Ag} + \mathrm{Cl}^- \rightleftharpoons \mathrm{AgCl} + e^-, \tag{12-1}$$

where Ag denotes the metallic silver of the electrode and e^- represents the electron that is retained in the metallic phase. The equilibrium condition of the electrode reaction (12-1) can be written

$$\mu_{\mathrm{Ag}} + \tilde{\mu}_{\mathrm{Cl}^-} = \mu_{\mathrm{AgCl}} + \tilde{\mu}_{e^-}. \tag{12-2}$$

The same reaction evidently takes place at each of the electrodes situated in the two compartments, I and II, so that we may write

$$\begin{aligned} \mu^{\mathrm{I}}_{\mathrm{Ag}} + \tilde{\mu}^{\mathrm{I}}_{\mathrm{Cl}^-} &= \mu^{\mathrm{I}}_{\mathrm{AgCl}} + \tilde{\mu}^{\mathrm{I}}_{e^-}, \\ \mu^{\mathrm{II}}_{\mathrm{Ag}} + \tilde{\mu}^{\mathrm{II}}_{\mathrm{Cl}^-} &= \mu^{\mathrm{II}}_{\mathrm{AgCl}} + \tilde{\mu}^{\mathrm{II}}_{e^-}. \end{aligned} \tag{12-3}$$

Since the solid silver has the same properties in both electrodes, $\mu_{Ag}^{I} = \mu_{Ag}^{II}$. Similarly, the chemical potential of the solid and electroneutral silver chloride is the same in both compartments and $\mu_{AgCl}^{I} = \mu_{AgCl}^{II}$. Hence by subtracting Eqs. (12-3) we obtain

$$\tilde{\mu}_{e^-}^{I} - \tilde{\mu}_{e^-}^{II} = \tilde{\mu}_{Cl^-}^{I} - \tilde{\mu}_{Cl^-}^{II} = \Delta\tilde{\mu}_{Cl^-}. \tag{12-4}$$

As discussed in Chapter 11, for two points in the same phase of equal composition but differing in electrical potential,

$$\tilde{\mu}_i^{I} - \tilde{\mu}_i^{II} = z_i\mathfrak{F}(\psi_I - \psi_{II}).$$

In the present case the difference in the electrochemical potential of the electron in the metallic-silver phase complies with this requirement, so that

$$\tilde{\mu}_{e^-}^{I} - \tilde{\mu}_{e^-}^{II} = -\mathfrak{F}(\psi_I - \psi_{II}).$$

The difference in electrostatic potential between the two electrodes $(\psi_I - \psi_{II})$ is the electromotive force E of the cell. Thus,

$$\tilde{\mu}_{e^-}^{I} - \tilde{\mu}_{e^-}^{II} = -\mathfrak{F}E, \tag{12-5}$$

and hence, according to Eq. (12-4),

$$\Delta\tilde{\mu}_{Cl^-} = -\mathfrak{F}E,$$
$$E = -\frac{\Delta\tilde{\mu}_{Cl^-}}{\mathfrak{F}}. \tag{12-6}$$

In general, for any pair of electrodes interacting reversibly with a z_i-valent ion, the electromotive force is related to the difference in electrochemical potential of the ith ion by the expression

$$E = \frac{\Delta\tilde{\mu}_i}{z_i\mathfrak{F}}. \tag{12-7}$$

Since the difference $\Delta\tilde{\mu}_i$ is between ions dissolved in the same medium we may write

$$\Delta\tilde{\mu}_i = \Delta\mu_i + z_i\mathfrak{F}\Delta\psi, \tag{12-8}$$

in which $\Delta\mu_i$ is the difference in chemical potential and $\Delta\psi$ is the difference in electrical potential across the membrane separating the compartments. The term $\Delta\psi$ is usually referred to as the membrane or liquid-junction potential and is related to the electromotive force by the expression

$$\Delta\psi = E - \frac{\Delta\mu_i}{z_i\mathfrak{F}}. \tag{12-9}$$

12.1.2. Following the reasoning used in Chapter 10, we may write for the dissipation of free energy accompanying the flow of ions and water across the boundary between the compartments

$$\Phi = J_1 \Delta\tilde{\mu}_1 + J_2 \Delta\tilde{\mu}_2 + J_w \Delta\mu_w. \tag{12-10}$$

In analyzing membrane processes, it is more convenient to transform Eq. (12-10) into an expression involving the flow of neutral salt J_s and the electric current I. We shall assume that it is ion 2 that interacts reversibly with the electrodes. In this case, the flow of ion 1 may be regarded as the flow of salt, since this ion is not produced or removed at the electrodes. As pointed out in Chapter 11, the flow of salt is given by $J_s = J_i/\nu_i$, so that in the present case,

$$J_1 = \nu_1 J_s. \tag{12-11}$$

Further, according to Eq. (11-45), the electric current is given by

$$I = z_1 \mathfrak{F} J_1 + z_2 \mathfrak{F} J_2 = \nu_1 z_1 \mathfrak{F} J_s + z_2 \mathfrak{F} J_2, \tag{12-12}$$

and, according to Eq. (11-52),

$$\Delta\mu_s = \nu_1 \Delta\tilde{\mu}_1 + \nu_2 \Delta\tilde{\mu}_2,$$

or

$$\Delta\tilde{\mu}_1 = \frac{\Delta\mu_s - \nu_2 \Delta\tilde{\mu}_2}{\nu_1}. \tag{12-13}$$

Introducing Eq. (12-13) into Eq. (12-10) and also making use of Eqs. (12-7) and (12-11), we obtain

$$\Phi = J_s \Delta\mu_s + (J_2 - \nu_2 J_s) z_2 \mathfrak{F} E + J_w \Delta\mu_w.$$

With the condition of electroneutrality,

$$z_1 \nu_1 + z_2 \nu_2 = 0,$$

this expression may be rewritten as

$$\Phi = J_s \Delta\mu_s + (z_1 \nu_1 \mathfrak{F} J_s + z_2 \mathfrak{F} J_2) E + J_w \Delta\mu_w,$$

which upon introduction of Eq. (12-12) yields the desired form of the dissipation function:

$$\Phi = J_s \Delta\mu_s + IE + J_w \Delta\mu_w. \tag{12-14}$$

It is important to note again that the electric force E is the potential difference between the reversible electrodes, not the membrane or liquid junction potential.

Equation (12-14) is a generalization of Eq. (10-4) and reduces, for the case $I = 0$, to the dissipation function for a nonelectrolyte solution that was discussed in Chapter 10. Indeed, we may use the equality

$$J_s \Delta\mu_s + J_w \Delta\mu_w = J_v \Delta P + J_D \Delta\pi_s,$$

which arises as a result of the transformation utilized in Chapter 10, and express Eq. (12-14) in the form

$$\Phi = J_v \Delta P + J_D \Delta\pi_s + IE. \tag{12-15}$$

Equation (12-15) also reduces to the expression for nonelectrolytes when $E = 0$ or $I = 0$. It is particularly useful when studying the coupled transport of volume and electricity across a membrane separating solutions of equal concentration. In this case, $\Delta\pi_s = 0$, and

$$\Phi = J_v \Delta P + IE. \tag{12-16}$$

Equation (12-16) is the fundamental expression for the quantitative description of electrokinetic phenomena, which will be treated in the following section.

For certain purposes, it is advantageous to use, in addition to the salt flow J_s and the electric current I, the volume flow J_v instead of the water flow J_w. The suitable dissipation function is obtained by introducing the explicit expressions,

$$\Delta\mu_s = \bar{V}_s \Delta P + \frac{\Delta\pi_s}{\bar{c}_s},$$

$$\Delta\mu_w = \bar{V}_w(\Delta P - \Delta\pi_s),$$

into Eq. (12-14) to yield

$$\Phi = J_s\left(\bar{V}_s \Delta P + \frac{\Delta\pi_s}{c_s}\right) + J_w \bar{V}_w(\Delta P - \Delta\pi_s) + IE,$$

$$\Phi = (J_s \bar{V}_s + J_w \bar{V}_w)(\Delta P - \Delta\pi_s) + J_s \frac{\Delta\pi_s}{\bar{c}_s}(1 + \bar{c}_s \bar{V}_s) + IE,$$

$$\Phi = J_v(\Delta P - \Delta\pi_s) + J_s \frac{\Delta\pi_s}{\bar{c}_s}(1 + \varphi_s) + IE.$$

As previously pointed out, the average volume fraction of the solute in free solution, φ_s, is ordinarily much smaller than unity, so that

$$\Phi = J_v(\Delta P - \Delta\pi_s) + J_s \frac{\Delta\pi_s}{\bar{c}_s} + IE, \tag{12-17}$$

or

$$\Phi = J_v(\Delta P - \Delta\pi_s) + J_s \Delta\mu_s^c + IE,$$

since, as shown previously, the concentration-dependent part of the chemical potential of salt may be given by the relation

$$\Delta\mu_s^c = \frac{\Delta\pi_s}{\bar{c}_s}.$$

The set of phenomenological equations relating the three flows and forces defined by Eq. (12-17) is

$$J_v = L_{11}(\Delta P - \Delta\pi_s) + L_{12}E + L_{13}\frac{\Delta\pi_s}{\bar{c}_s},$$

$$I = L_{21}(\Delta P - \Delta\pi_s) + L_{22}E + L_{23}\frac{\Delta\pi_s}{\bar{c}_s},$$

$$J_s = L_{31}(\Delta P - \Delta\pi_s) + L_{32}E + L_{33}\frac{\Delta\pi_s}{\bar{c}_s}.$$

These equations contain nine phenomenological coefficients, of which, as a result of the Onsager relations, six are independent. Complete characterization of the system requires, therefore, six independent experimental measurements to determine the coefficients. Although methods are available to do this for a three-flow system, the problem becomes formidable in systems containing more components and, hence, more coefficients. Thus, even though the thermodynamic formalism is able, in principle, to describe a system of any degree of complexity, practical considerations may limit the number of components that can be treated quantitatively. The three-flow system described by the foregoing equations has been discussed by Kedem and Katchalsky[1] and the original articles should be consulted for details. Here we shall consider only special cases in which one of the flows or one of the forces vanishes.

12.2. Electrokinetic Phenomena

12.2.1. The classical equipment for the study of electrokinetic phenomena consisted of a two-compartment system separated by a plug of porous charged material, such as wet clay or a fritted-glass filter. Modern experiments could also use an ion-exchange membrane separating two salt solutions of equal concentration ($\Delta\pi_s = 0$) and subjected to various pressure differences and electromotive forces. The interest in the coupling of volume flow and electric driving force or of electric flow and hydrostatic pressure goes back to the early 19th century, and through the decades a wealth of experimental material has accumulated for many combinations of flows and forces. The first theoretical explanations of the phenomena, advanced at the end of the 19th century, were based on the theory of the electrical double layer developed by Helmholtz, Smoluchowski, Gouy, and others.[2] All classical theories treated a simplified model which still serves as a very good approximation to the behavior of loose membranes such as glass filters or clay. The advantage of this approach is that it permits a direct evaluation of the coefficients and gives a tangible picture of the processes in the membrane. However, the theories reach their limit when dealing with very dense membranes containing a low percentage of water. In later years, Saxèn observed that several relations between coupled phenomena, derived from the simple theory, also remain valid in the region in which the theory itself fails to describe the experimental data. These Saxèn relations attracted the attention of thermodynamicists, and in 1951 Mazur and Overbeek[3] proved that they may be deduced in a general way from the phenomenological equations of nonequilibrium thermodynamics.

Since so many experimental data exist concerning these phenomena, the thermodynamic analysis will be considered in some detail. The condition of uniform concentration in the solutions bathing the membrane leads to a considerable simplification since the dissipation function assumes the form given by Eq. (12-16). The system can be described in terms of the two flows and two forces appearing in this expression and we may write immediately for the dependence of flows on forces (at $\Delta\pi_s = 0$),

$$J_v = L_{11}\Delta P + L_{12}E, \tag{12-18.1}$$

$$I = L_{21}\Delta P + L_{22}E, \tag{12-18.2}$$

or, alternatively, for the dependence of forces on flows,

$$\Delta P = R_{11}J_v + R_{12}I, \tag{12-19.1}$$

$$E = R_{21}J_v + R_{22}I. \tag{12-19.2}$$

The Onsager reciprocal relations take the form

$$L_{12} = L_{21} \quad \text{or} \quad R_{12} = R_{21}.$$

A considerable amount of evidence, summarized by Miller,[4] has provided experimental confirmation of these relations for electrokinetic systems.

It is worth noting that, although Eqs. (12-18) and (12-19) are equivalent mathematically, each equation is useful under different experimental conditions. To demonstrate this point, let us consider the straight coefficient relating volume flow to the pressure difference across the membrane. In one experimental arrangement, illustrated in Fig. 22*a*, we may short-circuit the electrodes so that $E = 0$ and observe J_v as a function of ΔP. According to Eq. (12-18.1),

$$\left(\frac{J_v}{\Delta P}\right)_{E=0} = L_{11}, \tag{12-20}$$

in which L_{11} is the *filtration coefficient at zero electromotive force.* When $E = 0$, the electric current does not vanish and the flow of ions coupled to the volume flow establishes a current given by Eq. (12-18.2): $(I)_{E=0} = L_{21}\Delta P$. If we are interested in the *filtration coefficient at zero electric current,*

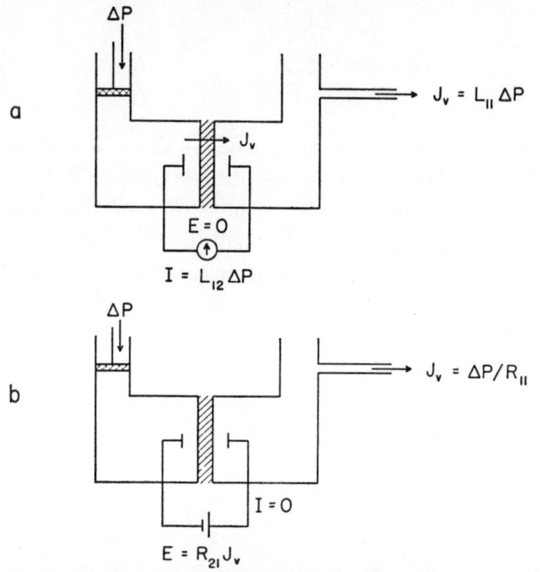

Fig. 22. Schematic arrangements for measurement of filtration coefficients of a membrane under different conditions. The electrodes are reversible to one of the ions in the solutions. A pressure is applied to one compartment and the volume change in the other compartment may be observed in the calibrated tube. Solutions of identical composition are placed in the two compartments. (*a*) The electrodes are short-circuited so that $E = 0$; (*b*) E is measured potentiometrically so that there is no current between the electrodes.

which will be denoted by L_P, a different experimental procedure, shown in Fig. 22*b*, is required. The electrodes have to be joined through a potentiometric arrangement so that $I = 0$ and J_v is measured in the presence of a pressure difference. Making use of Eq. (12-19.1) for the condition $I = 0$, we find that

$$L_P = \frac{1}{R_{11}} = \left(\frac{J_v}{\Delta P}\right)_{I=0}. \tag{12-21}$$

The relation between the coefficient L_{11} and L_P is readily found by solving Eq. (12-18.2) for E, to yield

$$E = \frac{I - L_{21}\Delta P}{L_{22}}.$$

Introducing this expression into Eq. (12-18.1) and rearranging, we obtain

$$J_v = \left(L_{11} - \frac{L_{12}L_{21}}{L_{22}}\right)\Delta P + \frac{L_{12}}{L_{22}}\,I, \tag{12-22}$$

and

$$\left(\frac{J_v}{\Delta P}\right)_{I=0} = L_P = L_{11} - \frac{L_{12}^2}{L_{22}}. \tag{12-23}$$

Thus, the filtration coefficient measured at $E = 0$ will be equal to the one measured at $I = 0$ only if no coupling exists, or if $L_{12} = 0$.

A similar behavior is observed in the study of the electrical conductance of the partition between the two solutions. Thus, we may determine the conductance in the conventional way when no volume flow takes place. As illustrated schematically in Fig. 23*a*, this measurement may be carried out by allowing the development of a pressure difference sufficient to prevent the transport of volume coupled with that of ions. The expression for the conductance κ of the membrane at $J_v = 0$ is readily evaluated from Eq. (12-19.2):

$$\kappa = \left(\frac{I}{E}\right)_{J_v=0} = \frac{1}{R_{22}}. \tag{12-24}$$

This conductance is, in general, different from the value observed at zero pressure difference when volume flow is allowed to take place (Fig. 23*b*). The conductance κ' at $\Delta P = 0$ is given by Eq. (12-18.2):

$$\kappa' = \left(\frac{I}{E}\right)_{\Delta P=0} = L_{22}, \tag{12-25}$$

and the relation between the two values of conductance is found by solving Eq. (12-18.1) for ΔP and introducing the result into Eq. (12-18.2), to yield

$$I = \left(L_{22} - \frac{L_{12}^2}{L_{11}}\right)E + \frac{L_{12}}{L_{11}} J_v. \tag{12-26}$$

From Eqs. (12-24), (12-25), and (12-26), we find that

$$\left(\frac{I}{E}\right)_{J_v=0} = \kappa = L_{22} - \frac{L_{12}^2}{L_{11}} = \kappa' - \frac{L_{12}^2}{L_{11}}. \tag{12-27}$$

Here again the two coefficients κ and κ' will be equal only if the cross coefficient L_{12} vanishes.

In order to complete this basic description of the electrokinetic phenomena, we shall define the electroosmotic permeability β as the coefficient relating the flow of volume caused by an electric current under conditions of zero pressure difference. Thus,

$$\beta = \left(\frac{J_v}{I}\right)_{\Delta P=0}. \tag{12-28}$$

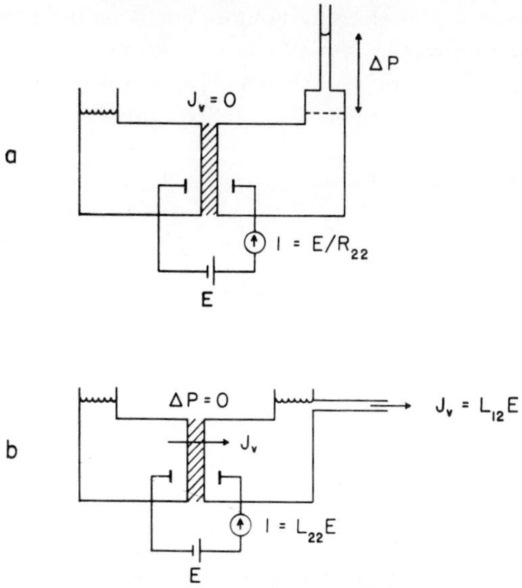

Fig. 23. Schematic arrangement for measurement of electrical conductivity of a membrane under different conditions. A known electromotive force is applied to the electrodes and the current is observed. (*a*) A pressure difference is allowed to develop so that $J_v = 0$. (*b*) There is no pressure difference and $J_v \neq 0$.

Introducing the condition $\Delta P = 0$ into Eqs. (12-18) and dividing Eq. (12-18.1) by Eq. (12-18.2), we find that

$$\beta = \frac{L_{12}}{L_{22}},$$

or, in view of Eq. (12-25),

$$\beta = \frac{L_{12}}{\kappa'}. \tag{12-29}$$

Making use of L_P from Eq. (12-23), κ from Eq. (12-24), κ' from Eq. (12-25), and β from Eq. (12-29), we can derive from Eqs. (12-18) a set of "practical equations" for the description of electrokinetic phenomena:

$$\begin{aligned} J_v &= L_P\Delta P + \beta I, \\ I &= \kappa'\beta\Delta P + \kappa' E, \end{aligned} \tag{12-30}$$

or, alternatively,

$$\begin{aligned} J_v &= L_P\Delta P + \beta I, \\ I &= \frac{\kappa\beta}{L_P} J_v + \kappa E. \end{aligned} \tag{12-31}$$

In these expressions, the thermodynamic coefficients have been replaced by conventional parameters which are well known in experimental practice. The relations between the thermodynamic coefficients L_{11}, L_{12}, and L_{22} and the practical coefficients L_P, κ', and β are

$$L_{11} = L_P + \kappa'\beta^2, \qquad L_{12} = \kappa'\beta, \qquad L_{22} = \kappa'.$$

Also

$$R_{11} = \frac{1}{L_P}, \qquad R_{12} = -\frac{\beta}{L_P}, \qquad R_{22} = \frac{1}{\kappa}.$$

12.2.2. We may now turn our attention to some of the conclusions that arise as a consequence of Onsager's law. Let us first consider the flow of volume induced by an electromotive force under conditions of uniform pressure. This electroosmotic volume flow is a typical coupling phenomenon, since it arises as a result of the nonconjugate electric force. From Eq. (12-18.1), we find that

$$\left(\frac{J_v}{E}\right)_{\Delta P=0} = L_{12}.$$

On the other hand, under conditions of short-circuited electrodes ($E = 0$), the application of a mechanical pressure results in an electric current, which is known as the streaming current. From Eq. (12-18.2),

$$\left(\frac{I}{\Delta P}\right)_{E=0} = L_{21}.$$

Thus, by applying the Onsager law, we obtain the relation

$$\left(\frac{J_v}{E}\right)_{\Delta P=0} = \left(\frac{I}{\Delta P}\right)_{E=0}. \tag{12-32}$$

The streaming current may also be expressed in a different manner by referring the current not to the pressure difference but to the associated volume flow. Introducing the condition $E = 0$ into Eqs. (12-18), we find that

$$\left(\frac{I}{J_v}\right)_{E=0} = \frac{L_{21}}{L_{11}}. \tag{12-33}$$

If an electromotive force is applied under conditions of zero volume flow, a pressure difference will develop across the barrier. The ratio of ΔP to E obtained from Eq. (12-18.1) is

$$\left(\frac{\Delta P}{E}\right)_{J_v=0} = -\frac{L_{12}}{L_{11}}. \tag{12-34}$$

Comparison of Eqs. (12-33) and (12-34) indicates that if the Onsager relation is valid

$$\left(\frac{I}{J_v}\right)_{E=0} = -\left(\frac{\Delta P}{E}\right)_{J_v=0}, \tag{12-35}$$

which is one of Saxèn's relations connecting a coupling of flows, $(I/J_v)_{E=0}$, to a coupling of forces, $(\Delta P/E)_{J_v=0}$.

The whole range of coupling possibilities, several of which have been tested and found to hold experimentally, is presented in Table 6. The coefficients in the table are obtained by dividing the symbols in the upper row by the symbols in the first column. The restrictions imposed on the values in the second and third columns are the vanishing of one of the forces, while those imposed on the fourth and fifth columns are the vanishing of one of the flows. The whole field is divided into the upper left-hand part containing the L_{ij} and the lower right-hand part containing the R_{ij}. The major diagonal from the upper left-hand corner to the lower right-hand corner comprises the straight coefficients, L_{11}, L_{22}, R_{11}, and R_{22}, and their conventional equivalents. The other coefficients represent coupling phenomena. Two coefficients equally distant from the main diagonal are equal in absolute magnitude according to Onsager's law. The reader is advised to study more carefully the numerous phenomena of classical colloid chemistry, such as streaming currents, electroosmotic flows, electroosmotic pressure, and streaming potential, which appear in the table as ordinary coefficients intimately related through the phenomenological relations of nonequilibrium thermodynamics.

12.3. Liquid-Junction Potentials

In our considerations of transport across a discontinuous junction between two phases, we have made use of two special cases derived from the more general equations (12-15) or (12-17). In Chapter 10, we dealt with transport under conditions of zero electric current when the solute was a nonelectrolyte. In the previous section, we considered transport of charged solutes under the simplified conditions of uniform concentration. Here we shall examine the third possible special case involving only two flows, a flow of solute and a flow of charge taking place under conditions of zero volume flow. The dissipation function for such a case is, according to Eq. (12-17),

$$\Phi = J_s \Delta\mu_s^c + IE = J_s \frac{\Delta\pi_s}{\bar{c}_s} + IE, \tag{12-36}$$

and the phenomenological equations are

$$I = L'_{22}E + L_{23}\frac{\Delta\pi_s}{\bar{c}_s}, \tag{12-37.1}$$

Table 6. Electrokinetic phenomena.

	J_v	I	E	ΔP
ΔP	$(J_v/\Delta P)_{E=0} = L_{11}$ Mechanical conductance	$(I/\Delta P)_{E=0} = L_{21} = \kappa'\beta$ Second streaming current	$(E/\Delta P)_{I=0} = -(L_{21}/L_{22}) = -\beta$ Streaming potential	1
E	$(J_v/E)_{\Delta P=0} = L_{12} = \kappa'\beta$ Second electroosmotic flow	$(I/E)_{\Delta P=0} = L_{22} = \kappa'$ Electrical conductance	1	$(\Delta P/E)_{J_v=0} = R_{21}/R_{22} = -\kappa\beta/L_P$ Electroosmotic pressure
I	$(J_v/I) = L_{12}/L_{22} = \beta$ Electroosmotic flow	1	$(E/I)_{J_v=0} = R_{22} = 1/\kappa$ Electric resistance	$(\Delta P/I)_{J_v=0} = R_{12} = -\beta/L_P$ Second electroosmotic pressure
J_v	1	$(I/J_v)_{E=0} = -R_{21}/R_{22} = \kappa\beta/L_P$ Streaming current	$(E/J_v)_{I=0} = R_{21} = -\beta/L_P$ Second streaming potential	$(\Delta P/J_v)_{I=0} = R_{11} = 1/L_P$ Mechanical resistance
	One of the forces is zero		One of the flows is zero	

$$J_s = L_{32}E + L_{33}\frac{\Delta\pi_s}{\bar{c}_s}, \tag{12-37.2}$$

with the reciprocal relation

$$L_{23} = L_{32}.$$

(The subscript 3 has been introduced in the phenomenological coefficients in order to avoid confusion with those used in the previous section, and L'_{22} is used to indicate that this coefficient is not identical with the L_{22} appearing in Eq. (12-18.2).)

As was done in the previous section, the phenomenological coefficients appearing in Eqs. (12-37) can be translated into conventional parameters that are well known from general electrochemistry. From Eq. (12-37.1), we note that

$$\left(\frac{I}{E}\right)_{J_v=0,\Delta\pi=0} = L'_{22}.$$

The ratio on the left-hand side is simply the membrane conductance at zero volume flow, as expressed in Eq. (12-27), so that

$$L'_{22} = \kappa.$$

Solving Eq. (12-37.1) for E, introducing the resulting expression into Eq. (12-37.2), and rearranging, we obtain

$$J_s = \left(L_{33} - \frac{L_{23}^2}{L'_{22}}\right)\frac{\Delta\pi_s}{\bar{c}_s} + \frac{L_{23}}{L'_{22}}I. \tag{12-38}$$

The permeability coefficient ω of the membrane for the electroneutral salt is defined as

$$\omega = \left(\frac{J_s}{\Delta\pi_s}\right)_{J_v=0,I=0}, \tag{12-39}$$

so that

$$L_{33} - \frac{L_{32}^2}{L'_{22}} = \bar{c}_s\omega. \tag{12-40}$$

Further, in analogy to the considerations of Chapter 11, the transference number of ion 1, the ion that does not interact with the reversible electrode, may be defined as the fraction of the current transported by ion 1 under conditions of zero volume flow and uniform concentration. We may, therefore, write for the transference number of the z_1-valent ion in the membrane,

$$t_1 = \left(\frac{z_1\mathfrak{F}J_1}{I}\right)_{J_v=0,\Delta\pi_s=0} = \left(\frac{z_1\mathfrak{F}\nu_1 J_s}{I}\right)_{J_v=0,\Delta\pi_s=0}. \tag{12-41}$$

The flow J_s can be evaluated from Eq. (12-38), which holds for $J_v = 0$. Imposing the condition $\Delta\pi_s = 0$, we obtain

$$(J_s)_{J_v=0,\Delta\pi_s=0} = \frac{L_{23}}{L'_{22}} I,$$

so that Eq. (12-41) becomes

$$t_1 = \nu_1 z_1 \mathfrak{F} \frac{L_{23}}{L'_{22}}. \tag{12-42}$$

Introducing the equality $L'_{22} = \kappa$ into Eq. (12-42), we obtain for the coupling coefficient

$$L_{23} = L_{32} = \frac{t_1 \kappa}{\nu_1 z_1 \mathfrak{F}}. \tag{12-43}$$

The coefficients ω, κ, and t_1 are the conventional and well-studied parameters of a membrane which may be introduced into Eqs. (12-37) to give the practical phenomenological equations:

$$J_s = \omega \Delta\pi_s + \frac{t_1}{\nu_1 z_1 \mathfrak{F}} I, \tag{12-44.1}$$

$$I = \frac{\kappa t_1}{\nu_1 z_1 \mathfrak{F}} \frac{\Delta\pi_s}{\bar{c}_s} + \kappa E. \tag{12-44.2}$$

A particularly important quantity, which may be considered in terms of these expressions, is the potential difference across the membrane measured in a potentiometric experiment with $I = 0$. From Eq. (12-44.2) we obtain

$$(E)_{I=0,J_v=0} = -\frac{t_1}{\nu_1 z_1 \mathfrak{F}} \frac{\Delta\pi_s}{\bar{c}_s} = -\frac{t_1}{\nu_1 z_1 \mathfrak{F}} \Delta\mu_s^c . \tag{12-45}$$

As pointed out in Sec. 12.1.1, the electromotive force measured between the reversible electrodes is related to the liquid-junction or membrane potential $\Delta\psi$ by the expression

$$\Delta\psi = E - \frac{\Delta\mu_2}{z_2} \mathfrak{F}. \tag{12-46}$$

The potential difference $\Delta\psi$ is the one that would be measured between a pair of calomel electrodes placed in the two solutions. Since these electrodes make contact with the solution via a saturated KCl junction, they are not, in effect, reversible to ion 2 and measure only $\Delta\psi$, not $(\Delta\psi + \Delta\mu_2/z_2\mathfrak{F})$ as do reversible electrodes. Introducing the value of E from Eq. (12-45) into Eq. (12-46) and recalling that

$$\Delta\mu_s^c = \nu_1 \Delta\tilde{\mu}_1 + \nu_2 \Delta\tilde{\mu}_2,$$

we obtain

$$\Delta\psi = -\frac{t_1}{z_1\mathfrak{F}}\,\Delta\tilde{\mu}_1 - \frac{t_1\nu_2}{\nu_1 z_1\mathfrak{F}}\,\Delta\tilde{\mu}_2 - \frac{\Delta\mu_2}{z_2\mathfrak{F}}.$$

This expression may be simplified by making use of the condition of electroneutrality,

$$\nu_1 z_1 + \nu_2 z_2 = 0,$$

and the requirement, for a system containing only two ions, that

$$t_1 + t_2 = 1.$$

After introducing these relations and rearranging, we obtain

$$-\mathfrak{F}\Delta\psi = \frac{t_1}{z_1}\,\Delta\mu_1 + \frac{t_2}{z_2}\,\Delta\mu_2. \qquad (12\text{-}47)$$

Equation (12-47) is a special case of a more general expression first given by Planck[5] and by Henderson[6] and developed alternatively using the formalism of nonequilibrium thermodynamics by Staverman.[7] Although we have considered only the simple case of a single electrolyte, the generalization to an n-component system presents no fundamental difficulties.

Liquid-junction potentials play an important role in biology and appear to underlie many potential differences measured across cell and tissue membranes.[8] The study of the ionic species participating in the establishment of the potential and of its magnitude as a function of concentration and coupled reactions is, however, beyond the scope of this book.

12.4. Frictional Interpretation of Permeability Coefficients

12.4.1. In Chapter 10, we have considered the translation of the coefficients L_P, ω, and σ, describing membrane permeability to nonelectrolyte solutions, into terms of frictional coefficients. Three frictional coefficients were required for a complete description. They were f_{sw}, the friction between solute and water, f_{wm}, the friction between water and membrane, and f_{sm}, the friction between solute and membrane. Here we shall develop a similar analysis, based on the considerations of Kedem and Katchalsky, for the interpretation of the permeability coefficients for ionic transport through charged membranes. This treatment requires a larger number of frictional parameters than does the nonelectrolyte case. Since on a priori grounds the transport of each of the ionic species i is to be characterized by two coefficients f_{iw} and f_{im}, and there exists in principle also a coefficient of friction between ions of the ith and jth species f_{ij}, such a simple system as sodium$^{(1)}$-chloride$^{(2)}$-water is characterized by six parameters f_{1w}, f_{1m}, f_{12}, f_{2w}, f_{2m}, and f_{wm}. This is generally too large a set of unknowns to be of interest to the student of membrane behavior.

However, the situation is simplified considerably if the membrane is highly charged or if the concentration X of the fixed charges in the membrane matrix is much larger than the concentration of neutral salt at any point of the membrane.

Let us assume that the sign of the fixed charges is negative, and let the salt concentration at point x be C_s; then the concentration of the positive *counterions* is

$$C_1 = X + C_s, \tag{12-48}$$

while the concentration of the negative *coions* is

$$C_2 = C_s. \tag{12-49}$$

For highly charged membranes, $X \gg C_s$ and

$$C_1 \cong X.$$

We may now write the relations between forces and velocities for the flow of a monomonovalent salt in the same manner as was done in Chapter 10 for nonelectrolytes, using the general expression

$$X_i = f_{iw}(v_i - v_w) + f_{im}(v_i - v_m),$$

in which X_i is the force $d\tilde{\mu}_i/dx$, the f's are frictional coefficients and the v's are the velocities of the components. The basis of this type of equation is discussed in Sec. 10.4.2. Thus,

$$X_1 = -\frac{d\tilde{\mu}_1}{dx} = f_{1w}(v_1 - v_w) + f_{1m}(v_1 - v_m),$$

$$X_2 = -\frac{d\tilde{\mu}_2}{dx} = f_{2w}(v_2 - v_w) + f_{2m}(v_2 - v_m).$$

Since the concentration of the negative coion is small, we have assumed that the friction between the two mobile ions, f_{12}, may be neglected. If we introduce the flows J_1 and J_2 given by

$$J_1 = C_1 v_1, \qquad J_2 = C_2 v_2,$$

and the condition $v_m = 0$, the expressions become

$$-\frac{d\tilde{\mu}_1}{dx} = \frac{(f_{1w} + f_{1m})J_1}{C_1} - \frac{f_{1w}J_w}{C_w}; \tag{12-50}$$

$$-\frac{d\tilde{\mu}_2}{dx} = \frac{(f_{2w} + f_{2m})J_2}{C_2} - \frac{f_{2w}J_w}{C_w}. \tag{12-51}$$

For the case in which no electric potential difference is applied across the membrane, the ion flow is electroneutral, so that $J_1 = J_2 = J_s$. Further, it is clear from previous considerations that the force acting on the salt as a whole is

$$X_s = -\frac{d\mu_s}{dx} = -\frac{d\tilde{\mu}_1}{dx} - \frac{d\tilde{\mu}_2}{dx}.$$

Hence adding Eqs. (12-50) and (12-51) we obtain

$$-\frac{d\mu_s}{dx} = \left(\frac{f_{1w} + f_{1m}}{C_1} + \frac{f_{2w} + f_{2m}}{C_2}\right)J_s - \left(\frac{f_{1w} + f_{2w}}{C_w}\right)J_w. \qquad (12\text{-}52)$$

If $(f_{1w} + f_{1m})$ is of the same order of magnitude as $(f_{2w} + f_{2m})$, the fact that $C_1 \gg C_2$ makes the first term in parentheses on the right-hand side of Eq. (12-52) negligibly small in comparison with the second, so that, with the use of Eq. (12-49), we find that

$$-\frac{d\mu_s}{dx} = \frac{f_{2w} + f_{2m}}{C_s} J_s - \frac{f_{1w} + f_{2w}}{C_w} J_w. \qquad (12\text{-}53)$$

We shall first consider the case in which $J_w = 0$ (which is nearly equivalent to the condition $J_v = 0$), so that Eq. (12-53) reduces to

$$-\frac{d\mu_s}{dx} = \frac{f_{2w} + f_{2m}}{C_s} J_s. \qquad (12\text{-}54)$$

In the steady state when J_s is constant throughout the system, Eq. (12-54) may be integrated across the membrane to yield

$$K\Delta\pi_s = J_s(f_{2w} + f_{2m})\Delta x,$$

in which K is the distribution coefficient for the salt between aqueous solution and membrane and Δx is the thickness of the membrane. The details of the integration follow the development used in arriving at the analogous expression for a nonelectrolyte, Eq. (10-49). From the definition of ω, we find that

$$\omega = \left(\frac{J_s}{\Delta\pi_s}\right)_{J_w=0} = \frac{K}{\Delta x(f_{2w} + f_{2m})}. \qquad (12\text{-}55)$$

The reflection coefficient of the salt, $\sigma\ [= (\Delta P/\Delta\pi)_{J_v=0}]$ may be obtained by reasoning similar to that given in Eqs. (10-51) through (10-56). The resulting expression is

$$\sigma = 1 - \frac{\omega\bar{V}_s}{L_P} - \frac{K}{\varphi_w}\frac{f_{1w} + f_{2w}}{f_{2w} + f_{2m}} = 1 - \frac{\omega\bar{V}_s}{L_P} - \frac{\omega f_{sw}\Delta x}{\varphi_w}, \qquad (12\text{-}56)$$

in which $f_{sw} = f_{1w} + f_{2w}$.

It is of particular interest to apply Eqs. (12-55) and (12-56) to a highly charged membrane of very loose structure containing a large percentage of water. In this case, we may assume that the solutes pass through water-filled channels and that the friction f_{iw} between a solute and water in the membrane is equal to the friction f_{iw}^0 in free solution. Further, since a high concentration of charge within the membrane insures that the coion concentration C_2 is small, the friction between this ion and the membrane may be neglected relative to the friction between the ion and water, or $f_{2m} \ll f_{2w}$. Finally, the distribution coefficient K may be obtained from the requirements of a Donnan equilibrium, namely, that the activity of salt at every point in the aqueous channels is equal to the activity in the equivalent aqueous solution. Since the concentration in the membrane, C_i, is expressed as moles per unit volume of membrane, the concentration in the aqueous phase will be C_i/φ_w, where φ_w is the volume fraction of water in the membrane. Thus, the requirement of Donnan equilibrium takes the form

$$c_s^2 = \frac{C_1}{\varphi_w}\frac{C_2}{\varphi_w},$$

or, with Eqs. (12-48) and (12-49),

$$c_s^2 = \frac{C_s(C_s + X)}{\varphi_w^2},$$

and

$$K = \frac{C_s}{c_s} = \frac{c_s\varphi_w^2}{C_s + X} \cong \frac{c_s\varphi_w^2}{X}. \tag{12-57}$$

On the basis of these considerations, Eq. (12-55) may be written

$$\omega = \frac{\bar{c}_s\varphi_w^2\vartheta}{X\Delta x f_{2w}^0}. \tag{12-58}$$

The factor ϑ is a "tortuosity factor," which according to Mackie and Meares[9] must be introduced to take account of the fact that the path of the channels within the membrane is longer than the macroscopic thickness Δx. The true path length is given by $\Delta x/\vartheta$, so that $\vartheta < 1$. The effect of the increased path length may be most conveniently expressed in terms of an increase in the over-all friction between solute and water within the membrane, so that we may write

$$f_{1w} = \frac{f_{1w}^0}{\vartheta}, \qquad f_{2w} = \frac{f_{2w}^0}{\vartheta}. \tag{12-59}$$

Equation (12-58) illustrates two important points. First, it shows that the permeability coefficient for electrolyte permeation is not constant but rather is directly dependent on the average salt concentration, $\bar{c}_s$. Second, the frictional resistance governing salt permeability is not due to the friction of all ionic species but is given by that of the coions. The counterions, whose concentration in the membrane is rather large, contribute little to the over-all frictional resistance.

The reflection coefficient may also be expressed in similar terms by introducing Eqs. (12-57) and (12-59), as well as the assumption that $f_{2m} \ll f_{2w}$, into Eq. (12-56), to yield

$$\sigma = 1 - \frac{\omega \bar{V}_s}{L_P} - \frac{\bar{c}_s \varphi_w}{X} \left(\frac{f_{1w}^0 + f_{2w}^0}{f_{2w}^0} \right). \tag{12-60}$$

Equation (12-60) can be further modified by noting that the transference number of the counterions in free solution t_1^0 is given by

$$t_1^0 = \frac{u_1^0}{u_1^0 + u_2^0} = \frac{1/f_{1w}^0}{1/f_{1w}^0 + 1/f_{2w}^0} = \frac{f_{2w}^0}{f_{1w}^0 + f_{2w}^0}.$$

Introducing this expression into Eq. (12-60), we obtain

$$\sigma = 1 - \frac{\omega \bar{V}_s}{L_P} - \frac{\bar{c}_s \varphi_w}{X t_1^0}. \tag{12-61}$$

Equation (12-61) shows that for low electrolyte transport numbers σ decreases rapidly with increasing salt concentration. If t_1^0 is sufficiently small and X sufficiently large, σ readily becomes negative. The physical phenomenon accompanying negative values of σ is the negative anomalous osmosis discovered by Dutrochet in 1837, studied by Jacques Loeb[10] in the twenties of this century, and investigated more recently by Grim and Sollner.[11] It will be recalled that in an osmotic experiment volume flow in the absence of electric current is given by the equation

$$J_v = L_P(\Delta P - \sigma \Delta \pi).$$

At the quasi-equilibrium when $J_v = 0$, the stationary hydrostatic pressure difference ΔP in the osmometer is equal to $\sigma \Delta \pi$, where $\Delta \pi$ is the difference in osmotic pressure across the membrane. In an ideal case of a perfectly semipermeable membrane, $\sigma = 1$ and $\Delta P = \Delta \pi$; for cases with membranes of lesser selectivity, $\sigma < 1$ and $\Delta P < \Delta \pi$. However, in cases of negative σ, ΔP becomes negative and a pressure has to be applied to the external solution in order to prevent volume flow in the osmometer. This behavior is represented in Fig. 24 where the apparent osmotic pressure $\sigma \Delta \pi$ (normalized to RTX) is compared with the real osmotic pressure normalized to the ideal osmotic pressure of the membrane.

12.4.2. In concluding this section, we shall evaluate some of the permeability coefficients for electrolyte driven across a charged membrane by a gradient of electric potential. The membrane is again considered to be highly swollen and highly charged. For the sake of simplicity, we shall discuss only conditions of zero volume flow with equal concentrations of

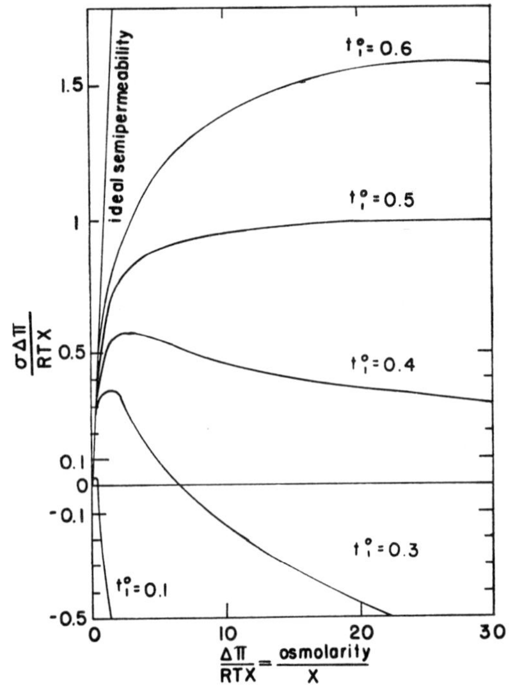

Fig. 24. The dependence of effective osmolarity, $\sigma \Delta\pi/RTX$, on the true osmolarity, $\Delta\pi/RTX$, across a charged membrane for various values of the transport number t_1^0 of the counter ion. Reproduced by permission of the Rockefeller Institute Press from A. Katchalsky and O. Kedem, *Biophys. J.* *2* (1962), 53.

salt in the solutions bathing both sides of the membrane. These are the conditions for the determination of the conductivity κ and the transference number t discussed in Sec. 12.2 and it is these coefficients that will be considered in terms of frictions and concentration.

If the condition $J_w = 0$ is introduced into Eqs. (12-50) and (12-51), the forces $d\tilde{\mu}_1/dx$ and $d\tilde{\mu}_2/dx$ may be written

$$-\frac{d\tilde{\mu}_1}{dx} = \frac{(f_{1w} + f_{1m})J_1}{C_1},$$
$$-\frac{d\tilde{\mu}_2}{dx} = \frac{(f_{2w} + f_{2m})J_2}{C_2}. \tag{12-62}$$

Under the conditions of high charge density within the membrane, $C_1 \cong X$ and, according to Eq. (12-57),

$$C_s = C_2 = \frac{c_s^2 \varphi_w^2}{X}.$$

Further, assuming that the membrane is a loose structure of high water content, $f_{1m} \ll f_{1w}$ and $f_{2m} \ll f_{2w}$. Thus, Eqs. (12-62) can be written

$$-\frac{d\tilde{\mu}_1}{dx} = \frac{f_{1w}J_1}{X}, \qquad -\frac{d\tilde{\mu}_2}{dx} = \frac{Xf_{2w}J_2}{c_s^2\varphi_w^2}. \tag{12-63}$$

Assuming that the system is in a steady state and that f_{1w} and f_{2w} may be taken as constant, Eqs. (12-63) may be integrated to yield

$$\Delta\tilde{\mu}_1 = \frac{f_{1w}J_1\Delta x}{X}, \tag{12-64}$$

$$\Delta\tilde{\mu}_2 = \frac{Xf_{2w}J_2\Delta x}{c_s^2\varphi_w^2}. \tag{12-65}$$

Since the solutions on the two sides of the membrane are of identical composition,

$$\Delta\mu_s = \Delta\tilde{\mu}_1 + \Delta\tilde{\mu}_2 = 0. \tag{12-66}$$

Further, as discussed in Sec. 12.1, if the measuring electrodes are reversible to ion 2,

$$\Delta\tilde{\mu}_2 = -\mathfrak{F}E,$$

so that Eq. (12-65) may be written

$$J_2 = -\frac{c_s^2\varphi_w^2\mathfrak{F}E}{X\Delta x f_{2w}}. \tag{12-67}$$

Introducing Eqs. (12-64) and (12-65) into Eq. (12-66) yields

$$\frac{f_{1w}J_1}{X} = -\frac{Xf_{2w}J_2}{c_s^2\varphi_w^2},$$

and with the use of Eq. (12-67) we find that

$$J_1 = \frac{\mathfrak{F}EX}{f_{1w}\Delta x}, \tag{12-68}$$

The electric current I may now be evaluated with the aid of Eqs. (12-67) and (12-68):

$$I = \mathfrak{F}(J_1 - J_2) = \frac{\mathfrak{F}^2E}{\Delta x}\left(\frac{X}{f_{1w}} + \frac{c_s^2\varphi_w^2}{Xf_{2w}}\right).$$

At low salt concentrations,

$$\frac{c_s^2\varphi_w^2}{X} \ll X,$$

so that

$$I = \frac{\mathfrak{F}^2 E X}{f_{1w} \Delta x}. \tag{12-69}$$

Thus, the conductance is given by

$$\kappa = \left(\frac{I}{E}\right)_{J_v=0,\Delta\pi_s=0} = \frac{\mathfrak{F}^2 X}{f_{1w} \Delta x}. \tag{12-70}$$

Using the concept of tortuosity introduced in the preceding section, we may replace f_{1w} by f_{1w}^0/ϑ, so that the expression for κ contains only one unknown factor, the tortuosity of the aqueous channels:

$$\kappa = \frac{\vartheta \mathfrak{F}^2 X}{f_{1w}^0 \Delta x}. \tag{12-71}$$

A numerical example might be useful in appreciating the content of Eq. (12-71). Let us consider a membrane of thickness $\Delta x = 10^{-2}$ cm having a charge density $X = 10^{-4}$ moles/cm^3 and in which ϑ is assumed to equal 0.5. If the electrolyte under consideration is KCl, K^+ being the counterion, $f_{1w}^0 = RT/D = 1.3 \times 10^{15}$ dyne sec/mole cm. The Faraday in absolute units is $\mathfrak{F} = 96{,}500$ coulombs/equivalent $= 2.9 \times 10^{14}$ e.s.u. Introducing all the figures, we get for κ,

$$\kappa = 3.2 \times 10^{11} \frac{\text{statamp}}{\text{statvolt cm}^2}.$$

In more conventional terms, since 1 statvolt $=$ 300 volts while 3×10^9 statamp $=$ 1 amp,

$$\kappa = 0.3 \text{ ohm}^{-1} \text{ cm}^{-2}.$$

The same equations may be used to evaluate the transference numbers of the counterions and the coions in the membrane. According to the considerations of Sec. 12.2, the transference number of the coion, t_2, will be given by

$$t_2 = \left(\frac{-\mathfrak{F} J_2}{I}\right)_{J_v=0,\Delta\pi_s=0}. \tag{12-72}$$

If we introduce J_2 from Eq. (12-67) and I from Eq. (12-69), Eq. 12-72 becomes

$$t_2 = \left(\frac{c_s \varphi_w}{X}\right)^2 \frac{f_{1w}}{f_{2w}}. \tag{12-73}$$

Since, for a system containing only two mobile ions,

$$t_1 + t_2 = 1,$$

we find that

$$t_1 = 1 - \left(\frac{c_s\varphi_w}{X}\right)^2 \frac{f_{1w}}{f_{2w}}. \tag{12-74}$$

Since, under the conditions considered here, $X \gg c_s\varphi_w$, the transference number t_2 of the coion is near zero while that of the counterion is close to unity.

The last coefficient to be translated into frictional terms is β. Applying the Gibbs–Duhem relation to the aqueous solution within the membrane, we may write

$$C_w \frac{d\mu_w}{dx} + C_1 \frac{d\tilde{\mu}_1}{dx} + C_2 \frac{d\tilde{\mu}_2}{dx} = 0,$$

or

$$-\frac{d\mu_w}{dx} = \frac{C_1}{C_w}\frac{d\tilde{\mu}_1}{dx} + \frac{C_2}{C_w}\frac{d\tilde{\mu}_2}{dx}. \tag{12-75}$$

Since the salt concentration is the same on both sides of the homogeneous membrane, it is reasonable to assume that there is no gradient of neutral salt concentration within the membrane phase, so that

$$\frac{d\mu_s}{dx} = \frac{d\tilde{\mu}_1}{dx} + \frac{d\tilde{\mu}_2}{dx} = 0,$$

or

$$\frac{d\tilde{\mu}_1}{dx} = -\frac{d\tilde{\mu}_2}{dx}. \tag{12-76}$$

Introducing $d\tilde{\mu}_1/dx$ from Eq. (12-76) into Eq. (12-75), we obtain

$$\frac{d\mu_w}{dx} = \left(\frac{C_1 - C_2}{C_w}\right)\frac{d\tilde{\mu}_2}{dx}. \tag{12-77}$$

Now the difference between counterion and coion concentrations in the membrane is evidently equal to the concentration of the charged groups fixed in the membrane, or

$$C_1 - C_2 = X = \text{constant}.$$

The water content of the membrane, C_w, may also be taken as a constant, so that Eq. (12-77) may be integrated across the membrane from 0 to Δx to give

$$\Delta\mu_w = \frac{X}{C_w}\Delta\tilde{\mu}_2. \tag{12-78}$$

Under the condition $\Delta\pi = 0$ the value of $\Delta\mu_w$ is $\bar{V}_w\Delta P$. If electrodes reversible to ion 2 are used to establish an electromotive force E, $\Delta\tilde{\mu}_2 = -\mathfrak{F}E$ as indicated by Eq. (12-7). Hence Eq. (12-78) may be rewritten

$$\bar{V}_w \Delta P = -\frac{X\mathfrak{F}E}{C_w}.$$

Since $C_w \bar{V}_w = \varphi_w$ is the volume fraction of water in the membrane,

$$\left(\frac{\Delta P}{E}\right)_{\Delta\pi=0,\,J_v=0} = -\frac{X\mathfrak{F}}{\varphi_w}.$$

An inspection of the phenomenological Eqs. (12-31) shows that

$$\left(\frac{\Delta P}{E}\right)_{\Delta\pi=0,\,J_v=0} = -\frac{\kappa\beta}{L_P},$$

and hence

$$\beta = \frac{L_P X\mathfrak{F}}{\kappa\varphi_w}. \tag{12-79}$$

For L_P, we may now introduce the expression given in Eq. (10-35) and for κ we may use the value given by Eq. (12-70), so that finally

$$\beta = \frac{f_{1w}\bar{V}_w}{f_{wm}\mathfrak{F}}. \tag{12-80}$$

In the capillary model of water penetration through a porous membrane the relation between volume flow of water and the pressure difference is given by Poiseuille's equation,

$$J_v = \frac{\varphi_w r^2 \Delta P}{8\eta\Delta x/\vartheta},$$

in which φ_w represents the membrane area available for permeation, $\Delta x/\vartheta$ is the "true" length of the capillaries, and r is their radius. This expression leads to a value of L_P given by

$$L_P = \left(\frac{J_v}{\Delta P}\right)_{I=0} = \frac{\varphi_w r^2 \vartheta}{8\eta\Delta x}.$$

Introducing this value of L_P into Eq. (12-79) and making use of Eq. (12-71) for κ, we obtain for β

$$\beta = \frac{f_{1w}^0 r^2}{8\eta\mathfrak{F}}.$$

Thus, for a membrane characterized by a capillary radius of $r = 10$ Å $= 10^{-7}$ cm, with K^+ as counterion [$f_{1w}^0 = 1.3 \times 10^{15}$ dyne sec/mole cm] and at a temperature at which $\eta = 10^{-2}$ poise,

$$\beta = \frac{1.3 \times 10^{15} \times 10^{-14}}{8 \times 10^{-2} \times 96{,}500} = 1.7 \times 10^{-3} \text{ cm}^3/\text{coulomb},$$

indicating that every coulomb of electricity will exert a drag effect sufficient to carry 1.7×10^{-3} cm^3 of water through 1 cm^2 of the membrane.

Although the considerations presented here are based on certain simplifying assumptions regarding the nature of the membrane and the bathing solutions, the resulting expressions should give a clearer insight into the physical basis of some of the membrane phenomena.

12.5. Composite Membranes

The treatment of single-phase homogeneous membranes developed in the previous sections serves a didactic purpose by introducing the basic concepts of membrane thermodynamics in a simple and straightforward manner. There is little doubt, however, that many biological membranes are neither simple nor single-phase homogeneous structures. An overwhelming amount of chemical and ultramicroscopic evidence indicates that the limiting barriers of single cells and of tissues are composite structures, sometimes consisting of several layers of substances differing in composition and permeability characteristics. Lack of sufficient information renders impossible discussion of any particular case taking into consideration specific properties of given biological structure. We would like, however, to outline the thermodynamic approach to the more complicated case of composite membranes. For the sake of simplicity we shall consider two elementary compositions, a membrane composed of different patches arranged in a *parallel array*, and a multilayer in which the phases overlie each other in a *series array* of different elements.

12.5.1. There are a few general statements that may be made about a parallel-membrane system. If the flow enters the elements perpendicularly and the area of contact between the membrane elements plays a negligible role in the permeation process, the total flow is equal to the sum of flows through all the elements. Thus if the fraction of the area occupied by the kth element is γ_k and the ith flow through the kth membrane element is J_i^k, then the total ith flow is

$$J_i = \sum_k \gamma_k J_i^k, \tag{12-81}$$

in which the summation is carried out over all k elements. Another evident statement is that the total macroscopic force acting on any of the membrane elements is the same. Thus we may write for the ith flow through the kth element the phenomenological expression

$$J_i^k = \sum_j L_{ij}^k X_j, \tag{12-82}$$

in which the summation is to be carried out over all j forces. Introducing Eq. (12-82) into Eq. (12-81) we obtain

$$J_i = \sum_k \gamma_k \sum_j L_{ij}^k X_j = \sum_j \left(\sum_k \gamma_k L_{ij}^k\right) X_j = \sum_j L_{ij} X_j. \tag{12-83}$$

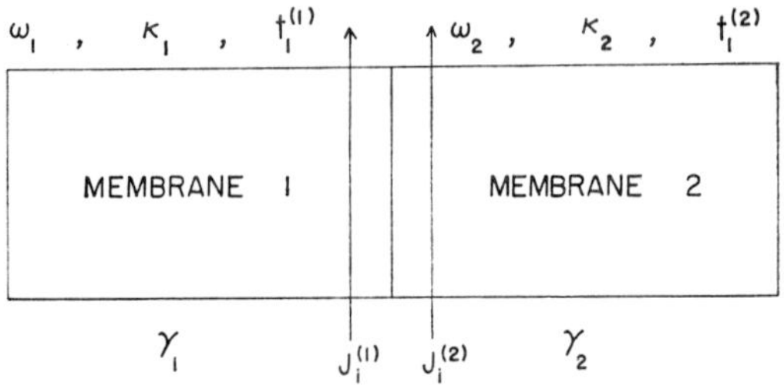

Fig. 25. A composite membrane of two elements in parallel arrangement; γ_i is the fractional area occupied by each element, ω_i is salt permeability, κ_i is electrical conductance, t_1^i is the transference number of the cation, and J_i^k is the flow of the ith solute across the kth membrane element.

Equation (12-83) shows that the over-all coefficients L_{ij} of a system of parallel membrane elements are composed additively of the coefficients for the single elements, weighted by the fraction of the area occupied by each element, or

$$L_{ij} = \sum_k \gamma_k L_{ij}^k. \tag{12-84}$$

The form of Eq. (12-84) resembles closely the familiar equation for the conductance of parallel electrical networks, only here the Onsager coefficients play the role of generalized conductances. This similarity, however, breaks down under certain experimental conditions which will be discussed in the following.

To bring out the new properties exhibited by such membrane systems, let us consider a parallel array of two charged membranes occupying the fractions γ_1 and γ_2 of the total membrane area, as illustrated in Fig. 25. For the sake of simplicity we shall assume that no water flow takes place through the elements, so that the behavior of each constituent may be represented by the phenomenological Eqs. (12-44), or

$$J_s^{(1)} = \omega_1 \Delta\pi_s + \frac{t_1^{(1)}}{\mathfrak{F}} I_1, \qquad J_s^{(2)} = \omega_2 \Delta\pi_s + \frac{t_1^{(2)}}{\mathfrak{F}} I_2, \tag{12-85}$$

$$I_1 = \frac{\kappa_1 t_1^{(1)}}{\mathfrak{F}} \frac{\Delta\pi_s}{\bar{c}_s} + \kappa_1 E, \qquad I_2 = \frac{\kappa_2 t_1^{(2)}}{\mathfrak{F}} \frac{\Delta\pi_s}{\bar{c}_s} + \kappa_2 E. \tag{12-86}$$

The forces $\Delta\pi_s$ and E are the same for both elements, but the flows I_1 and I_2, as well as J_s^1 and J_s^2, are different since both the straight coefficients ω and κ and the coupling coefficient t have different values for each of the constituent elements.

Let us now carry out an open-circuit (or a potentiometric) experiment on the parallel-membrane system. In this case, the electric current is zero, so that, according to Eq. (12-81),

$$I = \gamma_1 I_1 + \gamma_2 I_2 = 0. \tag{12-87}$$

Equation (12-87) does not imply that the vanishing of the total current leads to the disappearance of the flows I_1 and I_2. The only requirement is that the sum total of the electrical contributions from both elements be compensating and, as we shall see immediately, I_1 and I_2 are generally nonvanishing. Multiplying Eqs. (12-86) by γ_1 and γ_2 respectively and adding, we obtain, with the use of Eq. (12-87),

$$\gamma_1 I_1 + \gamma_2 I_2 = 0 = \frac{\gamma_1\kappa_1 t_1^{(1)} + \gamma_2\kappa_2 t_1^{(2)}}{\mathfrak{F}}\left(\frac{\Delta\pi_s}{\bar{c}_s}\right) + (\gamma_1\kappa_1 + \gamma_2\kappa_2)E,$$

or

$$E = -\frac{\gamma_1\kappa_1 t_1^{(1)} + \gamma_2\kappa_2 t_1^{(2)}}{\mathfrak{F}(\gamma_1\kappa_1 + \gamma_2\kappa_2)}\left(\frac{\Delta\pi_s}{\bar{c}_s}\right). \tag{12-88}$$

Introducing E from Eq. (12-88) into Eq. (12-86), we find readily the current through the separate membrane elements,

$$\gamma_1 I_1 = -\gamma_2 I_2 = \frac{\gamma_1\gamma_2\kappa_1\kappa_2(t_1^{(1)} - t_1^{(2)})}{\mathfrak{F}(\gamma_1\kappa_1 + \gamma_2\kappa_2)}\left(\frac{\Delta\pi_s}{\bar{c}_s}\right). \tag{12-89}$$

Since γ_1, γ_2, κ_1, κ_2, and $\Delta\pi/\bar{c}_s$ are nonvanishing quantities, $\gamma_1 I_1$ would vanish only in the case that $t_1^{(1)} = t_1^{(2)}$. For any other condition, $\gamma_1 I_1 \neq 0$ and there will be an electric current through element 1 of the composite membrane. This current will be compensated by an equal flow in the opposite direction through element 2, so that the net over-all current vanishes. Such a flow may be considered as an electric circulation, the existence of which has been demonstrated experimentally by Sollner and co-workers.[12]

This circulation of electric charge derives from enhanced permeability to salt, as may be shown by the direct evaluation of J_s. From Eq. (12-81),

$$J_s = \gamma_1 J_s^{(1)} + \gamma_2 J_s^{(2)}. \tag{12-90}$$

Introducing the values of I_1 and I_2 from Eq. (12-89) into Eq. (12-85) and using Eq. (12-87), we obtain

$$J_s = (\gamma_1\omega_1 + \gamma_2\omega_2)\Delta\pi_s + \frac{\gamma_1\gamma_2\kappa_1\kappa_2(t_1^{(1)} - t_1^{(2)})^2}{\mathfrak{F}(\gamma_1\kappa_1 + \gamma_2\kappa_2)}\left(\frac{\Delta\pi_s}{\bar{c}_s}\right),$$

or

$$J_s = \left[\gamma_1\omega_1 + \gamma_2\omega_2 + \frac{\gamma_1\gamma_2\kappa_1\kappa_2(t_1^{(1)} - t_1^{(2)})^2}{\mathfrak{F}\bar{c}_s(\gamma_1\kappa_1 + \gamma_2\kappa_2)}\right]\Delta\pi_s = \omega\Delta\pi_s. \tag{12-91}$$

Equation (12-91) shows that the over-all coefficient of salt permeability, ω, is now composed of two terms, the classical Kirchoff term, $\gamma_1\omega_1 + \gamma_1\omega_2$, and an additional term due to the circulation,

$$\frac{\gamma_1\gamma_2\kappa_1\kappa_2(t_1^{(1)} - t_1^{(2)})^2}{\mathfrak{F}\bar{c}_s(\gamma_1\kappa_1 + \gamma_2\kappa_2)}.$$

This additional term is positive-definite and may often be many times larger than the term expected from a simple additivity of the permeabilities. A rather impressive demonstration of these phenomena occurs when one of the membrane elements carries a high positive fixed charge and the other a high negative charge. In this case, $t_1^{(1)} \cong 1$ and $t_1^{(2)} \cong 0$. Since no transport of ions can take place through highly charged membranes at zero electric current owing to the impermeability of one of the ions and the restriction of electroneutrality, both ω_1 and ω_2 are close to zero. Equation (12-91) shows, however, that, despite the impermeability of the individual elements, the composite membrane will have a definite and rather large permeability, given by

$$\omega \cong \frac{\gamma_1\gamma_2\kappa_1\kappa_2}{\mathfrak{F}\bar{c}_s(\gamma_1\kappa_1 + \gamma_2\kappa_2)}.$$

The physical basis of this phenomenon is readily seen if we consider, for example, the transport of KCl through such a membrane. While the positive membrane, element 1, is impermeable to K^+ and therefore impermeable to the salt as a whole, and the negative membrane, element 2, is impermeable to Cl^- and therefore prevents the passage of KCl, there is no obstacle to the simultaneous transport of both ions through the two elements as long as electroneutrality is retained. Moreover, this example shows clearly the physical meaning of electric circulation. The flow of K^+ from the higher to the lower salt concentration corresponds to a positive direction of electric current, while the simultaneous flow of the Cl^- corresponds to a flow of electricity in the opposite or negative direction. Both flows together determine, therefore, a closed circuit, as predicted by Eq. (12-89) and illustrated in Fig. 26.

12.5.2. We shall now turn our attention to the second simple case of composite membranes, that of a series array of elements. The general statements that can be made about these systems for the case of stationary flow are that the flux of the ith type must be the same throughout the

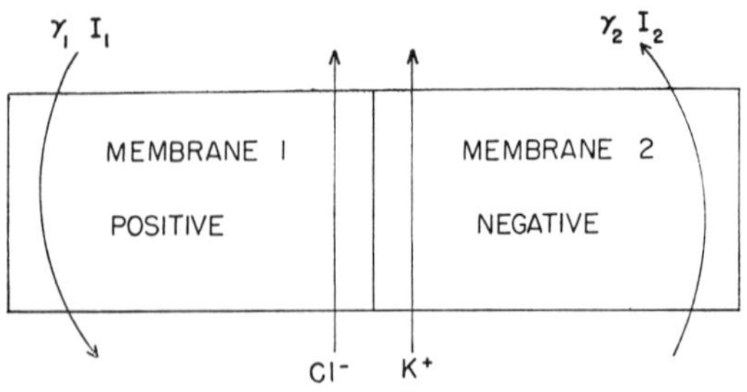

Fig. 26. Schematic illustration of ionic flows and electric current across a parallel composite membrane composed of cation- and anion-exchange elements.

constituent layers, and that the force, on the other hand, may be built up additively from the individual gradients operating across the layers. Thus if the force of the ith type acting on the kth element is X_i^k, we may write

$$X_i = \sum_k X_i^k. \tag{12-92}$$

In dealing with series systems, it is more convenient to utilize the inverse phenomenological equations, which may be written, for each membrane element,

$$X_i^k = \sum_j R_{ij}^k J_j, \tag{12-93}$$

in which the R_{ij}^k's are the inverse Onsager coefficients for the kth membrane. Introducing Eq. (12-93) into Eq. (12-92) we obtain

$$X_i = \sum_k \left(\sum_j R_{ij}^k J_j\right) = \sum_j \left(\sum_k R_{ij}^k J_j\right) = \sum_j R_{ij} J_j, \tag{12-94}$$

in which

$$R_{ij} = \sum_k R_{ij}^k \tag{12-95}$$

are the over-all generalized resistances of the composite membrane. Equation (12-93) again bears a formal resemblance to Kirchoff's law for the additivity of a series of resistances in an electric circuit. It is only in a more detailed analysis of the membrane behavior under specified experimental conditions that the prominent differences become apparent.

We shall consider a two-membrane array in series, assuming that the elements are electrically charged, permeable to ions but of sufficiently low permeability to water that $J_v = 0$. The experimental arrangement is illustrated in Fig. 27. In order to develop a clear representation of the forces operating in this system, it is advantageous to introduce between the membrane elements 1 and 2 an infinitely thin layer of aqueous solution in which the chemical potentials of salt and water are equal to those of the bordering surfaces. The salt concentration c_i in this intermediate layer is evidently different from those at the external surfaces of membranes c_1 and c_2. It is determined, however, by the external electrochemical potentials. Thus in terms of Eq. (12-92) the osmotic driving force for a monomonovalent salt, $\Delta\pi = 2RT(c_1 - c_2)$, may be written

$$\Delta\pi = 2RT(c_1 - c_i) + 2RT(c_i - c_2) = \Delta\pi_1 + \Delta\pi_2. \tag{12-96}$$

Similarly, the over-all electromotive force

$$E = E_1 + E_2, \tag{12-97}$$

in which, for example, E_1 would be the electromotive force between two Ag-AgCl electrodes inserted in compartment 1 and in the intermediate

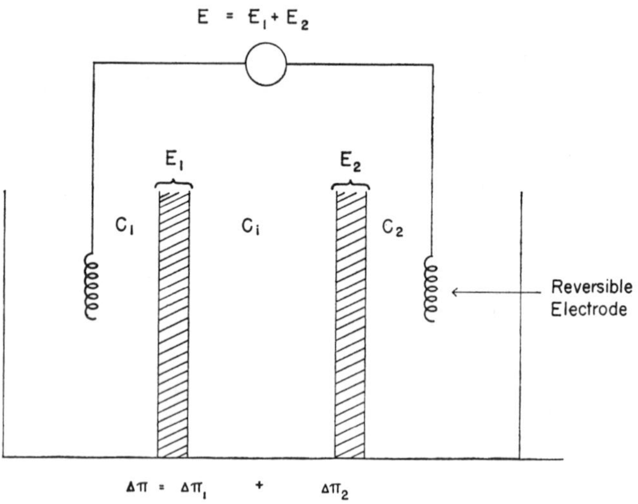

Fig. 27. A composite membrane of two elements in series arrangement; E is electromotive force between the reversible electrodes, c is salt concentration, and $\Delta\pi$ is osmotic-pressure difference.

solution. The concentration c_i is not an independent parameter but is determined by the values of the parameters outside the membrane, such as the external concentrations and the over-all value of E.

We may now proceed to the evaluation of the simple case in which the salt concentrations on the two sides of the complex membrane are equal ($\Delta\pi = 0$). According to Eq. (12-96) this condition requires that

$$\Delta\pi_1 = -\Delta\pi_2,$$

and we may therefore write the phenomenological equations for the membrane elements, Eqs. (12-44), as

$$J_s = \omega_1 \Delta\pi_1 + \frac{t_1^{(1)}}{\mathfrak{F}} I;$$
$$J_s = \omega_2 \Delta\pi_2 + \frac{t_1^{(2)}}{\mathfrak{F}} I = -\omega_2 \Delta\pi_1 + \frac{t_1^{(2)}}{\mathfrak{F}} I, \qquad (12\text{-}98)$$

in which the requirement of equality of J_s and I in both the constituents of the composite membrane has been introduced. Subtracting Eqs. (12-98) from each other yields an explicit expression for $\Delta\pi_1$,

$$-\Delta\pi_1 = \left(\frac{t_1^{(1)} - t_1^{(2)}}{\omega_1 + \omega_2}\right) \frac{I}{\mathfrak{F}}. \qquad (12\text{-}99)$$

Equation (12-99) reveals the remarkable fact that, if $t_1^{(1)} - t_1^{(2)}$ is positive, $\Delta\pi_1$ will be positive for negative values of I and negative for positive values of I. Since $\Delta\pi_1 = 2RT(c - c_i)$, this means that in the first case $c > c_i$, or that there will be a depletion of salt in the intermediate space when the electric current is in the negative direction (from compartment 2 to compartment 1), while when the current is in the positive direction $c_i > c$ and there will be an accumulation of salt in the space. For example, let membrane 1 be negatively charged and $t_1^{(1)} \cong 1$ and membrane 2 be positively charged so that $t_1^{(2)} \cong 0$. For a negative value of I, positive ions will tend to flow from compartment 2 to compartment 1. However, the positive membrane 2 prevents their movement into the intermediate space. On the other hand, the space loses positive ions which may pass readily through the negative membrane 1. Similar reasoning applies for the negative ions which tend to flow in the opposite direction so that the over-all result is a diminution of c_i, as predicted quantitatively by Eq. (12-99). If the direction of the current is reversed, positive ions from compartment 1 will enter the intermediate space through membrane 1, but no positive ions will leave the space since their movement toward the negative electrode will be blocked by the positive membrane 2. In a similar way an equivalent number of negative ions will accumulate in the intermediate space, making the over-all value of c_i larger than the external c, the stationary value of $\Delta\pi_1$ being again given by Eq. (12-99).

For the case in which c_i increases with the flow of electricity, the membrane system will become a better electric conductor; on the other hand, when c_i decreases and ultimately approaches zero, the membrane gradually becomes an insulator which will not permit the passage of electricity. The fact that the composite membrane behaves as conductor or insulator, dependent on the direction of the current, is an expression of the *polarity* of a series array of membrane elements and demonstrates the vectorial-anisotropic properties of such arrangements. A quantitative measure of polarity may be obtained by evaluating the over-all conductivity of a series membrane. For the present case we may write Eqs. (12-86) as

$$I = \frac{\kappa_1 t_1^{(1)}}{\mathfrak{F}} \frac{\Delta\pi_1}{\bar{c}_s} + \kappa_1 E_1 = \frac{\kappa_2 t_1^{(2)}}{\mathfrak{F}} \frac{\Delta\pi_2}{\bar{c}_s} + \kappa_2 E_2,$$

or

$$E_1 = \frac{I}{\kappa_1} - \frac{t_1^{(1)}}{\mathfrak{F}} \frac{\Delta\pi_1}{\bar{c}_s} \quad \text{and} \quad E_2 = \frac{I}{\kappa_2} - \frac{t_1^{(2)}}{\mathfrak{F}} \frac{\Delta\pi_2}{\bar{c}_s}.$$

The sum of the forces E_1 and E_2 is E, the over-all electromotive force of the system. Introducing the relation $\Delta\pi_2 = -\Delta\pi_1$ and substituting for $\Delta\pi_1$ its value from Eq. (12-99) we obtain

$$E = I\left[\frac{1}{\kappa_1} + \frac{1}{\kappa_2} + \frac{(t_1^{(1)} - t_1^{(2)})^2}{\mathfrak{F}^2 \bar{c}_s(\omega_1 + \omega_2)}\right].$$

Hence the over-all conductance, κ, is given by

$$\left(\frac{E}{I}\right)_{\Delta\pi=0,\,J_v=0} = \frac{1}{\kappa} = \frac{1}{\kappa_1} + \frac{1}{\kappa_2} + \frac{(t_1^{(1)} - t_1^{(2)})^2}{\mathfrak{F}^2\bar{c}_s(\omega_1 + \omega_2)}. \qquad (12\text{-}100)$$

The first two terms on the right-hand side of Eq. (12-100) correspond to the classical laws of Kirchoff by which we expect the over-all resistance to be additive in the constituent resistances, $1/\kappa_1$ and $1/\kappa_2$. The new term due to polarity is

$$\frac{(t_1^{(1)} - t_1^{(2)})^2}{\mathfrak{F}^2\bar{c}_s(\omega_1 + \omega_2)}.$$

When accumulation of salt takes place in the intermediate space and $\bar{c}_s$ becomes appreciable, the polarity term vanishes and Eq. (12-100) reduces to the conventional form. On the other hand, if the flow of electricity depletes the salt from the space and $\bar{c}_s$ approaches zero, the polarity term becomes dominant and determines the relation between current and electromotive force. Thus two charged membranes in series exhibit rectifying properties similar to those of a diode.

CHAPTER 13

SYSTEMS WITH TEMPERATURE GRADIENTS

In the previous chapters, we have considered the thermodynamic description of several systems in which the temperature was assumed to be uniform. We shall now remove this restriction and examine the effects of temperature gradients. A number of coupling phenomena involving thermal gradients have been observed in nonbiological systems and may be analyzed in terms of the thermodynamics of irreversible processes. In fact, the thermoelectric phenomena were among the first irreversible processes considered from a thermodynamic point of view. Although temperature gradients are usually assumed to be absent in biological systems, they cannot be completely ruled out and could play a role in biological processes as well.

13.1. Thermal Diffusion in Continuous Systems

13.1.1. One of the thermal phenomena that has been studied extensively since its first observation by Ludwig in 1856 is thermal diffusion. This represents a typical example of coupling, since a flow of matter is caused by a nonconjugated force, the temperature gradient. (An extensive bibliography of work on thermal diffusion may be found in the book of Jost.[1]) In order to develop an understanding of this phenomenon in thermodynamic terms, we shall begin by considering the entropy production for the general case of several diffusing substances in a continuous, nonisothermal system. Assuming that the components do not undergo chemical reaction, the expression for σ, Eq. (7-19), becomes

$$\sigma = \mathbf{J}_q \cdot \operatorname{grad} \frac{1}{T} + \sum_{i=1}^{n} \mathbf{J}_i \cdot \operatorname{grad} \left(-\frac{\mu_i}{T}\right). \tag{13-1}$$

The flows and forces defined by Eq. (13-1) could be used for the phenomenological description of the system. However, it is more convenient to transform this expression to obtain a new set of flows and forces. The force grad $(-\mu_i/T)$ may be written

$$\operatorname{grad} \left(-\frac{\mu_i}{T}\right) = \frac{1}{T} \operatorname{grad} (-\mu_i) - \mu_i \operatorname{grad} \frac{1}{T}. \tag{13-2}$$

According to Eq. (5-69), we may write

$$\operatorname{grad} \mu_i = -\bar{S}_i \operatorname{grad} T + \bar{V}_i \operatorname{grad} P + \operatorname{grad} \mu_{c_i}, \tag{13-3}$$

in which μ_i^c again represents the concentration-dependent part of the chemical potential. Since the system is considered to be in mechanical equilibrium, grad $P = 0$ and Eq. (13-3) becomes

$$\text{grad } \mu_i = -\bar{S}_i \text{ grad } T + \text{grad } \mu_i^c. \tag{13-4}$$

Introducing Eq. (13-4) into Eq. (13-2) and using also the relation

$$\bar{H}_i = T\bar{S}_i + \mu_i,$$

we obtain

$$\text{grad}\left(-\frac{\mu_i}{T}\right) = -\bar{H}_i \text{ grad } \frac{1}{T} + \frac{1}{T} \text{ grad } (-\mu_i^c).$$

Equation (13-1) may then be written

$$\sigma = (\mathbf{J}_q - \sum_{i=1}^{n} \bar{H}_i\mathbf{J}_i)\cdot\text{grad } \frac{1}{T} + \sum_{i=1}^{n} \frac{\mathbf{J}_i\cdot\text{grad } (-\mu_i^c)}{T},$$

or, in terms of the dissipation function,

$$\Phi = T\sigma = \frac{\mathbf{J}_q'\cdot\text{grad } (-T)}{T} + \sum_{i=1}^{n} \mathbf{J}_i\cdot\text{grad } (-\mu_i^c), \tag{13-5}$$

in which

$$\mathbf{J}_q' = \mathbf{J}_q - \sum_{i=1}^{n} \bar{H}_i\mathbf{J}_i. \tag{13-6}$$

The thermal flow, $\mathbf{J}_q'$, has been called the "reduced" heat flow;[2] it is the difference between the "total" heat flow and the heat flow caused by the flows of matter. The use of the dissipation function in the form given by Eq. (13-5) is advantageous when dealing with diffusion in systems of nonuniform temperature because the forces conjugate to the flows of matter do not contain grad T.

Equation (13-5) may be further modified by making use of the Gibbs–Duhem relation, which requires that

$$\sum_{i=1}^{n-1} c_i \text{ grad } \mu_i^c = -c_w \text{ grad } \mu_w^c, \tag{13-7}$$

in which the subscript w denotes solvent. Introducing Eq. (13-7) into Eq. (13-5) and rearranging, we obtain

$$\Phi = \frac{\mathbf{J}_q'\cdot\text{grad } (-T)}{T} + \sum_{i=1}^{n-1} \left(\mathbf{J}_i - \frac{c_i}{c_w}\mathbf{J}_w\right)\cdot\text{grad } (-\mu_i^c).$$

As previously discussed, the flows $\mathbf{J}_i - (c_i/c_w)\mathbf{J}_w$ are the flows of the solutes relative to solvent, $\mathbf{J}_i^d$, so that

$$\Phi = \frac{\mathbf{J}_q'\cdot\text{grad } (-T)}{T} + \sum_{i=1}^{n-1} \mathbf{J}_i^d\cdot\text{grad } (-\mu_i^c). \tag{13-8}$$

13.1.2. For a binary, solution Eq. (13-8) reduces to

$$\Phi = \frac{\mathbf{J}'_q \cdot \text{grad}\,(-T)}{T} + \mathbf{J}^d_s \cdot \text{grad}\,(-\mu^c_s), \tag{13-9}$$

in which $\mathbf{J}^d_s$ is the flow of the solute relative to solvent. Using the flows and forces defined by Eq. (13-9), the phenomenological equations may be written

$$\begin{aligned} \mathbf{J}^d_s &= -L_{11}\,\text{grad}\,\mu^c_s - L_{1q}\frac{\text{grad}\,T}{T} \\ \mathbf{J}'_q &= -L_{q1}\,\text{grad}\,\mu^c_s - L_{qq}\frac{\text{grad}\,T}{T}, \end{aligned} \tag{13-10}$$

and the reciprocal relation is

$$L_{1q} = L_{q1}. \tag{13-11}$$

With the relation between grad μ^c_s and grad c_s,

$$\text{grad}\,\mu^c_s = \frac{\partial \mu_s}{\partial c_s}\,\text{grad}\,c_s = \mu_{ss}\,\text{grad}\,c_s,$$

the equation for solute flow becomes

$$\mathbf{J}^d_s = -L_{11}\mu_{ss}\,\text{grad}\,c_s - L_{1q}\frac{\text{grad}\,T}{T}. \tag{13-12}$$

The total flow of solute is made up of two terms, the ordinary diffusional flow, proportional to the concentration gradient, and a thermal-diffusion flow, dependent on the temperature gradient. The coefficient of grad c_s in Eq. (13-12) is the diffusion coefficient D of the solute defined in Chapter 9. It is generally found that L_{1q} is linearly proportional to the solute concentration c_s. It is, therefore, convenient to define a thermal-diffusion coefficient D^T by the relation

$$\frac{L_{1q}}{T} = c_s D^T. \tag{13-13}$$

Equation (13-12) may, therefore, be written

$$\mathbf{J}^d_s = -D\,\text{grad}\,c_s - c_s D^T\,\text{grad}\,T. \tag{13-14}$$

The phenomenon of thermal diffusion in solution is often characterized by the Soret coefficient, s_T, defined as the ratio of the thermal-diffusion coefficient to the ordinary diffusion coefficient:

$$s_T = \frac{D^T}{D} = \frac{L_{1q}}{Dc_s T}. \tag{13-15}$$

The Soret coefficient is a measure of the concentration gradient of the solute that can be maintained as a result of a temperature gradient at a steady state, which is defined by the condition $\mathbf{J}_s^d = 0$, grad T = constant. In this case, Eq. (13-13) becomes

$$\frac{\text{grad } c_s}{\text{grad } T} = \frac{-c_s D^T}{D},$$

or, in view of Eq. (13-15),

$$\frac{\text{grad } \ln c_s}{\text{grad } T} = -s_T. \tag{13-16}$$

13.1.3. Thermal diffusion may also be discussed in terms of a new quantity, the heat of transfer, Q^*, which is defined as the reduced heat flow per unit flow of matter at uniform temperature. From Eq. (13-10),

$$\left(\frac{\mathbf{J}_q'}{\mathbf{J}_s^d}\right)_{\text{grad } T=0} = Q^* = \frac{L_{q1}}{L_{11}}. \tag{13-17}$$

From Eq. (13-17) together with the Onsager relation, Eq. (13-11), Eq. (13-12) may be written

$$\mathbf{J}_s^d = -L_{11}\mu_{ss} \text{ grad } c_s - L_{11}Q^* \frac{\text{grad } T}{T}.$$

The thermal-diffusion coefficient is then given by

$$D^T = \frac{L_{11}Q^*}{c_s T},$$

and the Soret coefficient by

$$s_T = \frac{D^T}{D} = \frac{L_{11}Q^*}{Dc_s T}.$$

Since $D = L_{11}\mu_{ss}$, the relation between the Soret coefficient and the heat of transport is

$$s_T = \frac{Q^*}{c_s\mu_{ss}T}. \tag{13-18}$$

For dilute solutions,

$$\mu_{ss} = \frac{\partial \mu_s}{\partial c_s} = \frac{\partial}{\partial c_s}(RT \ln c_s) = \frac{RT}{c_s},$$

or

$$c_s\mu_{ss} = RT.$$

Equation (13-18) for the ideal case gives, therefore,

$$s_T = \frac{Q^*}{RT^2},$$

and hence the constancy of the Soret coefficient s_T implies a constant heat of transfer Q^*. If an independent method of measuring Q^* were available, the verification of Eq. (13-18) would provide an experimental test of the reciprocal relation $L_{1q} = L_{q1}$. However, such measurements have not, as yet, been possible. The physical meaning of the heat of transport will be discussed in more detail in the following section; here we merely wish to show that this quantity can be ulitized for the description of thermal diffusion.

Thermal diffusion in binary systems has been studied rather extensively in gaseous, liquid, and solid phases. In practice, a cell is filled with a solution of uniform composition and the two end plates are maintained at different temperatures. The steady-state concentration gradient developed in the presence of the constant temperature gradient is observed in order to evaluate the thermal effect. The thermal-diffusion coefficient is found to be smaller by a factor of 10^2 to 10^3 than the ordinary diffusion coefficient for electrolytes, nonelectrolytes, and gases, so that the concentration gradient is small unless the temperature gradient is very large. (See, for example, the data compiled by Jost.[1] The quantity $\alpha = D^T T/D = Ts_T$ is often reported as a measure of the thermal-diffusion effect.) Thus, the phenomenon probably does not play a significant role in biological systems unless the thermal-diffusion coefficient is much greater than in free solution because any temperature gradient which exists must be small. Thermal diffusion has, however, found an important application in the separation of isotopes in the gaseous phase. Clusius and Dickel[3] found that efficient separation of, for example, Kr^{84} and Kr^{86} or HCl^{37} and HCl^{35} could be achieved by making use of a vertical tube equipped with a heating wire along its axis. In these cases, the separation is aided by convection since the component moving toward the heated wire is carried upward while the one moving outward toward the cold wall also moves downward. As a result, the separation is much more effective than that expected on the basis of the Soret coefficient itself.

13.2. Thermal Osmosis

13.2.1. Thermal diffusion in a discontinuous system is often called thermal osmosis. The simplest arrangement for demonstration of thermal osmosis is one of two well-mixed compartments separated by a permeable membrane or barrier that allows maintenance of pressure and temperature differences across it. An interrelation between the flow of matter and a temperature difference in such simple discontinuous systems has been demonstrated by Ernst and Homola[4] and by Denbigh and Raumann.[5] The latter have carried out experiments in which a rubber membrane separated two compartments containing either CO_2 or H_2. If the compartments were maintained at different temperatures, gas moved from one side of the membrane to the other, and a steady difference in pressure developed between the two compartments. In the case of CO_2, the pressure difference was of the order of 0.2 percent per degree temperature difference with the higher pressure on the warm side; with H_2, the pressure difference was smaller and the effect was in the opposite direction. A similar relation between pressure and temperature differences has been observed in liquid helium II by Kapitza[6] and by Meyer and Mellink.[7]

In order to analyze such a system, we shall make use of the dissipation function expressed in terms of the entropy flow $\mathbf{J}_S$, which, according to Eq. (7-22), has the form

$$\Phi = \mathbf{J}_S \cdot \text{grad}\,(-T) + \sum_{i=1}^{n} \mathbf{J}_i \cdot \text{grad}\,(-\mu_i), \tag{13-19}$$

under the condition of no chemical reaction. This expression is the local equation for any point within the barrier. In order to obtain an expression applicable to a discontinuous system, Eq. (13-19) must be integrated across the barrier, following the method introduced in Chapter 10. Assuming that the system is in a steady state, the integrated form of Eq. (13-19) is

$$\mathbf{\Phi} = J_S \Delta T + \sum_{i=1}^{n} J_i \Delta\mu_i, \tag{13-20}$$

in which $\mathbf{\Phi} = \int \Phi dx$ and ΔT and $\Delta\mu_i$ refer to the differences of temperature and chemical potential across the barrier. For a system containing only a single component, Eq. (13-20) becomes

$$\mathbf{\Phi} = J_S \Delta T + J_m \Delta\mu_m, \tag{13-21}$$

in which J_m is the flow of matter, and the phenomenological equations may be written

$$\begin{aligned} J_m &= L_{11}\Delta\mu_m + L_{12}\Delta T, \\ J_S &= L_{21}\Delta\mu_m + L_{22}\Delta T, \end{aligned} \tag{13-22}$$

with the reciprocal relation

$$L_{12} = L_{21}. \tag{13-23}$$

Equations (13-22) can be brought into a more useful form by introducing the explicit expression for $\Delta\mu_m$ which, for a system containing a single component, takes the form

$$\Delta\mu_m = -\bar{S}\Delta T + \bar{V}\Delta P. \tag{13-24}$$

The quantities $\bar{S}$ and $\bar{V}$ are respectively the partial molar entropy and the partial molar volume of the component. Introducing this expression into Eqs. (13-22) and rearranging yields

$$
\begin{aligned}
J_m &= L_{11}\bar{V}\Delta P + (L_{12} - L_{11}\bar{S})\Delta T, \\
J_S &= L_{21}\bar{V}\Delta P + (L_{22} - L_{21}\bar{S})\Delta T.
\end{aligned}
\tag{13-25}
$$

The case of interest is the steady state attained when a constant temperature difference is applied to the system. Under these conditions, a pressure difference develops across the barrier that makes $J_m = 0$. The magnitude of this stationary pressure can be ascertained from the first of Eqs. (13-25), which becomes, for $J_m = 0$,

$$
\left(\frac{\Delta P}{\Delta T}\right)_{J_m=0} = \frac{-(L_{12} - L_{11}\bar{S})}{\bar{V}L_{11}} = \frac{-L_{12}}{\bar{V}L_{11}} + \frac{\bar{S}}{\bar{V}}. \tag{13-26}
$$

Thus, the thermoosmotic effect is dependent on two factors, one proportional to the ratio of the cross coefficient L_{12} to the straight coefficient L_{11}, and one proportional to the partial molar entropy $\bar{S}$. The latter contribution is due to the fact that the difference in temperature gives rise directly to a difference in chemical potential as indicated by Eq. (13-24). It is, however, the term L_{12}/L_{11} that represents a coupling of the flows of matter and of entropy (or heat).

This coupling phenomenon may be considered in terms of a new quantity, the *entropy of transfer*, S^*, which is defined as the entropy transferred by a unit flow of matter under conditions of uniform temperature. Thus,

$$
\left(\frac{J_S}{J_m}\right)_{\Delta T=0} = \frac{L_{21}}{L_{11}} = S^*. \tag{13-27}
$$

Experiments on the nonisothermal diffusion of water vapor recently reported by Cary[8] have shown that the Onsager relation is verified to within a few percent for this system. Thus, making use of the reciprocal relation, Eq. (13-23), we can write Eq. (13-26)

$$
\left(\frac{\Delta P}{\Delta T}\right)_{J_m=0} = \frac{-(S^* - \bar{S})}{\bar{V}}. \tag{13-28}
$$

The steady-state pressure difference produced by a temperature difference depends, therefore, on the difference between the entropy of transport S^* and the partial molar entropy of the substance, $\bar{S}$.

13.2.2. In order to develop a better understanding of the effects of temperature on the flow of matter, the entropy of transfer and the heat of transfer, introduced in Sec. 13.1.3, will be considered in more detail. The interrelations between the quantities of transfer should, however, be examined first. As discussed in detail by de Groot,[9] several transformations of flows and forces can be utilized for the description of nonisothermal systems, each leading to a different heat flow. The three most important flows have already been introduced. In Chapter 7, we considered the total heat flow, denoted by J_q and defined by Eq. (7-14), as well as the entropy flow J_S, defined by the relation

$$TJ_S = J_q - \sum_{i=1}^{n} \mu_i J_i.$$

In Sec. 13.1.1, the "reduced" heat flow J'_q, given by the expression

$$J'_q = J_q - \sum_{i=1}^{n} \bar{H}_i J_i,$$

was used. For the present case of a system containing only a single component, these relations reduce to

$$TJ_S = J_q - \mu J_m, \tag{13-29}$$

$$J'_q = J_q - \bar{H} J_m, \tag{13-30}$$

in which $\bar{H}$ is the partial molar enthalpy.

Equations (13-29) and (13-30) can be used to define two additional quantities of transfer for the discontinuous system and to relate these to S^*. The introduction of Eq. (13-29) into Eq. (13-27) yields

$$S^* = \left(\frac{J_S}{J_m}\right)_{\Delta T=0} = \frac{1}{T}\left[\left(\frac{J_q}{J_m}\right)_{\Delta T=0} - \mu\right].$$

The quantity $(J_q/J_m)_{\Delta T=0}$ may be called the energy of transfer, U^*, so that

$$TS^* = U^* - \mu. \tag{13-31}$$

From Eq. (13-30) we find that

$$\left(\frac{J'_q}{J_m}\right)_{\Delta T=0} = \left[\left(\frac{J_q}{J_m}\right)_{\Delta T=0} - \bar{H}\right] = U^* - \bar{H}.$$

In analogy to Eq. (13-17),

$$\left(\frac{J'_q}{J_m}\right)_{\Delta T=0} = Q^*,$$

so that

$$Q^* = U^* - \bar{H}. \tag{13-32}$$

Thus, the heat of transfer Q^* is given by the difference between the energy of transfer and the partial molar enthalpy. Using Eqs. (13-31) and (13-32) as well as the relation

$$\bar{H} = \mu + T\bar{S},$$

we find that

$$Q^* = T(S^* - \bar{S}). \tag{13-33}$$

In view of Eq. (13-33), Eq. (13-28), describing the steady-state thermo-osmotic effect, could be written

$$\left(\frac{\Delta P}{\Delta T}\right)_{J_m=0} = \frac{-Q^*}{\bar{V}T}. \tag{13-34}$$

This relation can also be obtained directly if the system is described with the aid of the dissipation function in the form given by Eq. (13-5), in which J_q' appears.

The concept of quantities of transfer may be clarified by considering a rather general example discussed by Denbigh.[10] If two compartments are separated by a barrier that can be penetrated only by molecules of a relatively high energy, the energy of the transported molecules will be greater than the average energy of the molecules on the side from which they come. This side will lose internal energy as a result of the transfer process, while the opposite side will gain energy. Thus, to maintain a condition of uniform temperature, heat, equal to the heat of transfer, must be added to one side of the barrier and removed from the other side. If the energy of transfer across the barrier were equal to the molar enthalpy of the molecules, the energy transported would be equal to the average energy, and no heat would need to be added to or removed from the system in order to maintain a uniform temperature. The heat of transfer would then be zero, as indicated by Eq. (13-32).

A more specific example, such as that mentioned by Spanner,[11] may also prove instructive. Consider two water-filled compartments, 1 and 2, connected by a barrier consisting of a wide tube and maintained at the same temperature. In this case the transfer of a mole of water from 1 to 2 will not alter the temperature of either compartment. If, however, the barrier between the compartments is replaced by a vapor phase, the situation is altered. The transfer of water from 1 to 2 now requires vaporization of one mole in 1 and its condensation in 2; compartment 1 will thus lose an amount of heat equal to the heat of vaporization per mole of water, while compartment 2 will gain this amount of heat. In order to maintain the condition of uniform temperature, a quantity of heat, equal to the heat of vaporization, must be added to 1 and removed from 2 during the transport process.

It should be kept in mind that the quantities of transfer are macroscopic thermodynamic quantities defined in a general phenomenological sense; any attempt to interpret them in other terms must be based on a kinetic model and will be less general than the phenomenological definition. Nonetheless, the foregoing considerations may give some insight into the physical meaning of heat of transfer. In particular, they indicate that, in a system of the type under discussion, the nature of the barrier plays an important role in determining the heat of transfer. They further indicate that Q^*

may vanish under appropriate conditions and suggest the possibility that Q^* may, in general, have either positive or negative values.

Spanner[11] has presented an interesting discussion of the possible significance of thermal osmosis in the transfer of water in biological systems. He has estimated that $Q^*_{H_2O}$ for water movement across plant-cell membrances is approximately 17,000 cal/mole. If this value is introduced into Eq. (13-34) along with appropriate values of $\bar{V}$ and T, we find that a temperature difference of 0.01 C deg would give rise to a stationary pressure difference of 1.32 atm. However, as pointed out by Spanner, the maintenance of even this small temperature difference across biological membranes is rather unlikely. Since the membranes concerned are about 100 Å thick, a ΔT of 0.01 deg would correspond to a temperature gradient of 10,000 deg/cm. Unless the barrier has an extremely low heat conductivity, such a gradient could not be maintained. Nevertheless, since the many chemical reactions occurring within a cell are accompanied by production or consumption of heat, local temperature gradients cannot be completely ruled out and these might play some role in the transport of materials across biological membranes.

13.3. Thermoelectricity

The basic thermoelectric phenomena were observed early in the 19th century, and were the first coupled processes for which a detailed thermodynamic explanation was attempted. For nearly 100 years there was little practical application of thermoelectricity, with the exception of the use of thermocouples for temperature measurements. The recent development of transistor electronics provoked a renewed interest in the large thermoelectric effects of semiconductors and led to an intensive theoretical and experimental study of these phenomena. In this section, the thermodynamic description of the basic thermoelectric phenomena will be summarized; for a more detailed treatment, the reader should consult the papers of Callen[12] and Domenicali.[13]

13.3.1. In 1821, Seebeck observed that heating one junction of a bimetallic couple and cooling the other gave rise to an electromotive force in the circuit. The couple studied by Seebeck consisted of copper–iron and the electromotive force developed was small, only 2 mv/100 C deg. The effect may, however, be easily multiplied and thermoelectric potentials now constitute one of the most sensitive methods of temperature determination. Further, the study of semiconductors has shown that thermocouples made of these materials can develop electromotive forces of the order of 200 mv/100 C deg and higher. Thermoelectric potentials of this magnitude have made feasible the use of this phenomenon as a means of converting heat into electricity, with an efficiency of up to 10 percent. Although less efficient than more conventional methods, thermoelectric generators can be useful in cases where power requirements are low.

Thirteen years after Seebeck's observations, Peltier found that passage of electric current through a bimetallic circuit caused absorption of heat at one junction and liberation of heat at the other. The rate at which heat must be supplied to or removed from the junctions to maintain their temperature constant is proportional to the current and reverses sign when the direction of the current is reversed. Thus, the effect cannot be ascribed simply to overcoming resistance since this heat would be proportional to the square of the current and, hence, independent of its direction. The heat flow per unit current at constant temperature was called the Peltier heat Π, defined as

$$\Pi = \frac{\text{heat added or removed}}{I}.$$

Generally, Π is dependent on temperature, and if the junctions are held at different temperatures there will be a net influx or efflux of heat from or to the surroundings. The properties of semiconductors have made possible the utilization of the Peltier effect for rapid heating or cooling by passing electric current through a couple. With materials presently available, maximum temperature differences of 60–70 C deg can be maintained between hot and cold junctions, and such devices appear to have many potential uses in various branches of scientific research. Some recent information concerning thermoelectric properties of semiconductors may be found in *Selected Papers on New Techniques for Energy Conversion.*[14]

In 1854, Thomson (Lord Kelvin)[15] analyzed the energy balance of thermoelectric phenomena and found that the Peltier heat could not account fully for the electric energy conversion. He therefore postulated a third effect taking place also in the homogeneous wires. The phenonenon of the Thomson heat can be illustrated by the arrangement shown in Fig. 28. We consider a homogeneous wire heated to a temperature of 100°C with two neighboring points cooled to 0°C. The temperatures at the points A and B, equidistant between the hot and cold points, will be equal when there is no current in the wire. If, however, current is passed through the system we find that $T_A \neq T_B$. Thus, the current disturbs the temperature gradient and the original gradient can be maintained only

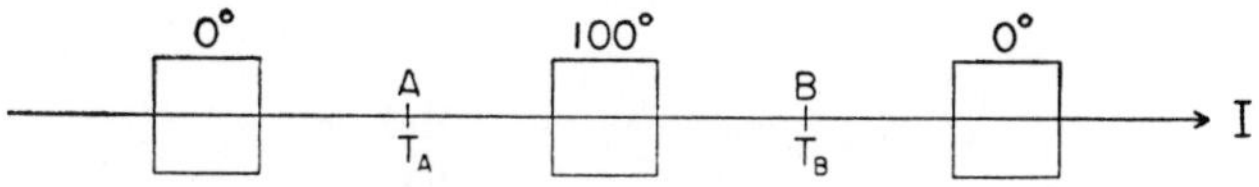

Fig. 28. System for demonstration of the Thomson heat. The uniform wire is heated to 100°C at its central point and held at 0°C at two equidistant points. A current is passed through the wire and the temperature at points A and B, equidistant between the hot and cold points is measured.

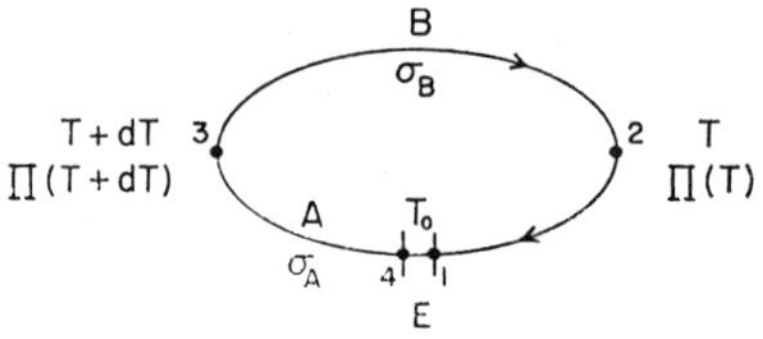

Fig. 29. A bimetallic couple of metals A and B. The two junctions are maintained at different temperatures, T and $T + dT$; σ_A and σ_B are Thomson heats, $\Pi(T)$ and $\Pi(T + dT)$ are Peltier heats, and E is electromotive force.

by addition or removal of heat. The heat required per unit current and per unit temperature gradient is called the Thomson heat and is denoted by $\sigma_A(T)$, indicating that it is a function of the nature of the metal, A, and of the temperature:

$$\sigma_A = \frac{1}{I}\frac{dQ}{dT}. \tag{13-35}$$

All three effects, the Seebeck, Peltier, and Thomson effects, demonstrate the existence of a coupling between thermal and electrical phenomena. In the following section, we shall characterize this coupling in more detail and elucidate the various factors involved.

13.3.2. The first satisfactory relation between electrical and thermal quantities was derived by Thomson in his fundamental paper of 1854. In order to develop these relations, we shall consider the system shown in Fig. 29 composed of metals A and B with one junction maintained at temperature T and the other at $T + dT$. An electromotive force E drives a current I through the system. A Peltier heat $\Pi(T + dT)$, per unit current, will be absorbed at the warm junction and an amount $\Pi(T)$ will be given off at the cool junction. In order to maintain a temperature gradient, Thomson heat $\sigma_A dT$ must be supplied to the metal A and, since the current is in the opposite direction in metal B, an amount of heat $\sigma_B dT$ must be removed from B. In a closed work cycle, the electrical energy is fully converted to heat, so that, by the first law of thermodynamics, the balance per unit current is

$$dE = \Pi(T + dT) - \Pi(T) + \sigma_A dT - \sigma_B dT. \tag{13-36}$$

We may now expand $\Pi(T + dT)$ in a Taylor series, retaining only the first two terms,

$$\Pi(T + dT) = \Pi(T) + \frac{d\Pi}{dT}\,dT.$$

Inserting this relation into Eq. (13-36), we obtain

$$dE = \frac{d\Pi}{dT}\,dT + (\sigma_A - \sigma_B)dT.$$

or

$$\frac{dE}{dT} = \frac{d\Pi}{dT} + (\sigma_A - \sigma_B). \tag{13-37}$$

Equation (13-37) is the famous first equation of Thomson for thermoelectricity.

13.3.3. Before considering the deduction of the second equation from the dissipation function, we shall analyze the bimetallic circuit in more detail in terms of the flows and forces for any element of the system. The most convenient form of Φ for the present purpose is

$$\Phi = \mathbf{J}_S \cdot \text{grad}\,(-T) + \sum_{i=1}^{n} \mathbf{J}_i \cdot \text{grad}\,(-\tilde{\mu}_i)$$

in which $\mathbf{J}_S$ is the flow of entropy. We may now assume that the metallic system under consideration is composed of only two components, electrons and ions, and that the electrons are the only flowing species. Under these conditions,

$$\Phi = \mathbf{J}_S \cdot \text{grad}\,(-T) + \mathbf{J}_e \cdot \text{grad}\,(-\tilde{\mu}_e), \tag{13-38}$$

in which $\mathbf{J}_e$ represents the absolute flow of electrons. Equation (13-38) defines a set of flows and forces for the system, and the corresponding phenomenological equations are

$$\begin{aligned} \mathbf{J}_S &= -L_{11}\,\text{grad}\,T - L_{12}\,\text{grad}\,\tilde{\mu}_e, \\ \mathbf{J}_e &= -L_{21}\,\text{grad}\,T - L_{22}\,\text{grad}\,\tilde{\mu}_e. \end{aligned} \tag{13-39}$$

Let us now consider the Seebeck experiment in which the two junctions of a couple, such as that illustrated in Fig. 29, are held at different temperatures. The points 1 and 4, assumed to be at the same temperature T_0, will be connected to a potentiomenter so that the electromotive force E can be measured with zero current ($\mathbf{J}_e = 0$). Under these conditions, Eq. (13-39) leads to the relation

$$\text{grad}\,\tilde{\mu}_e = \frac{-L_{21}}{L_{22}}\,\text{grad}\,T. \tag{13-40}$$

Before proceeding further, it will be convenient to introduce the entropy of transfer S^* discussed in Sec. 13.2.1. This quantity is defined as the entropy transferred per unit flow of electrons at uniform temperature. From Eqs. (13-39),

$$\left(\frac{\mathbf{J}_s}{\mathbf{J}_e}\right)_{\text{grad}\,T=0} = S^* = \frac{L_{12}}{L_{22}}. \tag{13-41}$$

Using the reciprocal relation $L_{12} = L_{21}$ and introducing Eq. (13-41) into Eq. (13-40), we obtain

$$\text{grad}\,\tilde{\mu}_e = -S^*\,\text{grad}\,T. \tag{13-42}$$

In order to evaluate the total electromotive force of the circuit shown in Fig. 29, Eq. (13-42) must be integrated between points 1 and 4. Assuming that the gradients depend only on the x-coordinate, the result is obtained by summing the following integrals:

$$\tilde{\mu}_{e2} - \tilde{\mu}_{e1} = -\int_{T_0}^{T} S_A^* dT,$$

$$\tilde{\mu}_{e3} - \tilde{\mu}_{e2} = -\int_{T}^{T+dT} S_B^* dT,$$

$$\tilde{\mu}_{e4} - \tilde{\mu}_{e3} = -\int_{T+dT}^{T_0} S_A^* dT,$$

or

$$\tilde{\mu}_{e(4)} - \tilde{\mu}_{e(1)} = \Delta\tilde{\mu}_e = \int_{T}^{T+dT} (S_A^* - S_B^*) dT. \tag{13-43}$$

However, since points 1 and 4 are at the same temperature and the condition of electroneutrality in the metal requires that there be no concentration gradient for the electrons, $\Delta\tilde{\mu}_e$ becomes simply

$$\Delta\tilde{\mu}_e = -\mathfrak{F}\Delta\psi,$$

and Eq. (13-43) becomes

$$E = \Delta\psi = -\frac{1}{\mathfrak{F}} \int_{T}^{T+dT} (S_A^* - S_B^*) dT. \tag{13-44}$$

Differentiating Eq. (13-44) with respect to T yields

$$\frac{dE}{dT} = -\frac{S_A^* - S_B^*}{\mathfrak{F}}. \tag{13-45}$$

This derivative is called the relative thermoelectric power of the metal A against B. It represents one expression of the coupling between the electrical and the thermal phenomena since the entropies of transfer depend on the cross coefficient L_{12} in Eq. (13-41).

Another expression of this coupling may be obtained by considering the Peltier experiment in which a heat flow accompanies a current under isothermal conditions. In order to do this, we shall examine in more detail the processes occurring at the junction between the two metals, A and B, during a steady current flow under isothermal conditions. As illustrated in Fig. 30, both the potentials and characteristic parameters are different in A and B. Hence by applying Eq. (13-39) to both metals, with grad $T = 0$, we find that

$$\mathbf{J}_e = \mathfrak{F} L_{22}^A \operatorname{grad} \psi = \mathfrak{F} L_{22}^B \operatorname{grad} \psi. \tag{13-46}$$

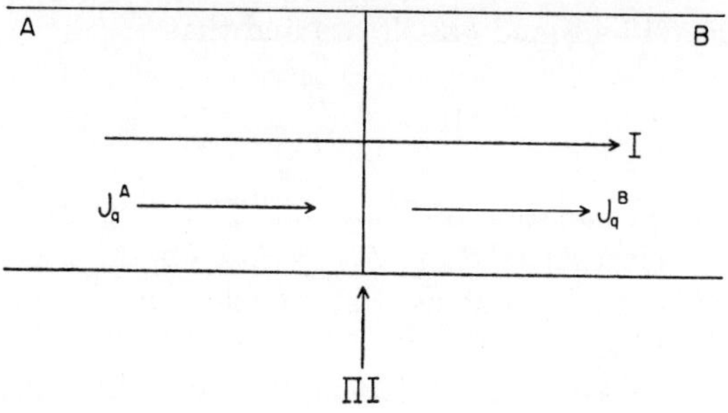

Fig. 30. Diagram of a junction between two metals A and B; $\mathbf{I}$ is electric current, $\mathbf{J}_q^A$ and $\mathbf{J}_q^B$ are heat flows in the two metals, and $\Pi\mathbf{I}$ is the Peltier heat absorbed at the junction.

If we introduce the current $\mathbf{I}$, given by

$$\mathbf{I} = -\mathfrak{F}\mathbf{J}_e, \tag{13-47}$$

Eq. (13-46) may be written in the form of Ohm's law,

$$-\mathbf{I} = \mathfrak{F}^2 L_{22}^A \operatorname{grad} \psi \tag{13-48}$$

and

$$-\mathbf{I} = \mathfrak{F}^2 L_{22}^B \operatorname{grad} \psi. \tag{13-49}$$

The flows of heat passing the two metals are given by $T\mathbf{J}_S^A$ and $T\mathbf{J}_S^B$. In general, these flows are not equal since an amount of heat given by $\Pi\mathbf{I}$ must be absorbed or injected at the junction in order to maintain constant temperature. Thus,

$$T\mathbf{J}_S^B = T\mathbf{J}_S^A - \Pi\mathbf{I}. \tag{13-50}$$

From Eq. (13-39) we find that for the condition grad $T = 0$

$$T\mathbf{J}_S^A = -TL_{12}^A \operatorname{grad} \tilde{\mu}_e, \tag{13-51}$$

$$T\mathbf{J}_S^B = -TL_{12}^B \operatorname{grad} \tilde{\mu}_e. \tag{13-52}$$

Dividing Eq. (13-51) by Eq. (13-48) and Eq. (13-52) by Eq. (13-49) yields

$$\left(\frac{T\mathbf{J}_S^A}{\mathbf{I}}\right)_{\text{grad } T=0} = \frac{-TL_{12}^A}{L_{22}^A} = \frac{-TS_A^*}{\mathfrak{F}},$$

$$\left(\frac{T\mathbf{J}_S^B}{\mathbf{I}}\right)_{\text{grad } T=0} = \frac{-TL_{12}^B}{L_{22}^B} = \frac{-TS_B^*}{\mathfrak{F}},$$

in which Eq. (13-41) has been used. Inserting these expressions into Eq. (13-50) we obtain

$$\Pi = T\,\frac{S_B^* - S_A^*}{\mathfrak{F}}. \tag{13-53}$$

Comparing Eqs. (13-45) and (13-53) we find that

$$\Pi = T\frac{dE}{dT}, \tag{13-54}$$

which is the second equation of Thomson. This equality depends on the validity of the reciprocal relation, $L_{12} = L_{21}$, for the coefficients in Eqs. (13-39), since this relation was used in introducing S^* into the expression for dE/dT (see Eqs. (13-40), (13-41), and (13-42)). Thus, the ample experimental verification[16] of Eq. (13-54) provides additional confirmation of the validity of Onsager's law.

In order to complete the formal relation between thermal and electrical phenomena, we shall consider Eq. (13-54) in more detail. Differentiating this expression with respect to temperature, we obtain

$$\frac{d\Pi}{dT} = \frac{dE}{dT} + T\frac{d^2E}{dT^2}, \tag{13-55}$$

and, in view of Eq. (13-37),

$$\sigma_A - \sigma_B = -T\frac{d^2E}{dT^2}. \tag{13-56}$$

Further, since

$$\frac{dE}{dT} = -\frac{S_A^* - S_B^*}{\mathfrak{F}},$$

$$\sigma_A - \sigma_B = T\frac{d^2E}{dT^2} = -\frac{T}{\mathfrak{F}}\frac{dS_A^*}{dT} + \frac{T}{\mathfrak{F}}\frac{dS_B^*}{dT}.$$

This expression identifies the Thomson heats with the specific entropies of transport of the individual metals A and B:

$$\sigma_A = -\frac{T}{\mathfrak{F}}\frac{dS_A^*}{dT}, \qquad \sigma_B = -\frac{T}{\mathfrak{F}}\frac{dS_B^*}{dT}. \tag{13-57}$$

Thus, with the use of Eqs. (13-54), (13-55), and (13-56), the Peltier heat, its variation with temperature, and the Thomson specific heat may be obtained from E and its first and second derivatives with respect to temperature.

13.3.4. The considerations of the previous section may be utilized for an additional interpretation of the physical content of the equations, by examining the exchange of energy between a single conductor, A, and its surroundings. Since the only external work performed by the present system is electrical work,

$$\mathbf{J}_u = \mathbf{J}_q + \mathbf{I}\psi,$$

in which $\mathbf{J}_u$ is the flow of energy and $\mathbf{J}_q$ is the flow of heat. Thus, the conservation equation for the energy, Eq. (6-16), becomes

$$\frac{\partial \rho_u}{\partial t} = -\text{div } \mathbf{J}_u = -\text{div } (\mathbf{J}_q + \mathbf{I}\psi),$$

in which ρ_u is the total energy per unit volume at any point. For the condition div $\mathbf{I} = -\mathfrak{F}$ div $\mathbf{J}_e = 0$ which, for the present system, is imposed by the requirement of electroneutrality,

$$\frac{\partial \rho_u}{\partial t} = -\text{div } \mathbf{J}_q - \mathbf{I}\cdot\text{grad } \psi. \tag{13-58}$$

According to the considerations of Sec. 13.2.2, the heat flow $\mathbf{J}_q$ is given by

$$\mathbf{J}_q = T\mathbf{J}_S + \mu_e\mathbf{J}_e. \tag{13-59}$$

Inserting Eq. (13-59) into Eq. (13-58), we obtain, after rearrangement,

$$\frac{\partial \rho_u}{\partial t} = -\mathbf{I}\cdot\text{grad } \psi - \mathbf{J}_e\cdot\text{grad } \mu_e - \text{div } T\mathbf{J}_S, \tag{13-60}$$

in which the condition div $\mathbf{J}_e = 0$ has also been used. Since $\mathbf{I} = -\mathfrak{F}\mathbf{J}_e$, Eq. (13-60) can be written

$$\frac{\partial \rho_u}{\partial t} = -\mathbf{J}_e\cdot\text{grad } \tilde{\mu}_e - \text{div } T\mathbf{J}_S. \tag{13-61}$$

The physical meaning of Eq. (13-61) can be more clearly demonstrated by making use of the phenomenological equations (13-39). The expression for $\mathbf{J}_e$ may be solved for grad $\tilde{\mu}_e$, to yield

$$-\text{grad } \tilde{\mu}_e = \frac{\mathbf{J}_e}{L_{22}} + \frac{L_{21}}{L_{22}} \text{grad } T. \tag{13-62}$$

Introducing Eq. (13-62) into the expression for $\mathbf{J}_S$ and rearranging, we obtain

$$\mathbf{J}_S = -\frac{L_{11}L_{22} - L_{12}L_{21}}{L_{22}} \text{grad } T + \frac{L_{12}}{L_{22}} \mathbf{J}_e. \tag{13-63}$$

Since $T\mathbf{J}_S$ is the heat flow at $\mathbf{J}_e = 0$, the coefficient of grad T in Eq. (13-63) may be related to the ordinary thermal conductivity λ by the expression

$$\lambda = T\frac{L_{11}L_{22} - L_{12}L_{21}}{L_{22}}$$

and Eq. (13-63) may then be written

$$\mathbf{J}_S = -\frac{\lambda}{T} \text{grad } T + \frac{L_{12}}{L_{22}} \mathbf{J}_e. \tag{13-64}$$

Further, under conditions of uniform temperature, grad $\tilde{\mu}_e$ becomes simply $-\mathfrak{F}$ grad ψ and Eq. (13-62) reduces to

$$\mathfrak{F} \text{ grad } \psi = \frac{\mathbf{J}_e}{L_{22}} = \frac{-\mathbf{I}}{\mathfrak{F}L_{22}},$$

which identifies the quantity $1/\mathfrak{F}^2L_{22}$ with the electrical resistance R at uniform temperature. Thus, Eq. (13-62) becomes

$$-\text{grad } \tilde{\mu}_e = R\mathfrak{F}^2\mathbf{J}_e + \frac{L_{21}}{L_{22}} \text{ grad } T. \tag{13-65}$$

Introducing Eqs. (13-64) and (13-65) into Eq. (13-61), we obtain

$$\frac{\partial \rho_u}{\partial t} = R\mathfrak{F}^2\mathbf{J}_e^2 + \mathbf{J}_e \cdot \frac{L_{21}}{L_{22}} \text{ grad } T - \text{div}\left(-\lambda \text{ grad } T + T\frac{L_{12}}{L_{22}}\mathbf{J}_e\right).$$

Introducing Eq. (13-47) and from (13-14) yields

$$\frac{\partial \rho_u}{\partial t} = \lambda \text{ div grad } T + R\mathbf{I}^2 + \mathbf{J}_e \cdot S^* \text{ grad } T - \text{div } TS^*\mathbf{J}_e, \tag{13-66}$$

in which the reciprocal relation $L_{12} = L_{21}$ has also been used. The last term on the right-hand side of Eq. (13-66) can be expanded to yield

$$-\text{div } (TS^*\mathbf{J}_e) = TS^* \text{ div } \mathbf{J}_e - \mathbf{J}_e \cdot S^* \text{ grad } T - T\mathbf{J}_e \cdot \text{grad } S^*. \tag{13-67}$$

Since S^* is a function of temperature only, the last term on the right-hand side becomes

$$T\mathbf{J}_e \cdot \text{grad } S^* = T\mathbf{J}_e \cdot \frac{\partial S^*}{\partial T} \text{ grad } T. \tag{13-68}$$

However, in accord with Eq. (13-57), Eq. (13-68) may also be written

$$T\mathbf{J}_e \cdot \text{grad } S^* = \mathfrak{F}\mathbf{J}_e \cdot \sigma_m \text{ grad } T, \tag{13-69}$$

in which σ_m is the Thomson heat of the metal. Inserting Eq. (13-69) into Eq. (13-67), using Eq. (13-47) and the condition div $\mathbf{J}_e = 0$, we finally obtain for $\partial\rho_u/\partial t$

$$\frac{\partial \rho_u}{\partial t} = \lambda \text{ div grad } T + R\mathbf{I}^2 + \mathbf{I} \cdot \sigma_A(-\text{grad } T). \tag{13-70}$$

Equation (13-70) shows in a clear way that the change in local energy at any point in the metal is composed of the heat dissipated in conduction (the Fourier heat, λ div grad T), the heat dissipated in overcoming the resistance to flow of electrons (the Joule heat, $R\mathbf{I}^2$), and the heat spent in maintaining the gradient of temperature against the electrical flow (the Thomson heat, $\mathbf{I} \cdot \sigma_A(-\text{grad } T)$). There is no Peltier heat in a single homogeneous conductor.

CHAPTER 14

RELATIONS BETWEEN CHEMICAL REACTIONS AND DIFFUSION PROCESSES

In discussing applications of thermodynamics to systems in which irreversible processes are taking place, we have not as yet considered chemical reactions specifically. In earlier chapters, the contribution of reactions to the over-all entropy production and the relation between the thermodynamic and the kinetic descriptions of chemical reactions have been examined, but the effects of reactions on the flow of matter have not been considered. These effects would appear to be of particular interest in the description of biological systems, whose functions are dependent, directly and indirectly, on interrelated sets of chemical reactions. In the present context, we are interested in the ways in which these reactions may influence transport processes and, particularly, in the role they may play in the widespread group of biological phenomena described as active transport. An active transport process is usually defined as one that can bring about a flow of a substance against an electrochemical potential gradient of the substance[1] and the name implies that specific biological activity is involved in the process. In principle, such flow could be anticipated on the basis of the thermodynamic equations without implying the operation of an active transport. A diffusional flow against its conjugate gradient driven by dissipation of another diffusional process would be regarded as an incongruent diffusion, not as active transport. Thus, the flow of the ith component across a membrane may be written

$$J_i = L_{ii}\Delta\mu_i + \sum_{\substack{k=1 \\ k\neq i}}^{n} L_{ik}\Delta\mu_k.$$

If $\Delta\mu_i = 0$, but $\Delta\mu_k \neq 0$, a flow of i may still take place. However, on the basis of biological experience we shall assume that active transport is based on the operation of internal metabolic processes *coupled* to external diffusional flows.[2] For this reason, the relation between transport processes and chemical reactions will be considered by examining several simple examples that illustrate different modes of coupling between these two types of phenomena.

In this relation, the Curie–Prigogine principle must be taken into account. As discussed in Chapter 8, this means that in an isotropic system a diffusional flow, which is a vector, cannot be coupled directly with the flow of a chemical reaction, which is a scalar. In terms of phenomenological equations, coupling coefficients may exist relating vectorial flows to any vectorial forces in the system, but there may be no coupling coefficients relating vectorial flows to the scalar affinities of chemical reactions. We shall, however, see that there may exist indirect coupling between diffusional flows and reactions and shall examine briefly the underlying reasons.

14.1. Chemical Reactions and Steady-state Concentration Gradients

14.1.1. As pointed out by Prigogine, maintenance of a steady state may impose an interdependence between the rate of a chemical reaction and diffusional flows for systems in which no direct coupling is permitted owing to the Curie–Prigogine principle. Jardetzky and Snell[3] have recently presented a general analysis of the relations between transport and chemical reactions, using the formalism of the thermodynamics of irreversible processes. The completely general analysis is rather involved and the interested reader should consult the original article for details. However, the principles can be illustrated by some simple examples.

We shall begin by considering a container or region of finite and constant volume into which an uncharged solute 1 enters by diffusion at a rate J_1, and is then converted into a substance 2 ($1 \rightarrow 2$) at a rate J_{ch}. For convenience, we shall assume that the region external to the container is of infinite volume so that its composition is independent of time. The phenomenological equations describing this system will be

$$J_1 = L_{11}\Delta\mu_1 + L_{12}\Delta\mu_2,$$

$$J_2 = L_{21}\Delta\mu_1 + L_{22}\Delta\mu_2,$$

$$J_{ch} = L_{ch}A,$$

in which A is the affinity of the reaction $1 \rightarrow 2$ taking place within the container, and the $\Delta\mu_i$ are the differences in chemical potential between the container and the surroundings. As required by the Curie principle, the equations contain no coefficients relating J_1 or J_2 to A. For the present case, it is convenient to solve these equations for the forces (see Sec. 8.2) to yield

$$\Delta\mu_1 = R_{11}J_1 + R_{12}J_2, \tag{14-1}$$

$$\Delta\mu_2 = R_{21}J_1 + R_{22}J_2, \tag{14-2}$$

$$A = R_{ch}J_{ch}, \tag{14-3}$$

in which the coefficients R_{ij} are given by Eq. (8-6).

We shall now impose the condition of a steady state and show how this condition leads to an interdependence between otherwise unrelated flows. For a system of volume V and area of permeation $\mathcal{A}$, the equation of continuity, Eq. (6-18), is

$$\frac{dn_i}{dt} = \int_V \frac{\partial c_i}{\partial t}\, dV = \int_{\mathcal{A}} J_i d\mathcal{A} + \int_V \nu_i J_{\text{ch}} dV.$$

In a steady state, $dn_i/dt = 0$ and the flows J_i and J_{ch} are constant, so that

$$J_i \int_{\mathcal{A}} d\mathcal{A} + \nu_i J_{\text{ch}} \int_V dV = \quad J_i \mathcal{A} + \nu_i J_{\text{ch}} V,$$

or

$$J_i = -\frac{\mathcal{A}}{V} \nu_i J_{\text{ch}}. \tag{14-4}$$

In the present case, $\nu_1 = -1$, $\nu_2 = 1$ and we shall assume that $\mathcal{A} = V = 1$, so that

$$J_1 = J_{\text{ch}}; \tag{14-5}$$

$$J_2 = -J_{\text{ch}}. \tag{14-6}$$

Equations (14-5) and (14-6) represent the steady-state coupling between chemical and diffusional flows. The rates of flow of 1 and 2 across the barrier are exactly balanced by addition or removal of the substances via the chemical reaction so that the concentrations remain constant.

Introducing Eqs. (14-5) and (14-6) into Eqs. (14-1) and (14-2), we find that

$$\Delta\mu_1 = (R_{11} - R_{12})J_{\text{ch}} = \frac{(R_{11} - R_{12})A}{R_{\text{ch}}}, \tag{14-7}$$

and

$$\Delta\mu_2 = -(R_{22} - R_{21})J_{\text{ch}} = \frac{-(R_{22} - R_{21})A}{R_{\text{ch}}}. \tag{14-8}$$

Thus, Eqs. (14-7) and (14-8) illustrate the expected result that in the steady state there exist differences in the chemical potentials of the substances on the two sides of the barrier that are determined directly by the rate of the chemical reaction. If $J_{\text{ch}} = 0$, there is no difference in composition of the two phases in the steady state.

14.1.2. The foregoing case involves consideration of the effect of reaction on the transfer of substances that participate directly in the reaction. A more interesting example, first suggested by Hearon,[4] will show how a steady-state concentration gradient of a solute can be maintained by a chemical reaction even though the solute is not involved in the reaction. We shall again consider the system described in the previous section but shall also assume that a third solute, 3, is present which flows into the container at a rate J_3 without participating in the chemical reaction. We shall further assume that the flow J_3 is coupled hydrodynamically to J_1 and that there is no coupling between J_2 and any of the other flows. The phenomenological equations may then be written (in inverted form)

$$\begin{aligned} \Delta\mu_1 &= R_{11}J_1 + R_{13}J_3, \\ \Delta\mu_2 &= R_{22}J_2, \\ \Delta\mu_3 &= R_{31}J_1 + R_{33}J_3, \\ A &= R_{ch}J_{ch}. \end{aligned}$$

If the system is in a steady state, Eqs. (14-5) and (14-6) apply and we have, in addition, the condition that

$$\frac{dc_3}{dt} = J_3 = 0. \tag{14-9}$$

Introducing Eqs. (14-5) and (14-9) in the expression for $\Delta\mu_3$ we obtain the interesting result that

$$\Delta\mu_3 = R_{31}J_{ch}, \tag{14-10}$$

indicating that the nonreactive substance may also have a nonequilibrium distribution between the container and the surroundings provided its flow is coupled to that of one of the reacting substances. This is shown more clearly by making use of the explicit expression for μ_3 in the simple form

$$\mu_3 = \mu_3^0 + RT \ln c_3.$$

If the standard potential, μ_3^0, is the same in both the container (I) and the surroundings (II),

$$\Delta\mu_3 = \mu_3^{\mathrm{I}} - \mu_3^{\mathrm{II}} = RT \ln \frac{c_3^{\mathrm{I}}}{c_3^{\mathrm{II}}},$$

and

$$RT \ln \frac{c_3^{\mathrm{I}}}{c_3^{\mathrm{II}}} = R_{13}J_{ch}. \tag{14-11}$$

Thus, in order to obtain a stationary difference in concentration there should be a nonvanishing coupling coefficient R_{12} (or L_{12}) and a nonvanishing rate of chemical reaction. If $J_{ch} = 0$, or $R_{12} = 0$, the concentrations of component 3 on the two sides of the barrier will be identical in the steady state. Equations (14-7), (14-8), and (14-10) express, in a formal manner, a condition frequently occurring in biological systems. Cells are often found to have steady-state concentration differences that are dependent on certain chemical reactions, the metabolic events in the cell. Although these considerations illustrate, in a simple manner, ways in which concentration differences can be maintained as a result of chemical reactions, the actual biological cases are more complex and are often thought to involve processes of the type discussed in the following section.

14.2. Diffusion with Chemical Reaction: A Carrier System

Many biological transport processes are thought to occur as a result of the combination of a substance with a membrane constituent to form a complex which then moves across the barrier.[5] In a more general sense we may envision that a substance i is converted, at some point in a system, to a substance j which migrates to a new position and is again reconverted to i. In such schemes, the membrane constituent or component j has been called a "carrier" and the over-all process may be referred to as carrier mediated transport. The existence of such transfer mechanisms in biological systems must still be regarded as a hypothesis, since no specific carrier has been isolated. However, a carrier-mediated transport has recently been demonstrated in a relatively simple artificial system by Scholander,[6] and the system has been discussed by several authors[7] in terms similar to a carrier model. Sufficient information on this system is available to permit a thermodynamic analysis and we shall use it as a specific example illustrating this aspect of the interaction of diffusion and chemical reaction.

The studies of Scholander involved investigation of the movement of a gas through an aqueous membrane containing a mobile substance or carrier with which the gas undergoes a reversible chemical reaction. The experimental arrangement is illustrated schematically in Fig. 31. The membrane is composed of a filter soaked in a solution of hemoglobin. Oxygen gas, at different pressures, P^{I} and P^{II}, was placed in the two compartments and the steady-state flow of oxygen across the membrane

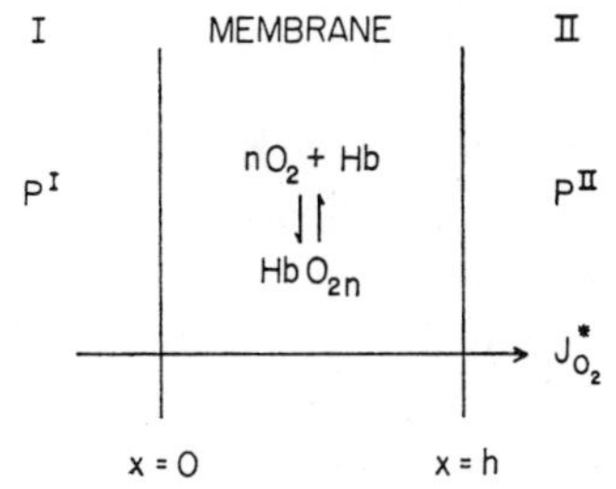

Fig. 31. Arrangement for measuring oxygen movement through a membrane containing hemoglobin.

was determined. Experimental results showed that the presence of hemoglobin in the membrane led to a greatly enhanced flow of oxygen at low O_2 pressures. However, this facilitation of O_2 transport virtually disappeared at higher pressures. In analyzing this system we shall consider only an ideal case, following a method suggested by Best and Hearon.[8] The formalism of the thermodynamics of irreversible processes will be used but several assumptions will be made that simplify the discussion appreciably without influencing the over-all results or seriously distorting the physical picture of the system.

In the experiments, a flow of oxygen J_1^* from one compartment to the other is observed as a result of a difference in oxygen pressure, $P^{\text{I}} > P^{\text{II}}$. However, it is dissolved rather than gaseous oxygen that is passing through the membrane and the true driving force for the movement of free oxygen in the barrier will be the chemical-potential gradient of dissolved oxygen. Further, the oxygen combines with the hemoglobin in the membrane, by the reaction

$$nO_2 + \text{Hb} \rightarrow \text{HbO}_{2n},$$

so that oxygen may move within the membrane in the form of HbO_{2n} as well as in the form of dissolved oxygen. The affinity of this reaction at any point in the membrane is given by

$$A = n\mu_1 + \mu_2 - \mu_3,$$

in which the subscripts 1, 2, and 3 refer to oxygen, hemoglobin (Hb), and oxyhemoglobin (HbO_{2n}) respectively. For simplicity and mathematical convenience, we shall assume that the rate of the chemical reaction is sufficiently more rapid than that of diffusion so that the reaction is at equilibrium at every point. Thus, at any point in the membrane, $A = 0$ and

$$n\mu_1 + \mu_2 = \mu_3. \tag{14-12}$$

This condition of equilibrium determines a relation among the driving forces acting on oxygen, hemoglobin, and oxyhemoglobin. Applying the gradient operator to Eq. (14-12), we obtain

$$n \text{ grad } \mu_1 + \text{grad } \mu_2 = \text{grad } \mu_3. \tag{14-13}$$

Equation (14-13) expresses a *chemical coupling* among the forces which, as we shall see, leads to a coupling of flows.

The flows passing any point in the membrane are those of free oxygen, J_1, of hemoglobin, J_2, and of oxyhemoglobin, J_3. Since under steady-state conditions the over-all flow of oxygen is constant throughout the system, the externally measured flow of oxygen, J_1^*, must be equal to the total transport within the membrane. The total flow of oxygen in the membrane is given by the sum of the flows of free oxygen and of oxygen carried by hemoglobin, so that

$$J_1^* = J_1 + nJ_3. \tag{14-14}$$

According to the same reasoning, the sum of the flows of hemoglobin and oxyhemoglobin should equal zero, since no over-all external flow of hemoglobin takes place:

$$J_2^* = J_2 + J_3 = 0. \tag{14-15}$$

Equation (14-15) states that the flows of hemoglobin and oxyhemoglobin are equal in magnitude but opposite in direction, and it therefore, describes a *circulation* of the hemoglobin within the membrane.

In order to proceed further, the phenomenological equations relating the flows to the appropriate forces must be defined. As in the preceding examples, this is done by making use of the dissipation function, which for the present case takes the form

$$\Phi = J_1 \text{ grad } (-\mu_1) + J_2 \text{ grad } (-\mu_2) + J_3 \text{ grad } (-\mu_3). \tag{14-16}$$

Equation (14-16) contains no term for the chemical reaction, since we have assumed that $A = 0$ at all points in the membrane. Under these conditions of chemical equilibrium, the forces are not independent as indicated by Eq. (14-13). In view of this relation, Eq. (14-16) can be written

$$\Phi = (J_1 + nJ_3) \text{ grad } (-\mu_1) + (J_2 + J_3) \text{ grad } (-\mu_2), \tag{14-17}$$

or, introducing the total flows defined by Eqs. (14-14) and (14-15),

$$\Phi = J_1^* \text{ grad } (-\mu_1) + J_2^* \text{ grad } (-\mu_2). \tag{14-18}$$

The flows and forces appearing in Eq. (14-18) can be related by the following phenomenological equations:

$$\begin{aligned} J_1^* &= -L_{11} \text{ grad } \mu_1 - L_{12} \text{ grad } \mu_2, \\ J_2^* &= 0 = -L_{21} \text{ grad } \mu_1 - L_{22} \text{ grad } \mu_2. \end{aligned} \tag{14-19}$$

However, this set of equations does not have the general validity of those previously discussed, since it depends on the assumption of local chemical equilibrium. For this reason, a consideration of the three flows appearing in Eq. (14-16) is more instructive and leads to a clearer physical picture of the system. For the present case, all cross coefficients relating the flows to nonconjugated forces will be neglected in order to concentrate on the effect of the chemical reaction on the transport of oxygen. Thus, we obtain the simplified equations,

$$\begin{aligned} J_1 &= -L_1 \text{ grad } \mu_1, \\ J_2 &= -L_2 \text{ grad } \mu_2, \\ J_3 &= -L_3 \text{ grad } \mu_3. \end{aligned} \tag{14-20}$$

Introducing Eqs. (14-20) into Eqs. (14-14) and (14-15) and making use of Eq. (14-13) to eliminate grad μ_3, we obtain a set of equations similar in form to Eqs. (14-19):

$$\begin{aligned} J_1^* &= (L_1 + n^2L_3)(-\text{ grad } \mu_1) + nL_3(-\text{ grad } \mu_2), \\ 0 &= nL_3(-\text{ grad } \mu_1) + (L_2 + L_3)(-\text{ grad } \mu_2). \end{aligned} \tag{14-21}$$

Equations (14-21) may be simplified by assuming ideal behavior for the components and requiring that the variation in the μ_i be confined to the x-coordinate only. Under these conditions,

$$\mu_i = \mu_i^0 + RT \ln c_i,$$

and

$$\text{grad } \mu_i = \frac{d\mu_i}{dx} = \frac{RT}{c_i}\left(\frac{dc_i}{dx}\right). \tag{14-22}$$

Further, according to Eq. (6-43), the proportionality coefficients L_i may be written

$$L_1 = c_1\omega_1, \qquad L_2 = c_2\omega_2, \qquad L_3 = c_3\omega_3, \tag{14-23}$$

in which the ω_i are the mobilities of the components. As previously discussed (Sec. 6.5), the c_i's are not constant but vary with x so that the L_i's are also functions of the x-coordinate. On the other hand, the mobilities ω_i are nearly independent of concentration over a relatively wide range and may be treated as constants in the following calculations. Introducing Eqs. (14-22) and (14-23) into Eqs. (14-21) yields

$$J_1^* = -\frac{RT}{c_1}(c_1\omega_1 + n^2c_3\omega_3)\frac{dc_1}{dx} - \frac{RTnc_3\omega_3}{c_2}\frac{dc_2}{dx}, \tag{14-24}$$

$$0 = -\frac{RT}{c_1}nc_3\omega_3\frac{dc_1}{dx} - \frac{RT}{c_2}(c_2\omega_2 + c_3\omega_3)\frac{dc_2}{dx}. \tag{14-25}$$

It is advantageous at this point to write the equilibrium condition, Eq. (14-12), in a conventional form,

$$c_1^n c_2 = Kc_3, \tag{14-26}$$

in which K is the equilibrium constant, and to assume that the mobility of hemoglobin is practically the same as of oxyhemoglobin,

$$\omega_2 \cong \omega_3. \tag{14-27}$$

By means of Eqs. (14-26) and (14-27), Eq. (14-25) is readily transformed to

$$0 = -RT\omega_3\left[\frac{nc_1^{n-1}c_2}{K}\frac{dc_1}{dx} + \left(1 + \frac{c_1^n}{K}\right)\frac{dc_2}{dx}\right], \tag{14-28}$$

or

$$0 = \frac{nc_1^{n-1}}{K + c_1^n}\frac{dc_1}{dx} + \frac{1}{c_2}\frac{dc_2}{dx} = \frac{d \ln (K + c_1^n)}{dx} + \frac{d \ln c_2}{dx}. \tag{14-29}$$

Equation (14-29) may be integrated directly to give

$$c_2(K + c_1^n) = \alpha,$$

in which α is an integration constant. Introducing Eq. (14-26) and rearranging, we obtain

$$c_2 + c_3 = \frac{\alpha}{K}. \tag{14-30}$$

The physical meaning of Eq. (14-30) is evident. If the mobilities of hemoglobin and oxyhemoglobin are the same, the sum of their concentrations will be constant throughout the membrane and equal to the average hemoglobin concentration $\bar{c}_{Hb} = \alpha/K$. On one side of the membrane the oxyhemoglobin concentration will be much larger than that of the hemoglobin, while the reverse will be true for the other side, but the total concentration will remain constant.

Making use of Eqs. (14-26) and (14-27), Eq. (14-24) may be written

$$J_1^* = -RT\omega_1 \frac{dc_1}{dx} - nRT\omega_2 \left(\frac{nc_1^{n-1}c_2}{K}\frac{dc_1}{dx} + \frac{c_1^n}{K}\frac{dc_2}{dx}\right). \tag{14-31}$$

From Eq. (14-28), we note that the term in brackets on the right-hand side of Eq. (14-31) is equal to $-dc_2/dx$, so that

$$J_1^* = -RT\omega_1 \frac{dc_1}{dx} + nRT\omega_2 \frac{dc_2}{dx}$$

or, using the definition $D_i = RT\omega_i$,

$$J_1^* = -D_1 \frac{dc_1}{dx} + nD_2 \frac{dc_2}{dx}. \tag{14-32}$$

In view of Eq. (14-30), we may also write

$$J_1^* = -D_1 \frac{dc_1}{dx} - nD_2 \frac{dc_3}{dx}. \tag{14-33}$$

Thus, as expressed by Eq. (14-33), the total oxygen flow has two components, the flow of free oxygen and the flow of bound oxygen transported by the hemoglobin carrier.

To obtain a fuller appreciation of the effect of the carrier, we may integrate Eq. (14-32) between $x = 0$ and $x = h$, assuming that J_1^*, D_1, and D_2 are constants:

$$J_1^* \int_0^h dx = D_1 \int_0^h -\frac{dc_1}{dx}\,dx - D_2 \int_0^h -\frac{dc_2}{dx}\,dx,$$

or

$$J_1^* = D_1 \frac{c_1^0 - c_1^h}{h} + nD_2 \frac{c_2^h - c_2^0}{h}. \tag{14-34}$$

As discussed in Chapter 6, the oxygen concentration at the boundaries of the aqueous-membrane phase is determined by the chemical potential of oxygen in the gaseous phase and will be the same whether hemoglobin is present in the membrane or not. Hence the term $D_1(c_1^0 - c_1^h)/h$ is determined entirely by the external oxygen pressure, and it is only in the second term on the right-hand side of Eq. (14-34) that the hemoglobin action is expressed. The values of c_2 at the two boundaries may be obtained from the equilibrium condition, Eq. (14-26), and the conservation equation, Eq. (14-30). Thus,

$$(c_1^0)^n c_2^0 = K(\bar{c}_{Hb} - c_2^0)$$

and

$$c_2^0 = \frac{\bar{c}_{Hb}}{K + (c_1^0)^n}. \tag{14-35}$$

An analogous expression holds for c_2^h, so that Eq. (14-34) becomes

$$J_1^* = J_1^0 + \frac{nD_2K\bar{c}_{Hb}}{h}\left[\frac{1}{K + (c_1^h)^n} - \frac{1}{K + (c_1^0)^n}\right], \tag{14-36}$$

in which J_1^0 is the diffusional flow of free oxygen and the second term represents the carrier-mediated flow. If $P^{\mathrm{I}} > P^{\mathrm{II}}$, $c_1^0 > c_1^h$ and the contribution of the carrier transport to the total oxygen flow is positive. Three aspects of the experimental observations of Scholander and Hemmingsen and Scholander are predicted by Eq. (14-36). First, the facilitated transport of oxygen increases with increasing hemoglobin concentration. Second, with $P^{\mathrm{II}} = 0$ ($c_1^h = 0$), the relative contribution of the facilitated transfer to total oxygen flow decreases with increase in P^{I}. Third, the facilitated transfer becomes negligible in the presence of rather low back pressures of oxygen, $P^{\mathrm{II}} \neq 0$. Such carrier systems have been proposed to explain both facilitated transfer and active transport in biological systems. In the latter case, additional coupling to metabolic reactions must be assumed. In the example given, flow will always be in the direction of the potential gradient and, for this reason, such a system would be described as one capable of facilitated transfer rather than active transport.

14.3. Phenomenological Description of Active Transport

14.3.1. As illustrated by the considerations of Sec. 14.2, a rather detailed knowledge of an active transport system is necessary in order to carry out an exact thermodynamic analysis. However, Kedem[9] has recently suggested an approach to the problem of relations between transport processes and metabolic reactions in biological systems that may prove useful. Kedem has assumed that active transport involves a metabolically dependent chemical reaction taking place within the membrane and that all flows may be considered interdependent, so that the phenomenological relations may be written (in inverted form)

$$\Delta\tilde{\mu}_i = \sum_{k=1}^{n} R_{ik}J_k + R_{ir}J_{ch}, \tag{14-37}$$

$$A_r = \sum_{k=1}^{n} R_{rk}J_k + R_{rr}J_{ch}, \tag{14-38}$$

in which the $\Delta\tilde{\mu}_i$ are the differences in electrochemical potential on the two sides of the membrane and J_{ch} is the rate of metabolic reaction. Kedem has suggested that the rate of oxygen consumption by a tissue may be a measure of J_{ch}. The coefficient R_{1r} expresses "coupling" between the flow of chemical reaction and the flow of matter. Since the flow of reaction is a scalar, the coefficient R_{ir} must be a vector. In view of the Curie–Prigogine principle, it is clear that Eqs. (14-37) and (14-38) may hold only in anisotropic systems. Hence the application of these equations presupposes an anisotropic structure of biological membranes. Equation (14-37) may be solved for J_i, to yield

$$J_i = \frac{\Delta\tilde{\mu}_i}{R_{ii}} - \sum_{\substack{k=1 \\ k\neq i}}^{n} \frac{R_{ik}}{R_{ii}} J_k - \frac{R_{ir}}{R_{ii}} J_{ch}. \tag{14-39}$$

The last term on the right-hand side should represent the "active transport" of component i. If $R_{ir} = 0$, the substance is not actively transported and the flow J_i should be that predicted on the basis of the equations that have been developed for nonliving systems. Kedem has applied expressions of the type given by Eq. (14-39) to a consideration of ion transport across frog skin.

14.3.2. To develop a clearer insight into the nature of the coefficient R_{ir}, we shall consider in some detail a model developed theoretically and experimentally by Kedem, Caplan, and Blumenthal (unpublished observations). The experiment permits a full evaluation of R_{ir} from the transport parameters of the system and from the rate constants for the chemical reaction. Let us consider a three-compartment system consisting of two large ("semi-infinite") compartments, I and II, separated by permselective membranes α and β from an inner compartment i. A chemical reaction takes place in the inner compartment in such a manner that a neutral substance, AB, is broken down enzymatically into a salt, A^+B^-. Such a reaction may be, for example, the hydrolysis of an organic amide,

$$H_2O + RCONH_2 \rightarrow RCOO^- + NH_4^+.$$

If membrane α is permeable to cations only and membrane β to anions only, the introduction of suitable electrodes into compartments I and II will make possible observation of an electric current with an intensity determined by the rate of the reaction. For the sake of simplicity, we assume that the membranes are permeable only to salt, not to water, that the concentrations of AB and A^+B^- in compartments I and II are identical so that $\Delta\mu_{AB}$ and $\Delta\mu_{A^+B^-}$ across the composite membrane are zero, and that the system has reached a stationary state so that all flows are constant and all concentrations in the inner compartment are time independent.

The rate of the chemical reaction is measured by $d\xi/dt$, the chemical breakdown of AB. If the volume of the inner compartment and the membrane areas are taken as unity, the condition of a stationary state requires that

$$\frac{dn^i_{AB}}{dt} = 0 = -\frac{d\xi}{dt} + J^\alpha_{AB} - J^\beta_{AB}. \tag{14-40}$$

Similar conditions apply for the ionic concentrations, so that

$$\frac{dn^i_A}{dt} = 0 = \frac{d\xi}{dt} + J^\alpha_A - J^\beta_A, \tag{14-41}$$

$$\frac{dn^i_B}{dt} = 0 = \frac{d\xi}{dt} + J^\alpha_B - J^\beta_B. \tag{14-42}$$

We may also write the dissipation function for the total system,

$$\Phi = (\Delta\mu^\alpha_{AB}J^\alpha_{AB} + \Delta\tilde{\mu}^\alpha_A J^\alpha_A + \Delta\tilde{\mu}^\alpha_B J^\alpha_B) + (\Delta\mu^\beta_{AB}J^\beta_{AB} + \Delta\tilde{\mu}^\beta_A J^\beta_A + \Delta\tilde{\mu}^\beta_B J^\beta_B) + A^i J_{ch}, \tag{14-43}$$

in which

$$\Delta\tilde{\mu}^\alpha_k = \tilde{\mu}^{\mathrm{I}}_k - \tilde{\mu}^i_k \quad \text{and} \quad \Delta\tilde{\mu}^\beta_k = \tilde{\mu}^i_k - \tilde{\mu}^{\mathrm{II}}_k, \tag{14-44}$$

$$A^i = \mu^i_{AB} - \tilde{\mu}^i_A - \tilde{\mu}^i_B, \tag{14-45}$$

and $J_{ch} = d\xi/dt$ is the rate of breakdown of substance AB.

From the condition of equality of concentration of AB and A^+B^- in compartments I and II we obtain the relations

$$\Delta\mu_{AB} = \Delta\mu^\alpha_{AB} + \Delta\mu^\beta_{AB} = 0,$$

or

$$\Delta\mu^\alpha_{AB} = -\Delta\mu^\beta_{AB}, \tag{14-46}$$

and

$$\Delta\mu_{A^+B^-} = \Delta\tilde{\mu}^\alpha_A + \Delta\tilde{\mu}^\beta_A + \Delta\tilde{\mu}^\alpha_B + \Delta\tilde{\mu}^\beta_B = \Delta\tilde{\mu}_A + \Delta\tilde{\mu}_B = 0,$$

or

$$\Delta\tilde{\mu}_A = -\Delta\tilde{\mu}_B. \tag{14-47}$$

Introducing Eqs. (14-41), (14-42), (14-46), and (14-47) into Eq. (14-43), we obtain

$$\mathbf{\Phi} = \Delta\mu^{\alpha}_{AB}(J^{\alpha}_{AB} - J^{\beta}_{AB}) + \Delta\tilde{\mu}^{\alpha}_{A}(J^{\beta}_{A} - J_{\text{ch}}) + \Delta\tilde{\mu}^{\beta}_{A}J^{\beta}_{A} + \Delta\tilde{\mu}^{\alpha}_{B}(J^{\beta}_{B} - J_{\text{ch}}) + \Delta\tilde{\mu}^{\beta}_{B}J^{\beta}_{B} + A^{i}J_{\text{ch}},$$

or, using Eq. (14-40),

$$\mathbf{\Phi} = J_{\text{ch}}(\Delta\mu^{\alpha}_{AB} - \Delta\tilde{\mu}^{\alpha}_{A} - \Delta\tilde{\mu}^{\beta}_{B} + A^{i}) + J^{\beta}_{A}\Delta\tilde{\mu}_{A} + J^{\beta}_{B}\Delta\tilde{\mu}_{B}. \tag{14-48}$$

Now, according to Eq. (14-44),

$$\Delta\mu^{\alpha}_{AB} - \Delta\tilde{\mu}^{\alpha}_{A} - \Delta\tilde{\mu}^{\alpha}_{B} + A^{i} = \mu^{\text{I}}_{AB} - \mu^{i}_{AB} - \tilde{\mu}^{\text{I}}_{A} + \tilde{\mu}^{i}_{A} - \tilde{\mu}^{\text{I}}_{B} + \tilde{\mu}^{i}_{B} + \mu^{i}_{AB} - \tilde{\mu}^{i}_{A} - \tilde{\mu}^{i}_{B}$$
$$= \mu^{\text{I}}_{AB} - \tilde{\mu}^{\text{I}}_{A} - \tilde{\mu}^{\text{I}}_{B} = A^{\text{I}},$$

or, denoting A^{I}, the affinity in compartment I, by A^{ext},

$$\Delta\mu^{\alpha}_{AB} - \Delta\tilde{\mu}^{\alpha}_{A} - \Delta\tilde{\mu}^{\alpha}_{B} + A^{i} = A^{\text{ext}}. \tag{14-49}$$

Since the composition of solution II is the same as that of solution I,

$$A^{\text{II}} = A^{\text{I}} = A^{\text{ext}}.$$

Further, as shown previously, $\Delta\tilde{\mu}_B = -\Delta\tilde{\mu}_A = -\mathfrak{F}E$, where E is the overall electromotive force between the reversible electrodes in compartments I and II. Finally, $(J^{\beta}_{A} - J^{\beta}_{B})\mathfrak{F} = I$ is the electric current in the system. Hence

$$\mathbf{\Phi} = J_{\text{ch}}A^{\text{ext}} + (J^{\beta}_{A} - J^{\beta}_{B})(-\Delta\tilde{\mu}_B) = J_{\text{ch}}A^{\text{ext}} + IE. \tag{14-50}$$

The interesting conclusion from Eq. (14-50) is that the dissipation function $\mathbf{\Phi}$ reduces to two terms, both involving external forces, the external affinity, A^{ext}, and the electromotive force, E. The inner compartment appears here as a "black box" in which a chemical reaction takes place, and it may be treated as a single complex membrane for which the phenomenological equations are

$$A^{\text{ext}} = R_{11}J_{\text{ch}} + R_{12}I, \tag{14-51}$$

$$E = R_{21}J_{\text{ch}} + R_{22}I. \tag{14-52}$$

Since the black box is, however, composed of known elements we may, in the present case, evaluate R_{12} and R_{21} explicitly and prove their equality.

According to our treatment of series membranes at zero volume flow (Sec. 12.5.2),

$$I = \kappa_\alpha E_\alpha + \frac{\kappa_\alpha t_1^\alpha}{\mathfrak{F}} \frac{\Delta\pi_\alpha}{\bar{c}_s^\alpha} = \kappa_\beta E_\beta + \frac{\kappa_\beta t_1^\beta}{\mathfrak{F}} \frac{\Delta\pi_\beta}{\bar{c}_s^\beta}, \tag{14-53}$$

in which $\Delta\pi_\alpha$ is the difference in the salt osmotic pressure between the internal membrane compartment and the external compartments, κ is the electrical conductance, and t_1 is the transference number of the ion which does not interact with the reversible electrodes. As in the case discussed in Sec. 12.5.2,

$$\Delta\pi_\alpha = -\Delta\pi_\beta = \Delta\pi \quad \text{and} \quad \bar{c}_s^\alpha = \bar{c}_s^\beta = \bar{c}_s. \tag{14-54}$$

The inner concentration is not, however, determined by the electromotive force only, but depends largely on the chemical reaction. From Eqs. (14-53) and (14-54), we find that

$$I\left(\frac{1}{\kappa_\alpha} + \frac{1}{\kappa_\beta}\right) = E + \frac{t_1^\alpha - t_1^\alpha}{\mathfrak{F}} \frac{\Delta\pi}{\bar{c}_s},$$

in which $E = E_\alpha + E_\beta$, and hence

$$\Delta\pi = \frac{\bar{c}_s I \mathfrak{F}\left(\frac{1}{\kappa_\alpha} + \frac{1}{\kappa_\beta}\right)}{t_1^\alpha - t_1^\beta} - \frac{\bar{c}_s E \mathfrak{F}}{t_1^\alpha - t_1^\beta}. \tag{14-55}$$

Further according to Eq. (12-98), the flows of salt at zero volume flow may be written

$$\begin{aligned} J_s^\alpha &= \omega_s^\alpha \Delta\pi_\alpha + \frac{t_1^\alpha}{\mathfrak{F}} I, \\ J_s^\beta &= \omega_s^\beta \Delta\pi_\beta + \frac{t_1^\beta}{\mathfrak{F}} I. \end{aligned} \tag{14-56}$$

Since salt also obeys the stationary condition given by Eq. (14-41) (note that salt flow is equal to the flow of the cation), we may write

$$\frac{d\xi}{dt} + J_s^\alpha - J_s^\beta = 0,$$

or, introducing Eqs. (14-56) and noting also Eq. (14-54),

$$\frac{d\xi}{dt} + (\omega_s^\alpha + \omega_s^\beta)\Delta\pi + \frac{t_1^\alpha - t_1^\beta}{\mathfrak{F}} I = 0. \tag{14-57}$$

Introducing $\Delta\pi$ from Eq. (14-55) and rearranging we obtain

$$E = \left[\frac{t_1^\alpha - t_1^\beta}{\bar{c}_s(\omega_s^\alpha + \omega_s^\beta)\mathfrak{F}}\right] J_{\text{ch}} + \left[\frac{1}{\kappa_\alpha} + \frac{1}{\kappa_\beta} + \frac{(t_1^\alpha - t_1^\beta)^2}{\bar{c}_s(\omega_s^\alpha + \omega_s^\beta)\mathfrak{F}^2}\right] I. \tag{14-58}$$

Equation (14-58) is equivalent to Eq. (14-52). As expected, R_{22} is equal to the resistance of a complex series membrane as discussed in Sec. 12.5.2, or

$$R_{22} = \frac{1}{\kappa_\alpha} + \frac{1}{\kappa_\beta} + \frac{(t_1^\alpha - t_1^\beta)^2}{\bar{c}_s(\omega_s^\alpha + \omega_s^\beta)\mathfrak{F}^2}. \tag{14-59}$$

It should, however, be borne in mind that $\bar{c}_s$ in Eq. (14-59) depends markedly on the rate of reaction, in contradistinction to the $\bar{c}_s$ in Eq. (12-100). The more interesting factor in the present case is the coupling coefficient,

$$R_{21} = \frac{t_1^\alpha - t_1^\beta}{\mathfrak{F}\bar{c}_s(\omega_s^\alpha + \omega_s^\beta)}. \tag{14-60}$$

We realize that the anisotropy appears here in the requirement that $t_1^\alpha \neq t_1^\beta$. When the membranes α and β are equal electrically and $t_1^\alpha = t_1^\beta$, $R_{21} = 0$ and no coupling will occur between electrical flow and chemical reaction.

To complete our argument we shall evaluate $d\xi/dt$ explicitly and thereby determine R_{12}. According to the thermodynamic formalism (Sec. 8.5.1), the phenomenological equation relating the rate of chemical reaction within the complex membrane to the affinity is

$$J_{\text{ch}} = L_{\text{ch}}A^i,$$

or, in view of Eq. (14-49),

$$J_{\text{ch}} = L_{\text{ch}}(A^{\text{ext}} - \Delta\mu_{AB}^\alpha + \Delta\tilde{\mu}_A^\alpha + \Delta\tilde{\mu}_B^\alpha). \tag{14-61}$$

Since $\Delta\mu_{A^+B^-}^\alpha = \Delta\tilde{\mu}_A^\alpha + \Delta\tilde{\mu}_B^\alpha$ and $\Delta\mu_{A^+B^-}^\alpha = \Delta\pi/\bar{c}_s$, Eq. (14-57) can be used to evaluate the last two terms on the right-hand side of Eq. (14-61). To evaluate $\Delta\mu_{AB} = \Delta\pi_{AB}/\bar{c}_{AB}$ we use again the condition of a stationary state given by Eq. (14-40),

$$J_{\text{ch}} = J_{AB}^\alpha - J_{AB}^\beta, \tag{14-62}$$

and write for the flow of the neutral substance AB at zero volume flow

$$J_{AB}^\alpha = \omega_{AB}^\alpha \Delta\pi_{AB}^\alpha, \qquad J_{AB}^\beta = \omega_{AB}^\beta \Delta\pi_{AB}^\beta.$$

Since

$$\Delta\pi_{AB}^\alpha = -\Delta\pi_{AB}^\beta = \Delta\pi_{AB},$$

$$J_{AB}^\alpha - J_{AB}^\beta = (\omega_{AB}^\alpha + \omega_{AB}^\beta)\Delta\pi_{AB},$$

or, in view of Eq. (14-62),

$$J_{\text{ch}} = (\omega_{AB}^\alpha + \omega_{AB}^\beta)\Delta\pi_{AB}.$$

Thus,

$$\Delta\mu_{AB} = \frac{J_{\text{ch}}}{\bar{c}_{AB}(\omega_{AB}^{\alpha} + \omega_{AB}^{\beta})}, \tag{14-63}$$

and, from Eq. (14-57),

$$\Delta\mu_{A^+B^-} = \frac{\Delta\pi}{\bar{c}_s} = -\frac{J_{\text{ch}}}{\bar{c}_s(\omega_s^{\alpha} + \omega_s^{\beta})} - \frac{t_1^{\alpha} - t_1^{\beta}}{\bar{c}_s(\omega_s^{\alpha} + \omega_s^{\beta})\mathfrak{F}} I. \tag{14-64}$$

Introducing Eqs. (14-63) and (14-64) into Eq. (14-61) yields

$$J_{\text{ch}} = L_{\text{ch}}\left[A^{\text{ext}} - \frac{J_{\text{ch}}}{\bar{c}_{AB}(\omega_{AB}^{\alpha} + \omega_{AB}^{\beta})} - \frac{J_{\text{ch}}}{\bar{c}_s(\omega_s^{\alpha} + \omega_s^{\beta})} - \frac{t_1^{\alpha} - t_1^{\beta}}{\bar{c}_s(\omega_s^{\alpha} + \omega_s^{\beta})\mathfrak{F}} I\right].$$

Rearranging terms we obtain

$$A^{\text{ext}} = \left[\frac{1}{L_{\text{ch}}} + \frac{1}{\bar{c}_{AB}(\omega_{AB}^{\alpha} + \omega_{AB}^{\beta})} + \frac{1}{\bar{c}_s(\omega_s^{\alpha} + \omega_s^{\beta})}\right]J_{\text{ch}} + \frac{t_1^{\alpha} - t_1^{\beta}}{\bar{c}_s(\omega_s^{\alpha} + \omega_s^{\beta})\mathfrak{F}} I. \tag{14-65}$$

Equation (14-65) is equivalent to Eq. (14-51) and permits the identification of the coefficients:

$$R_{11} = \frac{1}{L_{\text{ch}}} + \frac{1}{\bar{c}_{AB}(\omega_{AB}^{\alpha} + \omega_{AB}^{\beta})} + \frac{1}{\bar{c}_s(\omega_s^{\alpha} + \omega_s^{\beta})},$$

$$R_{12} = \frac{t_1^{\alpha} - t_1^{\beta}}{\bar{c}_s(\omega_s^{\alpha} + \omega_s^{\beta})\mathfrak{F}}. \tag{14-66}$$

Comparison of Eqs. (14-60) and (14-66) indicates that $R_{12} = R_{21}$.

It is also noteworthy that the "chemical resistance" R_{11} is composed not only of $1/L_{\text{ch}}$ but also of the resistance to the escape of the salt formed in the reaction $1/\bar{c}_s(\omega_s^{\alpha} + \omega_s^{\beta})$ as well as the resistance to the entry of the reactant into the reaction cell $1/\bar{c}_{AB}(\omega_{AB}^{\alpha} + \omega_{AB}^{\beta})$, which might be expected from a consideration of the availability of the components and their influence on the internal affinity.

14.3.3. The use of a phenomenological representation of active transport may be illustrated by considering a system discussed by Curran and his co-workers,[10] which is concerned with the relation between active solute transport and volume flow in complex membrane systems. The model system was proposed as one that could account for the close relation, observed in several biological systems, between volume flow and net solute transfer. We shall consider a system, illustrated in Fig. 32, composed of two membranes in series separated by a closed compartment. For simplicity we shall assume that the solutions contain a single solute that is actively transported across membrane I from compartment 1 to 2. Making use of

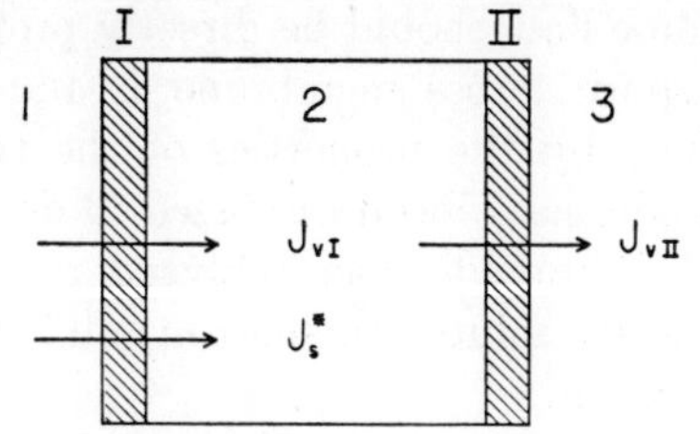

Fig. 32. Series membrane system. The central compartment is closed and the solute is actively transported across membrane I from compartment 1 to 2.

the considerations of Chapter 10, we may write for the volume flows across the two membranes,

$$J_{vI} = L_{PI}(\Delta P_I - \sigma_I \Delta\pi_I), \tag{14-67}$$

$$J_{vII} = L_{PII}(\Delta P_{II} - \sigma_{II} \Delta\pi_{II}), \tag{14-68}$$

and for the solute flows

$$J_{sI} = \bar{c}_{sI}(1 - \sigma_I)J_{vI} + \omega_I \Delta\pi_I + J_s^*, \tag{14-69}$$

$$J_{sII} = \bar{c}_{sII}(1 - \sigma_{II})J_{vII} + \omega_{II} \Delta\pi_{II}, \tag{14-70}$$

in which J_s^* represents the contribution of active transport to the solute flow across membrane I. Equation (14-69) is analogous to Eq. (14-39) given by Kedem, except that the phenomenological coefficients have been expressed in terms of L_P, ω, and σ, as discussed in Chapter 10, and the term $R_{1r}J_r/R_{11}$ has been replaced by the equivalent J_s^*.

If the system is in a steady state,

$$J_{vI} = J_{vII} = J_v,$$

$$J_{sI} = J_{sII} = J_s.$$

Further, assuming that solute concentrations and pressures are identical in the two end compartments, $\Delta P_I = -\Delta P_{II} = \Delta P$, $\Delta\pi_I = -\Delta\pi_{II} = \Delta\pi$, and $\bar{c}_{sI} = \bar{c}_{sII} = \bar{c}_s$. Equations (14-67) and (14-68) may then be used to eliminate ΔP to yield

$$J_v = -\frac{L_{PI}L_{PII}}{L_{PI} + L_{PII}}(\sigma_I - \sigma_{II})\Delta\pi = -\mathcal{L}(\sigma_I - \sigma_{II})\Delta\pi. \tag{14-71}$$

Setting Eqs. (14-69) and (14-70) equal and solving for $\Delta\pi$, we obtain

$$\Delta\pi = \frac{\bar{c}_s J_v(\sigma_I - \sigma_{II}) - J_s^*}{\omega_I + \omega_{II}}. \tag{14-72}$$

Introducing Eq. (14-72) into Eq. (14-71) and solving for J_v yields

$$J_v = \frac{\mathcal{L}(\sigma_I - \sigma_{II})J_s^*}{\omega_I + \omega_{II} + \mathcal{L}\bar{c}_s(\sigma_I - \sigma_{II})^2}. \tag{14-73}$$

Thus, the rate of volume flow should be directly proportional to the rate of active solute transport across membrane I, and the proportionality coefficient is determined by the properties of the two membranes. The implications of this model have been discussed in detail by Patlak, Goldstein, and Hoffman.[11] Diamond[12] has analyzed the connection between water movement and active solute transport in gall bladder using a similar, but not identical, approach.

The simple example given here is merely intended to illustrate that this general phenomenological description of active transport may be useful in certain cases. However, the problem of the specific relation between transport processes and chemical reactions remains a central one in the description of biological membrane phenomena. Although the equations of the thermodynamics of irreversible processes offer a formal framework within which these effects can be described, we do not as yet have sufficient information concerning the processes to make full use of the thermodynamic expressions. Nonetheless, some of the considerations presented in this chapter may prove useful in an attempt to develop a better understanding of the general problem of active transport.

CHAPTER 15

STATISTICAL DERIVATION OF ONSAGER'S LAW

15.1. Theory of Fluctuations

15.1.1. After a discussion of various applications of the formalism of the thermodynamics of irreversible processes, we return here to the consideration of fundamentals. As mentioned in Chapter 8, Onsager's law, which underlies many of the considerations of the previous chapters, can be derived by the methods of statistical mechanics.[1] In developing the proof, we shall assume that the reader is not conversant with the principles and procedures of statistical mechanics and shall provide the necessary concepts and theorems.

In order to become acquainted with the quantitative treatment of fluctuations, we shall first calculate the fluctuating number of noninteracting particles in a volume element of solution, following the method of Smoluchowski. We shall consider a large volume V, containing N particles, in which a small volume v is isolated for observation. The temporary, fluctuating number of particles in v will be denoted by n. The a priori probability p of finding any particle in v is given by

$$p = \frac{v}{V}. \tag{15-1}$$

The probability of finding the particle in the rest of the volume is

$$\frac{V - v}{V} = 1 - p. \tag{15-2}$$

Thus, the probability of finding n particles in v and $N - n$ in $V - v$ is proportional to $p^n(1 - p)^{N-n}$. Since the particles are indistinguishable, any way of selecting the n out of N will give a valid choice. According to the theory of probability, the number of ways of selecting n out of N particles is

$$\binom{N}{n} = \frac{N!}{(N - n)!n!}, \tag{15-3}$$

so that the total probability $\mathcal{P}(n)$ of finding n particles in the volume v is

$$\mathcal{P}(n) = \binom{N}{n} p^n(1 - p)^n. \tag{15-4}$$

Poisson has shown that, for very large values of N, Eq. (15-4) assumes the simple form

$$\mathcal{P}(n) = \frac{\nu^n e^{-\nu}}{n!}, \tag{15-5}$$

in which ν is the average value of n, given in our case by the condition

$$\frac{\nu}{v} = \frac{N}{V}. \tag{15-6}$$

Equation (15-5) is normalized so that the sum of all probabilities of finding any number of particles in v is unity, or

$$\sum_{n=0}^{\infty} \mathcal{P}(n) = e^{-\nu} \sum_{n=0}^{\infty} \frac{\nu^n}{n!} = e^{-\nu} e^{\nu} = 1. \tag{15-7}$$

Moveover, the average value of n is implied in Eq. (15-5). The numerical value $\bar{n}$ of the average is the sum over all values of n weighted by their respective probabilities:

$$\bar{n} = \sum_{n=0}^{\infty} n\mathcal{P}(n) = e^{-\nu} \sum_{n=0}^{\infty} \frac{n\nu^n}{n!} = \nu e^{-\nu} \sum_{n=1}^{\infty} \frac{\nu^{n-1}}{(n-1)!} = \nu e^{-\nu} e^{\nu} = \nu. \tag{15-8}$$

The fluctuation in the number of particles in the volume v is defined as the deviation of the actual number n from the mean, or $n - \nu$. For noninteracting particles, the probability of positive and negative deviations should be equal and hence the average fluctuation, $\overline{n - \nu}$, should be zero. This is easily verified by means of Eqs. (15-7) and (15-8):

$$\overline{n - \nu} = \sum_{n=0}^{\infty} (n - \nu)\mathcal{P}(n) = \sum_{n=0}^{\infty} n\mathcal{P}(n) - \nu \sum_{n=0}^{\infty} \mathcal{P}(n) = 0. \tag{15-9}$$

For this reason, the usual measure of fluctuations is not the linear average, but the average of the square of the fluctuations. This value is always positive and serves as an important indicator of the extent of fluctuations observable in a system. In general,

$$\overline{(n - \nu)^2} = \overline{n^2 - 2n\nu + \nu^2} = \overline{n^2} - 2\bar{n}\nu + \nu^2.$$

In view of Eq. (15-8), this becomes

$$\overline{(n - \nu)^2} = \overline{n^2} - 2\nu^2 + \nu^2 = \overline{n^2} - \nu^2, \tag{15-10}$$

and thus

$$\overline{(n - \nu)^2} = \overline{n^2} - \bar{n}^2. \tag{15-11}$$

The mean-square fluctuation is given by the difference between the mean value of n^2 and the square of the mean number of particles in v. Since

$\bar{n} = \nu$ is known, the evaluation of the mean-square fluctuation reduces to the evaluation of the mean of the square, $\overline{n^2}$. This is done as follows:

$$\overline{n^2} = \sum_{n=0}^{\infty} n^2 \mathcal{P}(n) = \sum_{n=0}^{\infty} [n(n-1) + n]\mathcal{P}(n).$$

Using Eqs. (15-5) and (15-8), we may write this expression as

$$\overline{n^2} = \nu + e^{-\nu} \sum_{n=1}^{\infty} \frac{n(n-1)}{n!} \nu^n = \nu + \nu^2 e^{-\nu} \sum_{n=2}^{\infty} \frac{\nu^{n-2}}{(n-2)!},$$

or

$$\overline{n^2} = \nu + \nu^2 e^{-\nu} e^{\nu} = \nu + \nu^2. \tag{15-12}$$

Introducing Eq. (15-12) into Eq. (15-10), we obtain the remarkable result that

$$\overline{(n-\nu)^2} = \nu. \tag{15-13}$$

Usually, we are not concerned with the absolute value of the fluctuations, but with their ratio to the average number of particles. We thus define a quantity Δ, by the following relations:

$$\Delta^2 = \overline{\left(\frac{n-\nu}{\nu}\right)^2},$$

or

$$\Delta = \sqrt{\overline{\left(\frac{n-\nu}{\nu}\right)^2}} = \frac{1}{\sqrt{\nu}}. \tag{15-14}$$

Equation (15-14) is the basis of the common notion that relative fluctuations decrease with the square root of the average number of particles in v. This concept is the basis of the stimulating discussion by Schrödinger,[2] in his book *What is Life?* on the question, "Why are the cells so large?" Schrödinger's conclusion is that, in order to permit the operation of regular macroscopic laws, the fluctuations in the system must be sufficiently small. Since fluctuations diminish with $1/\sqrt{\nu}$, ν has to be large enough to make the fluctuations in the cell of minor importance. The discussion in this section is valid only for fluctuations of independent particles. The treatment does not hold for interacting particles, and, since we are interested in coupled phenomena, based on particle interaction, we must consider a more powerful method that can predict the magnitude of fluctuations in all cases. The method applied below is based on the well-known analysis by Einstein, developed primarily for the explanation of light scattering. However, the conclusions hold for any type of fluctuation.

15.1.2. The analysis begins with the equation of Boltzmann relating entropy and the number of configurations in which a system may be realized. As discussed in Sec. 2.3,

$$S = k \ln \Omega, \tag{15-15}$$

in which Ω is the configuration number and k is the Boltzmann constant. The equilibrium entropy of a system is given by

$$S_0 = k \ln \Omega_0, \tag{15-16}$$

in which Ω_0 is the configurational number of an equilibrium state.

Let us now consider a fluctuation of the entropy from its equilibrium value such that $\Delta S = S - S_0$. This may be due to the fluctuation of any parameter ξ_i of the system from its equilibrium value ξ_i^0, and we may define such a fluctuation by a parameter $\alpha_i = \xi_i - \xi_i^0$. From Eqs. (15-15) and (15-16), the fluctuation in entropy is given by

$$\Delta S = k \ln \frac{\Omega}{\Omega_0} = k \ln \mathcal{P}, \tag{15-17}$$

in which $\mathcal{P}$ is the probability of finding the system in the given state of fluctuation. From Eq. (15-17),

$$\mathcal{P} = Ke^{\Delta S/k}, \tag{15-18}$$

in which the constant K is a normalization factor introduced to satisfy the requirement that the probability of finding the system in any state characterized by the fluctuation of any parameter is unity:

$$\int \cdots \int \mathcal{P} d\alpha_1 d\alpha_2 \cdots d\alpha_n = K \int e^{\Delta S/k} d\alpha_1 d\alpha_2 \cdots d\alpha_n = 1. \tag{15-19}$$

According to the second law of thermodynamics, the entropy is maximal at equilibrium. Thus, any fluctuating value of S must be smaller than S_0, and $\Delta S < 0$. We shall now assume that large spontaneous fluctuations in S will be generally improbable so that, to a good approximation, S may be obtained by expanding it in a Taylor's series around the equilibrium value, retaining only three terms:

$$S = S_0 + \sum_{i=1}^{n} \left(\frac{\partial S}{\partial \xi_i}\right)^0 (\xi_i - \xi_i^0) + \frac{1}{2} \sum_{i,j=1}^{n} \left(\frac{\partial^2 S}{\partial \xi_i \partial \xi_j}\right)^0 (\xi_i - \xi_i^0)(\xi_j - \xi_j^0), \tag{15-20}$$

in which the superscript 0 indicates that the partial derivatives are taken at equilibrium. Since S has a maximum at equilibrium, $(\partial S/\partial \xi_i)^0 = 0$ for all ξ_i, and Eq. (15-20) reduces to

$$\Delta S = \frac{1}{2} \sum_{i,j=1}^{n} \left(\frac{\partial^2 S}{\partial \xi_i \partial \xi_j}\right)^0 (\xi_i - \xi_i^0)(\xi_j - \xi_j^0).$$

Introducing the symbol $-g_{ij}$ for $(\partial^2 S/\partial\xi_i\partial\xi_j)^0$ and α_i for $(\xi_i - \xi_i^0)$ we obtain

$$\Delta S = -\tfrac{1}{2} \sum_{i,j=1}^{n} g_{ij}\alpha_i\alpha_j. \tag{15-21}$$

Inserting Eq. (15-21) into Eq. (15-18), we find the probability of observing the system in a given state of fluctuation is

$$\mathcal{P} = K \exp\left(-\frac{1}{2k} \sum_{i,j} g_{ij}\alpha_i\alpha_j\right). \tag{15-22}$$

In accord with our notions of thermodynamic forces, we may now introduce the forces X_i, attempting to restore the system to equilibrium:

$$X_i = \frac{\partial \Delta S}{\partial \alpha_i} = -\sum_{j=1}^{n} g_{ij}\alpha_j = K\frac{\partial \ln \mathcal{P}}{\partial \alpha_i}. \tag{15-23}$$

In order to master the application of Einstein's probability treatment, some space will be devoted to the solution of several of simple problems. We shall first prove that the average numerical fluctuation of a single parameter, $\alpha = \xi - \xi^0$, is zero. This is shown as follows:

$$\bar{\alpha} = \int_{-\infty}^{\infty} \alpha\mathcal{P}(\alpha)d\alpha = K\int_{-\infty}^{\infty} e^{-g\alpha^2/2k}\alpha d\alpha,$$

in which Eq. (15-22) has been used for a single parameter. If we put $x = g\alpha^2/2k$ and $\alpha d\alpha = kdx/g$, the integral may be evaluated to yield

$$\bar{\alpha} = \frac{kK}{g}\int_{-\infty}^{\infty} e^{-x}dx = \frac{kK}{g}[-e^{-x}]_{-\infty}^{\infty} = \frac{kK}{g}[-e^{-g\alpha^2/2k}]_{-\infty}^{\infty} = 0. \tag{15-24}$$

A second average, which plays an important role in the theory of light scattering by solutions, is the average of the square of the fluctuation of a single quantity, $\overline{\alpha^2}$:

$$\overline{\alpha^2} = \int_{-\infty}^{\infty} \alpha^2\mathcal{P}(\alpha)d\alpha = K\int_{-\infty}^{\infty} \alpha e^{-g\alpha^2/2k}\alpha d\alpha$$

$$= -\frac{kK}{g}\int_{-\infty}^{\infty} d(e^{-g\alpha^2/2k}).$$

The last integral can be readily evaluated by partial integration to yield

$$\overline{\alpha^2} = -\frac{kK}{g}[\alpha e^{-g\alpha^2/2k}]_{-\infty}^{\infty} + \frac{k}{g}\int_{-\infty}^{\infty} Ke^{-g\alpha^2/2k}d\alpha.$$

The first term on the right-hand side vanishes at both $-\infty$ and ∞. The second integral is

$$\int_{-\infty}^{\infty} Ke^{-g\alpha^2/2k}d\alpha = \int_{-\infty}^{\infty} \mathcal{P}(\alpha)d\alpha = 1$$

by the condition of normalization, Eq. (15-19). Hence,

$$\overline{\alpha^2} = \frac{k}{g} = -\frac{k}{(\partial^2 S/\partial\alpha^2)^0}. \tag{15-25}$$

This important equation may be cast in another and more useful form if we assume that the fluctuation takes place under isothermal, isobaric conditions. The volume v in which fluctuation α takes place will be taken as a part of a larger and constant volume V. We shall assign energy u and entropy s to the volume v and U and S to the total volume V and shall assume that the total energy U is constant. At constant P and T, the change in free energy accompanying the fluctuation will be

$$dG = du - Tds + pdv.$$

The change in internal energy of the volume $V - v$ will be

$$d(U - u) = Td(S - s) - Pd(V - v).$$

Adding these two equations and noting that dU and dV are zero, we find that

$$dG = -TdS,$$

or

$$-\frac{\partial^2 S}{\partial\alpha^2} = \frac{1}{T}\frac{\partial^2 G}{\partial\alpha^2}.$$

Thus, Eq. (15-25) may be transcribed into terms of the second-order differential of the Gibbs free energy,

$$\overline{\alpha^2} = \frac{kT}{(\partial^2 G/\partial\alpha^2)^0}. \tag{15-26}$$

It is worth showing that in the ideal case of noninteracting particles Eq. (15-26) gives the same mean-square fluctuation as is found from the Poisson distribution. Let $\alpha = n - \nu$ be the fluctuation in the number of particles counted in the volume v. Then,

$$\frac{\partial G}{\partial\alpha} = \frac{\partial G}{\partial n} = \mu,$$

in which μ is the chemical potential per particle. Now, in an ideal solution,

$$\mu = \mu^0 + P\bar{V} + kT\ln\frac{n}{V}.$$

At constant P, T, and V,

$$\left(\frac{\partial^2 G}{\partial\alpha^2}\right)^0 = \left(\frac{\partial\mu}{\partial n}\right)^0 = \left(\frac{kT}{n}\right)^0 = \frac{kT}{\nu}, \tag{15-27}$$

in which, as before, ν is the average number of particles in the volume v. Introducing Eq. (15-27) into Eq. (15-26), we obtain

$$\overline{\alpha^2} = \overline{(n - \nu)^2} = \nu, \tag{15-28}$$

which is identical with Eq. (15-13). The reader should, however, be aware of the fact that Eq. (15-26) will give different results for nonideal solutions, and can represent the fluctuation for any solution with any possible dependence of chemical potential on concentration.

As a third example, we shall consider the average of the product of two fluctuating parameters, $\overline{\alpha_i\alpha_j}$, such as the average of the product of the fluctuations in the concentrations of two components. It may be shown by direct calculation that

$$\overline{\alpha_j\alpha_i} = kg_{ij}^{-1},$$

in which g_{ij}^{-1} is not the reciprocal of g_{ij} but the i, jth term of the reciprocal matrix of the matrix g_{ij}. Thus, in the case of two fluctuating parameters,

$$g_{11}^{-1} = \frac{g_{22}}{|g|},$$

$$g_{12}^{-1} = \frac{-g_{12}}{|g|},$$

$$g_{22}^{-1} = \frac{g_{11}}{|g|},$$

in which $|g| = g_{11}g_{22} - g_{12}^2$. If the case to be considered is the isothermal fluctuation in the number of particles of types 1 and 2,

$$g_{ij} = -\frac{1}{T}\mu_{ij},$$

in which $\mu_{ij} = \partial\mu_i/\partial n_j$. Thus,

$$g_{11}^{-1} = \frac{T\mu_{22}}{|\mu|},$$

$$g_{12}^{-1} = \frac{T\mu_{12}}{|\mu|},$$

$$g_{22}^{-1} = \frac{T\mu_{11}}{|\mu|},$$

in which $|\mu| = \mu_{11}\mu_{22} - \mu_{12}^2$. The mean square fluctuations are

$$\overline{(n_1 - \nu_1)^2} = \frac{kT\mu_{22}}{|\mu|},$$

$$\overline{(n_1 - \nu_1)(n_2 - \nu_2)} = -\frac{kT\mu_{12}}{|\mu|},$$

$$\overline{(n_2 - \nu_2)^2} = \frac{kT\mu_{11}}{|\mu|}.$$

When the chemical potential of one component is independent of the number of particles of the other component, which will be the case for noninteracting substances, $\mu_{12} = 0$. In this case, the number of particles of components 1 and 2 will each fluctuate as if the other were not present:

$$\overline{(n_1 - \nu_1)^2} = \frac{kT}{\mu_{11}},$$

$$\overline{(n_2 - \nu_2)^2} = \frac{kT}{\mu_{22}},$$

in correspondence with the result of a simple fluctuation. Moreover, the average

$$\overline{(n_1 - \nu_1)(n_2 - \nu_2)} = 0.$$

Reversing the argument, we may say that if $\overline{\alpha_i\alpha_j} = 0$ there is no correlation between the fluctuating parameters. The requirement that $\overline{\alpha_i\alpha_j}$ vanish for noncorrelated quantities may also be deduced in the following general manner. If the ith and jth parameters fluctuate independently, $\overline{\alpha_i\alpha_j} = \overline{\alpha_i}\cdot\overline{\alpha_j}$ and, since both $\overline{\alpha_i} = 0$ and $\overline{\alpha_j} = 0$, $\overline{\alpha_i\alpha_j} = 0$.

15.1.4. For the proof of Onsager's law, we require the correlation average of fluctuations α_i in parameters ξ_i and of the force X_j, or $\overline{X_j\alpha_i}$. By definition of the average values, this correlation may be written

$$\overline{X_j\alpha_i} = \int \cdots \int X_j\alpha_i\mathcal{P}(\alpha_1\alpha_2 \cdots \alpha_n)d\alpha_1 d\alpha_2 \cdots d\alpha_n, \tag{15-29}$$

in which n is the total number of fluctuating parameters. According to Eq. (15-23),

$$X_j = \frac{k}{\mathcal{P}}\frac{\partial\mathcal{P}}{\partial\alpha_j},$$

and hence the term $X_j\mathcal{P}$ appearing in the integral of Eq. (15-29) is $k\partial\mathcal{P}/\partial\alpha_j$. Thus,

$$\begin{aligned}\overline{X_j\alpha_i} &= k\int \cdots \int \alpha_i \frac{\partial\mathcal{P}}{\partial\alpha_j}\, d\alpha_1 \cdots d\alpha_n \\ &= k\int \cdots \int d\alpha_1 \cdots d\alpha_{j-1}d\alpha_{j+1} \cdots d\alpha_n\alpha_i \frac{\partial\mathcal{P}}{\partial\alpha_j}\, d\alpha_j.\end{aligned} \tag{15-30}$$

The last term in Eq. (15-30) may be subjected to partial integration to yield

$$\int_{-\infty}^{\infty} \alpha_i \frac{\partial\mathcal{P}}{\partial\alpha_j}\, d\alpha_j = [\alpha_i\mathcal{P}]_{-\infty}^{\infty} - \int_{-\infty}^{\infty} \mathcal{P}\frac{\partial\alpha_i}{\partial\alpha_j}\, d\alpha_j.$$

It is clear that the probability $\mathcal{P}$ of finding an infinite positive or negative fluctuation is zero, so that $[\alpha_i \mathcal{P}]_{-\infty}^{\infty}$ must be zero. Further, since α_i and α_j are independent fluctuating parameters,

$$\frac{\partial \alpha_i}{\partial \alpha_j} = 0, \qquad (i \neq j),$$

$$\frac{\partial \alpha_i}{\partial \alpha_j} = 1, \qquad (i = j).$$

This result may be written in a simple expression by introducing the Kronecker delta $\delta_{ij}[= 0$ for $i \neq j$ and 1 for $i = j]$:

$$\frac{\partial \alpha_i}{\partial \alpha_j} = \delta_{ij}$$

and

$$\int_{-\infty}^{\infty} \alpha_i \frac{\partial \mathcal{P}}{\partial \alpha_j} d\alpha_j = -\delta_{ij} \int_{-\infty}^{\infty} \mathcal{P} d\alpha_j.$$

Introducing this expression back into Eq. (15-30) we find that

$$\overline{X_j \alpha_i} = k\delta_{ij}, \tag{15-31}$$

in which we have used the normalization condition,

$$\int \overset{\infty}{\underset{-\infty}{\cdots}} \int \mathcal{P} d\alpha_1 d\alpha_2 \cdots d\alpha_n = 1.$$

Thus, Eq. (15-31) shows that for nonconjugated forces and fluctuating parameters the correlational fluctuation is zero, while for conjugated forces and parameters,

$$\overline{X_i \alpha_i} = -k. \tag{15-32}$$

15.2. The Principle of Microscopic Reversibility and Onsager's Hypothesis

15.2.1. We shall now generalize the concept of correlational fluctuations to embrace time-dependent phenomena. Let a fluctuating parameter α_i have the value $\alpha_i(t)$ at time t. Then, as discussed above,

$$\overline{\alpha_i(t)\alpha_j(t)} = \overline{\alpha_j(t)\alpha_i(t)} \neq 0 \tag{15-33}$$

indicates that there exists a correlation between the parameters. It is, however, important to find out whether the fact that the ith parameter had the value $\alpha_i(t)$ at time t influences the magnitude of the jth parameter after the lapse of an additional time τ. That is, we would like to know whether $\alpha_j(t + \tau)$ is correlated with $\alpha_i(t)$. To answer this question, we have to ask about the correlation in time given by the average $\overline{\alpha_i(t)\alpha_j(t + \tau)}$.

The meaning of this time average can be given in the following way. Consider the time interval Θ on the time coordinate shown in Fig. 33.

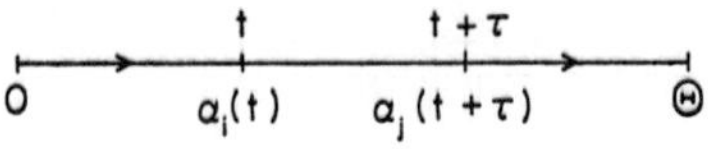

Fig. 33. Illustration of the concept of correlation in time of the fluctuation $\alpha_i(t)$ and $\alpha_j(t + \tau)$.

Let the value of α_i at any time be $\alpha_i(t)$ and the value of α_j at time τ later be $\alpha_j(t + \tau)$, both t and $t + \tau$ being in the time interval Θ. Then the correlational time average over the interval Θ will be

$$\overline{\alpha_i(t)\alpha_j(t + \tau)} = \frac{1}{\Theta} \int_0^\Theta \alpha_i(t)\alpha_j(t + \tau)dt.$$

The average for any time interval is obtained by letting Θ go to infinity, so that

$$\overline{\alpha_i(t)\alpha_j(t + \tau)} = \lim_{\Theta \to \infty} \frac{1}{\Theta} \int_0^\Theta \alpha_i(t)\alpha_j(t + \tau)dt.$$

15.2.2. The concept of the correlational time average permits a precise mathematical expression for the principle of microscopic reversibility which was stated qualitatively in Sec. 8.5.2. The essential meaning of this principle is that, on a microscopic level, processes going in one direction have the same probability as processes going in the opposite direction. In other words, the arrow of time has no direction in the microscopic realm. In terms of fluctuations, this means that the relation of the fluctuating value of α_i at time t to α_j at time $t + \tau$ may, in the inverse time scale, be looked upon as the relation of α_i at time $t + \tau$ to α_j at time t. Thus, averaging over all times, microscopic reversibility means that

$$\overline{\alpha_i(t)\alpha_j(t + \tau)} = \overline{\alpha_i(t + \tau)\alpha_j(t)}, \tag{15-34}$$

as illustrated in Fig. 34. Equation (15-34) may be further transformed to give additional information. Subtracting Eq. (15-33) from Eq. (15-34), we obtain

$$\overline{\alpha_i(t)\alpha_j(t + \tau) - \alpha_i(t)\alpha_j(t)} = \overline{\alpha_i(t + \tau)\alpha_j(t) - \alpha_i(t)\alpha_j(t)},$$

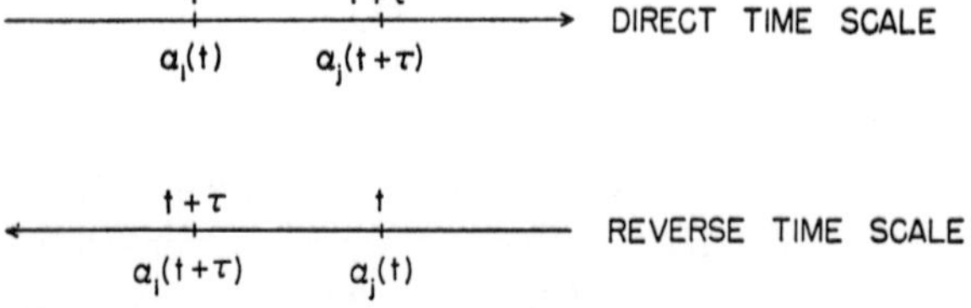

Fig. 34. The principle of microscopic reversibility. The correlation in time between α_i and α_j is independent of the direction of the time scale.

or

$$\overline{\alpha_i(t)[\alpha_j(t+\tau) - \alpha_j(t)]} = \overline{\alpha_j(t)[\alpha_i(t+\tau) - \alpha_i(t)]}. \tag{15-35}$$

Dividing both sides of Eq. (15-35) by τ yields

$$\overline{\alpha_i(t)\,\frac{\alpha_j(t+\tau) - \alpha_j(t)}{\tau}} = \overline{\alpha_j(t)\,\frac{\alpha_i(t+\tau) - \alpha_i(t)}{\tau}},$$

or, allowing τ to approach zero,

$$\overline{\alpha_i(t)\,\frac{d\alpha_j(t)}{dt}} = \overline{\alpha_j(t)\,\frac{d\alpha_i(t)}{dt}}. \tag{15-36}$$

The choice of τ and allowing τ to approach zero are not trivial mathematical processes. Small values of τ are physically small, but must always be sufficiently large compared to the time of a single collision process, τ_0, for it is only in this case that statistical averaging can be applied. On the other hand, large values of τ must be no larger than the time required for the fluctuation to relax and disappear, since for values of τ larger than the relaxation time of the fluctuation, τ_r, the correlation average given by Eq. (15-34) loses its meaning. Thus, $\tau_0 \ll \tau \ll \tau_r$. However, the time interval $\tau_r - \tau_0$ is sufficiently wide to leave the validity of the equation without any change.

15.2.3. We must now introduce the hypothesis of Onsager which underlies the law of symmetry of phenomenological coefficients. This hypothesis states that the rate of change of a fluctuating parameter, or the average rate of decay of a fluctuation, $\overline{d\alpha_i/dt}$, has the same linear dependence on the thermodynamic forces as is observed in macroscopic flows. In mathematical terms, this hypothesis states that

$$\overline{\left(\frac{d\alpha_i}{dt}\right)} = \sum_{k=1}^{n} L_{ik}X_k = J_i, \tag{15-37}$$

in which the L_{ik} are the over-all macroscopic coefficients introduced in Chapter 8. Introducing Eq. (15-37) into Eq. (15-36) we obtain

$$\overline{\alpha_i \sum_{k=1}^{n} L_{jk}X_k} = \overline{\alpha_j \sum_{k=1}^{n} L_{ik}X_k}, \tag{15-38}$$

or

$$\sum_{k=1}^{n} L_{jk}\overline{\alpha_i X_k} = \sum_{k=1}^{n} L_{ik}\overline{\alpha_j X_k}. \tag{15-38}$$

In view of Eq. (15-31), Eq. (15-38) may also be written

$$-k \sum_{k=1}^{n} L_{jk}\delta_{ik} = -k \sum_{k=1}^{n} L_{ik}\delta_{jk}. \tag{15-39}$$

Since $\delta_{ik} \neq 0$ only when $k = i$ and $\delta_{jk} \neq 0$ when $k = j$, all terms except the ith on the left-hand side of Eq. (15-39) vanish, as do all terms except the jth on the right-hand side. Thus, we obtain directly the reciprocal relation

$$L_{ji} = L_{ij}. \tag{15-40}$$

Several points regarding the proof of Eq. (15-40) should be mentioned. The flows and forces used in the phenomenological equations must satisfy the relation

$$\sigma = \sum J_i X_i. \tag{15-41}$$

Further, as presented here, the proof is, strictly speaking, valid only if the flows and forces satisfy Eqs. (15-23) and (15-37). This means that the flows must be time derivatives of thermodynamic variables. However, in the case of vectorial flows, this condition is not satisfied; it is the divergence of the flow that is equal to the time derivative. For example, $\partial c_i/\partial t = -\text{div } \mathbf{J}_i$. This problem has been considered in detail by several authors,[3,4] and they have demonstrated that the proof can be extended to include the various flows and forces that have been used in the previous chapters. As pointed out clearly by Casimir,[3] the proof is also based directly on the hypothesis that the regression of fluctuations follows the same laws as macroscopic irreversible processes. Thus, in the final analysis, the use of Eq. (15-40) in the description of macroscopic phenomena must be based on experimental verification. In the previous chapters, we have frequently mentioned evidence indicating that Eq. (15-40) is experimentally valid for several types of irreversible processes.[5] It may, therefore, be considered as a reasonably well-established law.

CHAPTER 16

STATIONARY STATES: THE PRINCIPLE OF MINIMUM ENTROPY PRODUCTION

16.1. Principle of Minimum Entropy Production

THROUGHOUT our discussion of the application of the thermodynamic theory, the notion of stationary states has appeared frequently. We recognized that in such a state the parameters of a system do not change with time, and this led to the important conclusion that

$$\sigma = \text{div } J_S. \tag{16-1}$$

Moreover, since the flows of conservative properties are characterized by the requirement that in a steady state,

$$\text{div } J_i = 0, \tag{16-2}$$

the condition J_i = constant for the unidimensional case could be used for the analysis of many phenomena that would be difficult to treat with variable flows. Numerous authors have realized that stationary states play a role in the thermodynamics of irreversible processes similar to that played by states of equilibrium in classical thermodynamics.[1,2,3] It is, therefore, of interest to inquire whether a steady state can be characterized by more general principles, similar to the extremum and stability conditions of a state of equilibrium. Thus, Eq. (16-1) indicates that steady states can be maintained only in diathermal or open systems in which entropy production can be balanced by the outflow of entropy, but we would like to know if it is possible to make a more definite statement concerning σ in a state of stationary flow. The answer is given by the principle of minimum production of entropy discovered by Prigogine.[1]

To derive this principle from the phenomenological equations, the properties of a stationary state must be considered from a different point of view. If no restraints are imposed on a system and it is left to age, it will eventually reach a state of equilibrium in which all the flows vanish. We may, however, impose a number of constant constraints on the system; for example, the forces X_1, X_2, $\cdots$ X_k may be fixed at constant values and the other forces in the system, X_{k+1}, X_{k+2}, $\cdots$ X_n, may be allowed to change freely. After a sufficiently long time the system will attain a steady state characterized by the vanishing of certain local derivatives, such as $\partial c_i/\partial t$, which leads to Eq. (16-2) and to the conclusion that $J_i =$ constant. On the other hand, in several examples treated in previous chapters, we have considered stationary those states in which the constant value of some of the flows J_i was zero. Certain forces in a system were fixed and the stationary state in which the flows conjugate to the nonfixed forces vanished was studied. According to this criterion the system described above will attain a steady state when all the flows corresponding to the unrestrained forces vanish ($J_i = 0$ for $i > k$). The flows corresponding to the fixed forces will assume constant values and the parameters of the system will become independent of time, as assumed in the previous discussions. Here, however, the vanishing of the flows J_i ($i > k$) is taken as the characteristic property of the stationary state and it may be shown that this is equivalent to a state of minimum entropy production (or of least dissipation of free energy).

We shall first consider a simple system in which there are two flows and two forces. The entropy production and phenomenological equations for such a case are

$$\sigma = J_1X_1 + J_2X_2, \tag{16-3}$$

$$\begin{aligned} J_1 &= L_{11}X_1 + L_{12}X_2, \\ J_2 &= L_{21}X_1 + L_{22}X_2. \end{aligned} \tag{16-4}$$

Introducing Eqs. (16-4) into Eq. (16-3), we obtain

$$\sigma = L_{11}X_1^2 + (L_{12} + L_{21})X_1X_2 + L_{22}X_2^2. \tag{16-5}$$

Let us now impose the restriction that $X_1 =$ constant and allow X_2 to vary. Differentiating σ with respect to the variable X_2 at constant X_1, we obtain

$$\frac{\partial\sigma}{\partial X_2} = (L_{12} + L_{21})X_1 + 2L_{22}X_2. \tag{16-6}$$

If Onsager's law holds, $L_{12} + L_{21} = 2L_{21}$ and, thus,

$$\frac{\partial\sigma}{\partial X_2} = 2(L_{21}X_1 + L_{22}X_2) = 2J_2. \tag{16-7}$$

Now according to the new condition for stationary states, if X_2 is unrestricted the conjugate flow must vanish and Eq. (16-7) becomes

$$\frac{\partial\sigma}{\partial X_2} = 0,$$

which indicates that entropy production has an extreme value in the steady state. Since σ is positive-definite, this extremum must be a minimum and the stationary state of the system is that state in which the entropy production assumes the minimal value consistent with the restraints imposed. The considerations may be easily extended to the general case for which

$$\sigma = \sum_{i=1}^{n} J_i X_i, \tag{16-8}$$

$$J_i = \sum_{k=1}^{n} L_{ik} X_k, \qquad (i = 1, 2, \cdots, n) \tag{16-9}$$

and hence

$$\sigma = \sum_{i,k=1}^{n} L_{ik} X_i X_k. \tag{16-10}$$

Assuming that the forces $X_1, \cdots, X_k$ are fixed and allowing $X_{k+1}, \cdots, X_n$ to vary, we may differentiate Eq. (16-10) with respect to X_i $(i > k)$, obtaining

$$\frac{\partial \sigma}{\partial X_i} = 2 \sum_{j=1}^{n} L_{ij} X_j = 2J_i = 0, \qquad (i = k + 1, k + 2, \cdots, n) \tag{16-11}$$

which again shows that the entropy production in a steady state is a minimum with respect to the variable forces.

This conclusion is, however, valid only under the following conditions: (*a*) the system obeys linear phenomenological laws; (*b*) the Onsager reciprocal relations are valid; (*c*) the phenomenological coefficients are independent of the forces. Thus, the principle of minimum entropy production in stationary states cannot be taken as universally valid. Further, this principle implies a restriction on the actual values of the fluxes, J_i, rather than on their divergence as does the more conventional definition of a steady state, Eqs. (16-1) and (16-2). Prigogine[1] has considered this difference and has shown, in the case of chemical reactions close to equilibrium, that the conditions $dc_i/dt = 0$ and the condition of minimum entropy production are equivalent.

16.2. Stability of Stationary States

It may further be shown that, upon removal of some of the restraints, the system will change in a manner resulting in a decrease in entropy production. This implies that stationary states are stable since any fluctuation in a system maintained in such a state gives rise to forces that tend to bring the system back to the stable configuration. To demonstrate this point, we shall consider only the case of two flows and two forces, although the generalization to a larger number presents no fundamental difficulties.

Differentiation of Eq. (16-5) with respect to time, assuming that the coefficients L_{ik} are independent of time, yields

$$\frac{d\sigma}{dt} = 2(L_{11}X_1 + L_{12}X_2)\frac{dX_1}{dt} + 2(L_{21}X_1 + L_{22}X_2)\frac{dX_2}{dt},$$

or

$$\frac{1}{2}\frac{d\sigma}{dt} = J_1\frac{dX_1}{dt} + J_2\frac{dX_2}{dt}. \tag{16-12}$$

The forces are functions of the parameters of the system, for example α_1 and α_2, so that their dependence on time is due to the change in the α_i with time, or

$$\frac{dX_1}{dt} = \frac{\partial X_1}{\partial \alpha_1}\frac{d\alpha_1}{dt} + \frac{\partial X_1}{\partial \alpha_2}\frac{d\alpha_2}{dt}.$$

As pointed out in the previous chapter,

$$X_1 = \frac{\partial \Delta S}{\partial \alpha_1},$$

and, thus,

$$\frac{\partial X_1}{\partial \alpha_1} = \frac{\partial^2 \Delta S}{\partial \alpha_1^2} = -g_{11},$$

$$\frac{\partial X_1}{\partial \alpha_2} = \frac{\partial^2 \Delta S}{\partial \alpha_1 \partial \alpha_2} = -g_{12} = -g_{21} = \frac{\partial X_2}{\partial \alpha_1},$$

$$\frac{\partial X_2}{\partial \alpha_2} = \frac{\partial^2 \Delta S}{\partial \alpha_2^2} = -g_{22},$$

in which the g_{ij} are defined by Eq. (15-21). Further, $d\alpha_i/dt$ is the flow J_i of the property α_i and, therefore,

$$\frac{dX_1}{dt} = J_1(-g_{11}) + J_2(-g_{12}),$$

$$\frac{dX_2}{dt} = J_1(-g_{12}) + J_2(-g_{22}).$$

Introducing these expressions into Eq. (16-12) we obtain the important result:

$$\frac{1}{2}\frac{d\sigma}{dt} = J_1^2(-g_{11}) + 2J_1J_2(-g_{12}) + J_2^2(-g_{22}) < 0. \tag{16-13}$$

The condition $d\sigma/dt < 0$ is due to the fact implied in Eq. (15-21) that the coefficients $(-g_{ij})$ constitute a negative matrix and therefore the quadratic form $[(-g_{11})J_1^2 + (-g_{12})J_1J_2 + (-g_{22})J_2^2]$ is negative-definite. Equation (16-13) constitutes the proof for the statement that σ decreases with time and in an aged system will reach a minimal value. Moreover, it implies the condition of stability or the natural tendency of any fluctuation to give rise to restoring forces bringing the system back to its most probable state.

This is perhaps more clearly seen by the following considerations which are due to DeGroot.[2] We shall consider a system in a steady state with the forces $X_1, \cdots, X_k$ fixed and other with nonrestrained forces, $X_{k+1}, \cdots, X_n$. A perturbation δX_j is applied to the nonfixed force X_j, all other forces being kept at their original values. The flow J_j then becomes

$$J_j = J_j^0 + L_{jj}\delta X_j, \tag{16-14}$$

in which J_j^0 is the unperturbed flow which, by the foregoing considerations, must be zero. Thus,

$$J_j = L_{jj}\delta X_j. \tag{16-15}$$

From the considerations of Chapter 8,

$$L_{jj} > 0$$

and thus

$$L_{jj}(\delta X_j)^2 > 0. \tag{16-16}$$

Inserting Eq. (16-15) into this inequality, we obtain

$$J_j\delta X_j > 0. \tag{16-17}$$

Thus, the flow caused by the perturbation must have the same sign as the perturbation. This means that the flow will tend to reduce the perturbation and the system will return to its original stable state.

The conclusions of the previous sections are illustrated diagramatically in Fig. 35, which shows a three-dimensional representation of σ as a function of X_1 and X_2. Since σ is equal to or greater than zero, it is represented by a quadratic surface of positive values passing through the origin. Let us start with a point of constant X_1' and X_2', designated as point 1, with an entropy production $\sigma_1(X_1', X_2')$. If one of the restraints is removed and X_2 is allowed to vary, X_1 being kept constant, the point describing σ will move along the parabola obtained by the intersection of the plane X_1 = constant with the surface $\sigma(X_1, X_2)$, until it reaches the minimal point designated σ_2. If both constraints are removed, σ will continue to decrease until the point $\sigma = 0$ is reached and the system will then be in a state of thermodynamic equilibrium.

16.3. The Principle of Least Dissipation and Biological Stability[4]

There are several remarkable analogies between open system approaching a steady state and living organisms in their development toward maturity. The decrease in entropy production during the maturation process, which may in certain cases be accompanied by an actual decrease in the entropy itself, seems to follow the general laws of thermodynamics

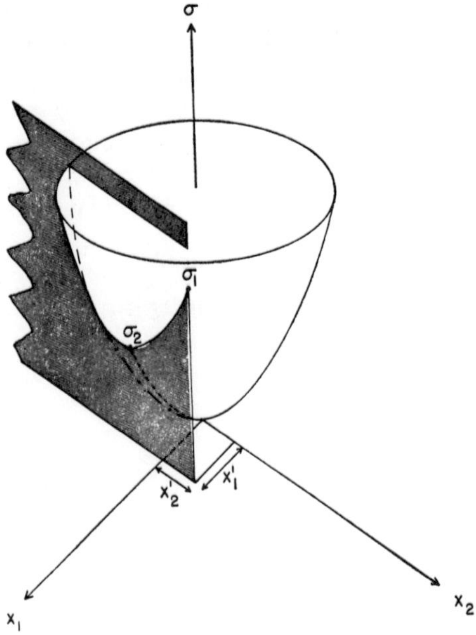

Fig. 35. Geometric illustration of the principle of minimum entropy production in the steady state of a two-component system. The entropy production σ is shown as a function of the two forces X_1 and X_2. The value σ_1 is attained when both forces are fixed, at X_1' and X_2'; σ_2 is the entropy production in the steady state reached when X_2 is held fixed at X_2' and X_1 is allowed to vary. The absolute minimum, $\sigma = 0$, represents the equilibrium state of the system reached when neither force is fixed.

of irreversible systems. Further, the recognition that in the steady state a system loses minimal amounts of free energy and is most economical from the energetic standpoint led many theoreticians to believe that the concept of least dissipation is the physical principle underlying the evolution of the phenomena of life. It is rather interesting to point out that living systems are endowed with a series of regulating mechanisms that preserve the steady state and bring the organism back to its unperturbed condition in a way resembling, in principle, the action of the restoring force coming into play in any fluctuation from a stationary state in a physical system.

The attempts to discover a universal physical principle underlying the phenomenon of life bring to mind the older attempts of scientists of the 18th century to show that all mechanical and optical phenomena could be founded in variational principles. Thus, the great principle of least action governing the natural mechanical paths and the Fermat principle of least time for optical tracks served scientists and philosophers as an outstanding demonstration of the mathematical structure of the universe. The Phythagorean belief that "the world is the number," that there is an intrinsic mathematical logic underlying all natural phenomena, was recently projected into the study of life and found its justification in the principle of least dissipation, which has many characteristics in common with the great principles of the 18th century.

The aesthetic satisfaction derived from this approach should not dim recognition of the limitation of the principle of minimum entropy production. The range of its validity is restricted to phenomena close to equilibrium obeying Onsager's law. For rapid metabolic processes, the phenomenological equations may not hold and the general laws applicable to all possible rate phenomena are still lacking. Although there is no doubt that the formal approach of the thermodynamics of irreversible processes is a powerful tool and one of the most promising approaches to the physical description of biological phenomena, there is much to be done before the all-embracing formulas, similar to the first and second laws, will be formulated. Attempts are being made to extend the range of validity of the variational principles so as to include stationary states far from equilibrium. Thus Glansdorff and Prigogine[5] decomposed the change in entropy production into two terms, one due to the change in the forces and the other due to the change in the flows,

$$d\sigma = d_X\sigma + d_J\sigma = \sum J_i dX_i + \sum X_i dJ_i,$$

and have shown that the first term is negative-definite even in cases for which the linear and symmetric phenomenological equations do not hold. Thus, the integral of $d_X\sigma$ over the volume;

$$d\Phi = \int (\sum J_i dX_i) dV \leq 0, \tag{16-18}$$

is regarded by these authors as a general criterion of evolution in macroscopic physics. They were able to show not only that Eq. (16-18) holds for the dissipative forces discussed in this book but that it may also include terms due to mechanical flow processes. The differential quantity is generally not a total differential and in some cases, as in periodic irreversible phenonena, it may be shown that it cannot describe the approach to a stationary state. In other cases, however, a function Φ can be evaluated for which $d\Phi$ is a total differential and which assumes a minimum value under conditions of stationary flow. The function Φ is useful for the description of the approach of a system toward a stationary state, as was shown by Hays[6] for viscous flow. A series of important studies on the statistical mechanical foundation of the description of irreversible processes have been published recently.[7] However, many points await further elucidation and the material may not yet be summarized within the framework of this book.

LIST OF SYMBOLS

A,	affinity of a chemical reaction
$\tilde{A}$,	electrochemical affinity of a chemical reaction
$\mathcal{A}$,	area
a_i,	external parameter of a system
C_i,	concentration of component i in a membrane
c_i,	molar concentration of component i
c_s,	molar concentration of solute in a binary solution
c_w,	molar concentration of water (solvent)
$\bar{c}_i$,	mean concentration of component i
D,	diffusion coefficient in a binary solution
D_{ik},	generalized diffusion coefficient
D^T,	thermal diffusion coefficient
E,	electrical potential difference between reversible electrodes
$\mathcal{E}$,	electric field
e,	quantity of electric charge
F,	Helmholtz free energy
$\mathfrak{F}$,	the faraday, 96,500 coulombs/mole
f,	external force
f_{ik},	coefficient of friction between components i and k
G,	Gibbs free energy
h,	enthalpy of a small volume element
H,	enthalpy
$\bar{H}_i$,	partial molar enthalpy of component i
$\mathbf{I}$,	electric current
$\mathbf{J}_i$,	absolute flow of component i in moles per unit area per unit time
$\mathbf{J}_e$,	flow of electrons
$\mathbf{J}_i^d$,	flow of component i relative to solvent
$\mathbf{J}_i^m$,	flow of component i relative to center of mass velocity
$\mathbf{J}_s^d$,	flow of solute relative to solvent in a binary solution
$\mathbf{J}_q$,	flow of heat
$\mathbf{J}_S$,	flow of entropy
J_v,	flow of volume
J_D,	velocity of solute relative to solvent in a membrane system
J_{ch},	rate of chemical reaction

k, Boltzman constant
k_i, k_{-i}, rate coefficients for the ith step in a chemical reaction
K, equilibrium constant for a chemical reaction
K_i, distribution coefficient of component i between solution and a membrane
L_{ik}, phenomenological coefficient relating the ith flow to the kth force
L_P, filtration coefficient of a membrane
l, length
M, mass
M_i, molecular weight of component i
n_i, number of moles of component
P, pressure
$\mathcal{P}$, probability
dq, heat change in a small volume element
Q, heat
Q^*, heat of transport
r, radial coordinate
R, gas constant
R_{ik}, resistance coefficient relating the ith force to the kth flow
S, entropy
$\bar{S}_i$, partial molar entropy of component i
S^*, entropy of transfer
d_iS, entropy produced within a system
d_eS, entropy exchanged with the environment of a system
$\mathcal{S}$, sedimentation coefficient
s, entropy of a small volume element
s_v, local entropy per unit volume
s_T, Soret coefficient
T, absolute temperature
t, time
t_i, transference number of component i
U, internal energy
U^*, energy of transport
u, energy of a small volume element
u_v, local internal energy per unit volume
u_i, mobility of ion i
u_{ii}, reduced phenomenological mobility
V, volume
$\bar{V}_i$, partial molar volume of component i
v, volume of a small volume element
v_i, partial specific volume (volume per unit mass) of component i
$\mathbf{v}$, velocity of center of mass
$\mathbf{v}_i$, velocity of component i

$\mathbf{v}_s$, velocity of the solute in a binary system
$\mathbf{v}_w$, velocity of water (solvent)
W, work
X, concentration of fixed charge in a membrane
$\mathbf{X}_i$, thermodynamic force acting on component i
X_{ik}, frictional force between components i and k
z_i, valence of component i
α_i, deviation of the ith parameter of a system from its equilibrium value
β, coefficient of electroosmosis
γ_i, activity coefficient of component i
ϑ, tortuosity factor for a membrane
κ, electrical conductance
λ, thermal conductance
λ_i, equivalent conductance of component i
μ_i, chemical potential of component i
μ_i^0, standard chemical potential of component i
$\tilde{\mu}_i$, electrochemical potential of component i
μ_i^c, concentration-dependent part of the chemical potential of component i
μ_s, chemical potential of the solute in a binary system
μ_w, chemical potential of water (solvent)
ν_i, stoichiometric coefficient of component i in a chemical reaction
ν, average value of a fluctuating quantity
$d\xi$, degree of advancement of a chemical reaction
ξ_i, internal parameter of a system
Π, Peltier coefficient
π, osmotic pressure
ρ, density
ρ_u, local energy density
σ, local entropy production
σ, reflection coefficient of solute in a binary system
σ_i, reflection coefficient for component i
σ_A, Thomson coefficient of metal A
τ, time interval
φ_i, volume fraction of component i
φ_s, volume fraction of solute in a binary system
φ_w, volume fraction of solvent in a binary system
Φ, local dissipation function
$\boldsymbol{\Phi}$, dissipation function in a discontinuous system
ψ, local electrical potential
Ω, configuration number
ω_i, mobility of component i

REFERENCES

INTRODUCTION

1. Lord Rayleigh (J. W. Strutt), *Proc. Math. Soc. (London) 4* (1873), 357; W. Thomson (Lord Kelvin) *Proc. Roy. Soc. Edinburgh 3* (1854), 225; H. Helmholtz, *Wied. Ann. 3* (1876), 201; W. Nernst, *Z. Physik. Chem. 4* (1889), 129; L. Natanson, *Z. Physik. Chem. 21* (1896), 193.

2. L. Onsager, *Phys. Rev. 37* (1931), 405; *38* (1931), 2265.

3. H. B. G. Casimir, *Rev. Mod. Phys. 17* (1945), 343.

4. I. Prigogine, *Étude Thermodynamique des Processus Irreversibles* (Desoer, Liège, 1947).

5. S. R. de Groot, *L'Effet Soret* (North-Holland, Amsterdam, 1945); J. Phys. Rad. *8* (1947), 188, 193.

6. J. Meixner, *Ann. Physik. 39* (1941), 333; *40* (1941), 165; *41* (1942), 409; *43* (1943), 244.

7. C. Eckart, *Phys. Rev. 58* (1940), 267, 269; H. B. Callen, *Phys. Rev. 73* (1948), 1349; R. T. Cox, *Rev. Mod. Phys. 22* (1950), 238; B. Leaf, *Phys. Rev. 70* (1946), 748.

8. K. G. Denbigh, *The Thermodynamics of the Steady State* (Methuen, London, 1951).

9. S. R. de Groot, *Thermodynamics of Irreversible Processes* (North-Holland, Amsterdam, 1952).

10. I. Prigogine, *Introduction to the Thermodynamics of Irreversible Processes* (Thomas, Springfield, Illinois, 1955).

11. D. D. Fitts, *Nonequilibrium Thermodynamics* (McGraw-Hill, New York, 1962).

12. S. R. de Groot and P. Mazur, *Non-Equilibrium Thermodynamics* (North-Holland, Amsterdam; Wiley, New York, 1962).

CHAPTER 1

1. G. N. Lewis and M. Randall, *Thermodynamics* (2nd ed., rev. by K. S. Pitzer and L. Brewer; McGraw-Hill, New York, 1961).

2. J. G. Kirkwood and I. Oppenheim, *Chemical Thermodynamics* (McGraw-Hill, New York, 1961).

3. M. W. Zamansky, *Heat and Thermodynamics* (3rd ed., McGraw-Hill, New York, 1951).

4. A. B. Pippard, *Classical Thermodynamics* (Cambridge University Press, Cambridge, England, 1961).

5. E. A. Guggenheim, *Thermodynamics* (North-Holland, Amsterdam, 1950).

6. H. B. Callen, *Thermodynamics* (Wiley, New York, 1960).

CHAPTER 2

1. W. Thomson (Lord Kelvin), *Trans. Roy. Soc. Edinburgh 20* (1853), 261.

2. C. Carathédory, *Math. Ann. 67* (1909), 355.

3. M. Born, *Physik. Z. 22* (1922), 218, 249, 282; see also M. Born, *Natural Philosophy of Cause and Chance* (Oxford University Press, New York, 1949; Dover, New York, 1951).

4. H. Margenau and G. M. Murphy, *The Mathematics of Physics and Chemistry* (Van Nostrand, Princeton, New Jersey, 1956).

5. J. G. Kirkwood and I. Oppenheim, *Chemical Thermodynamics* (McGraw-Hill, New York, 1961).

6. S. Carnot, *Reflections on the Motive Power of Fire* (1824), trans. and ed. by R. H. Thurston (Macmillan, New York, 1890; Dover, New York, 1960).

7. R. Clausius, *Poggendorffs Ann. Physik. 125* (1865), 390.

CHAPTER 3

1. J. W. Gibbs, *The Collected Works of J. Willard Gibbs* (Yale University Press, New Haven, 1948).

2. A. Katchalsky, S. Lifson, I. Michaeli, and M. Zwick, in A. Wasserman, ed., *Size and Shape of Contractile Polymers* (Pergamon Press, New York, 1960).

3. J. N. Brønsted, *Principles and Problems in Energetics* (Interscience, New York, 1955).

CHAPTER 4

1. J. G. Kirkwood and I. Oppenheim, *Chemical Thermodynamics* (McGraw-Hill, New York, 1961).

2. R. Clausius, *Poggendorffs Ann. Physik. 125* (1865), 390.

3. A. S. Eddington, *The Nature of the Physical World* (Macmillan, New York, 1929).

4. I. Prigogine, *Étude Thermodynamique des Processus Irreversibles* (Desoer, Liège, 1947); *Introduction to the Thermodynamics of Irreversible Processes* (Thomas, Springfield, Illinois, 1955); S. R. de Groot, *Thermodynamics of Irreversible Processes* (North-Holland, Amsterdam, 1952).

CHAPTER 5

1. T. DeDonder and P. van Rysselberghe, *The Thermodynamic Theory of Affinity* (Stanford University Press, Stanford, California, 1936).

2. J. Meixner, *Z. Naturforsch. 4A* (1949), 594.

CHAPTER 6

1. J. Meixner, *Ann. Phys. 43* (1943), 244.

CHAPTER 7

1. S. R. de Groot and P. Mazur, *Non-Equilibrium Thermodynamics* (North-Holland, Amsterdam, 1962).

2. J. Meixner, *Ann. Phys. 43* (1943), 244.

3. E. A. Guggenheim, *J. Phys. Chem.* 33 (1929), 842.

4. I. Prigogine, *Étude Thermodynamique des Processus Irreversibles* (Desoer, Liège, 1947).

CHAPTER 8

1. L. Onsager, *Phys. Rev. 37* (1931), 405; *38* (1931), 2265.

2. J. G. Kirkwood, in H. T. Clark, ed., *Ion Transport across Membranes* (Academic Press, New York, 1954), p. 119.

3. P. Curie, *Oeuvres* (Gauthier-Villars, Paris, 1908), p. 129.

4. S. R. de Groot and P. Mazur, *Non-Equilibrium Thermodynamics* (North-Holland, Amsterdam, 1962).

5. D. D. Fitts, *Nonequilibrium Thermodynamics* (McGraw-Hill, New York, 1962).

6. D. G. Miller, *Chem. Rev. 60* (1960), 15.

7. I. Prigogine, P. Outer, and C. Herbo, *J. Phys. Coll. Chem. 52* (1948), 321.

8. R. C. Tolman, *The Principles of Statistical Mechanics* (Oxford University Press, New York, 1938).

CHAPTER 9

1. I. Prigogine, *Introduction to the Thermodynamics of Irreversible Processes* (Thomas, Springfield, Illinois, 1955).

2. H. Fujita, *Mathematical Theory of Sedimentation Analysis* (Academic Press, New York, 1962).

3. J. G. Kirkwood, R. L. Baldwin, P. J. Dunlop, L. J. Gosting, and G. Kegeles, *J. Chem. Phys. 33* (1960), 1505.

4. S. R. de Groot and P. Mazur, *Non-Equilibrium Thermodynamics* (North-Holland, Amsterdam, 1962).

5. D. D. Fitts, *Nonequilibrium Thermodynamics* (McGraw-Hill, New York, 1962).

6. L. Onsager, *Ann. N. Y. Acad. Sci. 46* (1945), 241; R. L. Baldwin, P. J. Dunlop, and L. J. Gosting, *J. Am. Chem. Soc. 77* (1955), 5235.

7. P. J. Dunlop and L. J. Gosting, *J. Phys. Chem. 63* (1959), 86; H. Fujita and L. J. Gosting, *J. Phys. Chem. 64* (1960), 1256; P. J. Dunlop, *J. Phys. Chem. 61* (1957), 994.

8. T. Svedberg and K. O. Pedersen, *The Ultracentrifuge* (Oxford University Press, London, 1940); H. K. Schachman, *Ultracentrifugation in Biochemistry* (Academic Press, New York, 1959).

9. G. J. Hooyman, H. Holtan, P. Mazur, and S. R. de Groot, *Physica 19* (1953), 1095; G. J. Hooyman, *Physica 22* (1956), 761.

10. W. J. Archibald, *J. Phys. Colloid Chem. 51* (1947), 1204.

CHAPTER 10

1. J. G. Kirkwood, in H. T. Clark, ed., *Ion Transport across Membranes* (Academic Press, New York, 1954), p. 119.

2. O. Kedem and A. Katchalsky, *Biochim. Biophys. Acta 27* (1958), 229.

3. S. R. de Groot, *Thermodynamics of Irreversible Processes* (North-Holland, Amsterdam, 1952).

4. S. R. de Groot and P. Mazur, *Non-Equilibrium Thermodynamics* (North-Holland, Amsterdam, 1962).

5. A. J. Staverman, *Rec. trav. chim. 70* (1951), 344.

6. B. Andersen and H. H. Ussing, *Acta Physiol. Scand. 39* (1957), 228.

7. V. W. Sidel and A. K. Solomon, *J. Gen. Physiol. 41* (1957), 243; D. A. Goldstein and A. K. Solomon, *J. Gen. Physiol. 44* (1960), 1; D. Savitz and A. K. Solomon, unpublished observations.

8. J. Dainty and B. Z. Ginzburg, *Biochim. Biophys. Acta 79* (1964), 102, 112, 122, 129.

9. B. Z. Ginzburg and A. Katchalsky, *J. Gen. Physiol. 47* (1963), 403.

10. F. Helfferich, *Ion Exchange* (McGraw-Hill, New York, 1962).

11. J. Dainty, *Adv. Botan. Res. 1* (1963), 279.

12. O. Kedem and A. Katchalsky, *J. Gen. Physiol. 45* (1961), 143.

13. K. S. Spiegler, *Trans. Faraday Soc. 54* (1958), 1409.
14. R. Schlögl, *Stofftransport durch Membranen* (Steinkopff, Darmstadt, 1964).

CHAPTER 11

1. E. A. Guggenheim, *J. Phys. Chem. 33* (1929), 842.
2. D. G. Miller, *Chem. Rev. 60* (1960), 15
3. P. Debye and E. Hückel, *Physik. Z. 24* (1933), 185, 305.
4. L. Onsager and R. M. Fuoss, *J. Phys. Chem. 36* (1932), 2689.

CHAPTER 12

1. A. Katchalsky and O. Kedem, *Biophys. J. 2,* suppl. (1962), 53; O. Kedem and A. Katchalsky, *Trans. Faraday Soc. 59* (1963), 1918.
2. H. Helmholtz, *Wied. Ann. 7* (1879), 337; M. V. Smoluchowski, in Graetz, ed., *Handbuch der Elektrizitat und des Magnetismus* (Barth, Leipzig, 1914), vol. 2, p. 366; A. Gouy, *J. Physique 9* (1910), 457; J. Perrin, *J. Chem. Phys. 2* (1904), 601.
3. P. Mazur and J. T. Overbeek, *Rec. trav. chim. 70* (1951), 83.
4. D. G. Miller, *Chem. Rev. 60* (1960), 15.
5. M. Planck, *Ann. Physik. 39* (1890), 161; *40* (1890), 561.
6. P. Henderson, *Z. Physik. Chem. 59* (1907), 118; *63* (1908), 325.
7. A. J. Staverman, *Trans. Faraday Soc. 48* (1952), 176.
8. See, for example, H. H. Ussing, P. Kruhøffer, J. Hess Thaysen, and N. A. Thorn, *The Alkali-Metal Ions in Biology* (Springer-Verlag, Berlin, 1960); E. J. Harris, *Transport and Accumulation in Biological Systems* (Butterworths, London, 1960).
9. J. S. Mackie and P. Meares, *Proc. Roy. Soc. (A) 232* (1955), 498, 510.
10. J. Loeb, *J. Gen. Physiol. 2* (1920), 577; *4* (1922), 463, 621; *5* (1922), 89.
11. E. Grim and K. Sollner, *J. Gen. Physiol. 40* (1957), 887; *44* (1960), 381.
12. R. Neihof and K. Sollner, *J. Gen. Physiol. 38* (1955), 613; C. W. Carr and K. Sollner, *Biophys. J. 4* (1964), 189.

CHAPTER 13

1. J. Jost, *Diffusion in Solids, Liquids and Gases* (Academic Press, New York, 1960).
2. I. Prigogine, *Étude Thermodynamique des Processus Irreversibles* (Desoer, Liège, 1947).
3. K. Clusius and G. Dickel, *Naturwissenschaften 26* (1938), 546; *Z. Physik. Chem B44* (1939), 397, 451.
4. E. Ernst and L. Homola, *Acta Physiol. Acad. Sci. Hung. 3* (1952), 487.
5. K. G. Denbigh, *Nature 163* (1949), 60; K. G. Denbigh and G. Raumann, *Nature 165* (1950), 199; *Proc. Roy. Soc. (A) 210* (1951), 377, 518.
6. P. L. Kapitza, *J. Phys. Moscow 5* (1941), 59.
7. L. Meyer and J. M. Mellink, *Physica 13* (1947), 197.
8. J. W. Cary, *J. Phys. Chem. 67* (1963), 126.
9. S. R. de Groot, *Thermodynamics of Irreversible Processes* (North-Holland, Amsterdam, 1952).
10. K. G. Denbigh, *The Thermodynamics of the Steady State* (Methuen, London, 1951).
11. D. C. Spanner, *Symp. Soc. Exptl. Biol. 8* (1954), 76.
12. H. B. Callen, *Phys. Rev. 73* (1948), 1349.

13. C. A. Domenicali, *Rev. Mod. Phys. 26* (1954), 237.

14. S. N. Levine, ed., *Selected Papers on New Techniques for Energy Conversion* (Dover, New York, 1961)

15. W. Thomson, *Proc. Roy. Soc. Edinburgh 3* (1854), 225.

16. D. G. Miller, *Chem. Rev. 60* (1960), 15.

CHAPTER 14

1. T. Rosenberg, *Acta Chem. Scan. 2* (1948), 14; *Symp. Soc. Exptl. Biol. 8* (1954), 27.

2. A. Kleinzeller and A. Kotyk, eds., *Membrane Transport and Metabolism* (Czechoslovak Academy of Sciences; dist. by Academic Press, New York, 1961).

3. O. Jardetzky and F. M. Snell, *Proc. Nat. Acad. Sci. 46* (1960), 616.

4. J. Z. Hearon, *Bull. Math. Biophys. 12* (1950), 135.

5. H. H. Ussing, *Adv. Enzymology 13* (1952), 21.

6. P. F. Scholander, *Science 131* (1960), 585; E. Hemmingsen and P. F. Scholander, *Science 132* (1960), 1379.

7. R. E. Collins, *Science 133* (1961), 1593; *Bull. Math. Biophysics 23* (1961), 223; I. Fatt and R. C. LaForce, *Science 133* (1961), 1919; J. H. Wang, *Science 133* (1961), 1770; *J. Theo. Biol. 4* (1963), 175.

8. J. B. Best and J. Z. Hearon, in C. L. Comar and F. Bronner, eds., *Mineral Metabolism* (Academic Press, New York, 1960), vol 1A, p. 11.

9. O. Kedem, in A. Kleinzeller and A. Kotyk, eds., *Membrane Transport and Metabolism* (Academic Press, New York, 1961), p. 87.

10. P. F. Curran, *J. Gen. Physiol. 43* (1960), 1137; P. F. Curran and J. R. McIntosh, *Nature 193* (1962), 347; J. T. Ogilvie, J. R. McIntosh, and P. F. Curran, *Biochim. Biophys. Acta 66* (1963), 441.

11. C. S. Patlak, D. A. Goldstein, and J. F. Hoffman, *J. Theoret. Biol. 5* (1963), 426.

12. J. M. Diamond, *J. Physiol. 161* (1962), 503.

CHAPTER 15

1. L. Onsager, *Phys. Rev. 37* (1931), 405; *38* (1931), 2265.

2. E. Schrödinger, *What Is Life?* (Cambridge University Press, New York, 1944; Doubleday, New York, 1956).

3. H. B. G. Casimir, *Rev. Mod. Phys. 17* (1945), 343.

4. P. Mazur and S. R. de Groot, *Physica 19* (1953), 961; S. R. de Groot and P. Mazur, *Phys. Rev. 94* (1954), 218; P. Mazur and S. R. de Groot, *Phys. Rev. 94* (1954), 224; R. Fieschi, S. R. de Groot, and P. Mazur, *Physica 20* (1954), 67; R. Fieschi, S. R. de Groot, P. Mazur and J. Vlieger *Physica 20* (1954), 245.

5. D. G. Miller, *Chem. Rev. 60* (1960), 15.

CHAPTER 16

1. I. Prigogine, *Étude Thermodynamique des Processus Irreversibles* (Desoer, Liège, 1947); *Introduction to the Thermodynamics of Irreversible Processes* (Thomas, Springfield, Illinois, 1955).

2. S. R. de Groot, *Thermodynamics of Irreversible Processes* (North-Holland, Amsterdam, 1952).

3. K. G. Denbigh, *The Thermodynamics of the Steady State* (Methuen, London, 1951); S. R. de Groot and P. Mazur, *Non-Equilibrium Thermodynamics* (North-Holland, Amsterdam, 1962).

4. I. Prigogine and J. M. Wiame, *Experientia 2* (1946), 451.

5. P. Glansdorff and I. Prigogine, *Physica 30* (1964), 351; I. Prigogine in *The Law of Mass Action* (Norske Videnskaps-Akademi Universitetsforlaget, Oslo, 1964), p. 95.

6. D. F. Hays, *Acad. Roy. Belg. Bull. Classe Sci. 43* (1963), 526.

7. P. Glansdorff and I. Prigogine, *Physica 20* (1954), 773; L. Onsager and S. Machlup, *Phys. Rev. 91* (1953), 1505; S. Machlup and L. Onsager, *Phys. Rev. 91* (1953), 1512; see also S. R. de Groot and P. Mazur, *Non-Equilibrium Thermodynamics,* chaps. 7, 8, and 9.

INDEX